HIGHER STILL
PHYSICS

HIGHER LEVEL

Geoff Cackett

Portobello High School, Edinburgh

Jim Lowrie

Edinburgh's Telford College, Edinburgh

Alastair Steven

Wester Hailes Education Centre, Edinburgh

OXFORD
UNIVERSITY PRESS

OXFORD
UNIVERSITY PRESS

Great Clarendon Street, Oxford OX2 6DP

Oxford New York

Auckland Cape Town Dar es Salaam Hong Kong Karachi
Kuala Lumpur Madrid Melbourne Mexico City Nairobi
New Delhi Shanghai Taipei Toronto

With offices in

Argentina Austria Brazil Chile Czech Republic France
Greece Guatemala Hungary Italy Japan Poland Portugal
Singapore South Korea Switzerland Thailand Turkey
Ukraine Vietnam

Oxford is a registered trade mark of Oxford University Press
in the UK and in certain other countries

First published 1983
Second edition 1992
Third edition 1998

British Library Cataloguing in Publication Data

Data available

ISBN 0 19 914737 X

10 9 8 7 6 5 4

Typeset by Tradespools Limited, Frome, Somerset
Printed in Hong Kong

Cover photo supplied by The Stock Market Photo Agency Inc.

Preface

This book is written for students preparing for the Higher Level Physics course of the Scottish Higher Still programme of study. The course incorporates the relevant National Certificate modules and is divided into three mandatory Units:

Mechanics and Properties of Matter
Electricity and Electronics
Radiation and Matter

This book is divided into the same three Units. Each Unit is divided into Topics. Each Topic is followed by Topic Tests which cover all the content statements of the course. There are three versions of each Test to give students the opportunity to assess their knowledge thoroughly.

The aims of the Higher Level Physics course are that students should acquire:

- increased knowledge and understanding of facts and ideas, of techniques, and of the application of physics in society
- skill in applying their knowledge and understanding in a wide variety of theoretical and practical problem-solving contexts
- skills associated with carrying out experimental and investigative work in physics and analysing the information obtained.

The text is designed to equip students with understanding, basic knowledge, and problem-solving skills required at this level. The third objective is best achieved through practical work in class. However, the book includes a section on Measurements and Uncertainty, which contributes to the acquisition of skills in the experimental and investigative area.

The practical nature of the course is emphasised in the book by frequent reference to experiments, to sample results, and to worked examples that reinforce understanding of the concepts dealt with in the laboratory. Each chapter begins with the topic content statement and concludes with a summary and a set of ten questions which illustrate the standard of examination papers. Numerical answers to all problems are at the end of the book.

We would like to express our appreciation to the many people who have assisted in this work, and to Ellice, Eleanor and Sylvia for their support and encouragement. We gratefully acknowledge permission granted by the Scottish Qualifications Authority for allowing us to include past examination questions and by those listed on page 296 for the use of diagrams and photographs.

Geoff Cackett, Jim Lowrie, Alastair Steven
Edinburgh 1998

Contents

Contents

Unit 1
Mechanics and Properties of Matter

Topics

Topic 1.1
Vectors

Objectives

When you have completed the work of this topic you should be able to:

1 distinguish between distance and displacement;
2 distinguish between speed and velocity;
3 define and classify vector and scalar quantities;
4 use scale diagrams, or otherwise, to find the magnitude and direction of the resultant of a number of displacements or velocities;
5 state what is meant by the resultant of a number of forces;
6 carry out calculations to find the rectangular components of a vector;
7 use scale diagrams, or otherwise, to find the magnitude and direction of the resultant of a number of forces.

1.1 Vectors

Distance and displacement

Distance has magnitude only and can be described in terms of a number and unit; for example, 10 metres. Such a quantity defined by a number and a unit is called a **scalar** quantity.

Displacement has magnitude and direction; for example, 10 m due West. This is a **vector** quantity which is defined by a number, a unit and a direction.

To illustrate the difference between distance and displacement, consider an object moving from point A taking an irregular route and ending up at point B, shown in Figure 1.

The distance is the length of the irregular path from A to B. The displacement is the straight line path between the starting point A and the finishing point B.

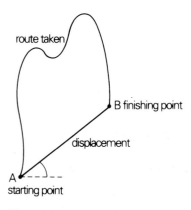

Figure 1

The displacement can be represented by an arrow drawn in the direction of the displacement and of length proportional to the magnitude of the displacement. This arrow is called a **vector** and represents the vector quantity shown in Figure 2.

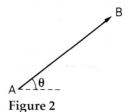

Figure 2

Resultant displacement

A person starts at A, crosses a pelican crossing to B and walks along the pavement to C.

In going from A to C what is
a) the distance travelled
b) the resultant displacement?

a) distance travelled = (A to B) then (B to C)
    = 9 + 12
    = 21 m

b) Drawing a scale diagram of the route allows the resultant displacement to be found.

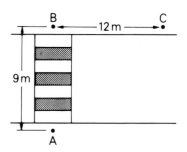

Figure 3

If we choose 1 cm to represent 3 m the resultant displacement is found by measuring the length of AC and the angle BAC
    AB = 9 m represented by 3 cm
    BC = 12 m represented by 4 cm
    by measurement length of AC = 5 cm
    this represents 5 × 3 = 15 m
    angle BAC = 53°

The resultant displacement is 15 m at an angle of 53° to direction AB.

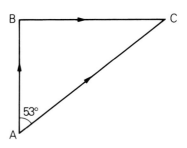

Figure 4

Example 1

A person starts walking into a maze, the direction of the first section being due North.

   If the starting point is X, find the distance to point Y and also determine the displacement of Y from X.

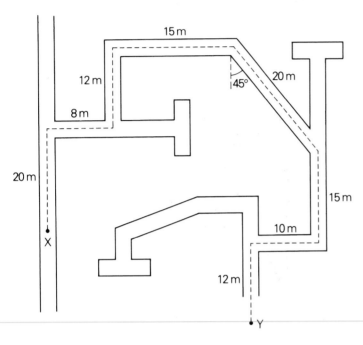

a)   total distance walked = 20 + 8 + 12 + 15 + 20 + 15 + 10 + 12
                                    = 112 m

b)   using a scale diagram with 1 cm to represent 10 m

   length of XY = 2.8 cm
   displacement of Y = 28 m

The displacement of Y from X is 28 metres at an angle of 20° South of East.

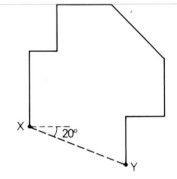

Velocity and speed

Speed is a scalar quantity with magnitude only: it tells only how fast an object is travelling.

Velocity is a vector quantity which provides the direction of travel as well as the speed.

Two cars approach a cross-roads at 70 mph. They each have the same speed, 70 mph, but they have different velocities:

   car A velocity is 70 mph due North

   car B velocity is 70 mph due West.

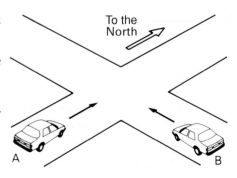

Figure 5

Resultant velocity

The velocity of an object can be the result of combining two separate velocities.

A swimmer attempts to swim due West across a river without allowing for the current.
   The actual velocity of the swimmer is the resultant of his velocity through the water and the velocity of the current.

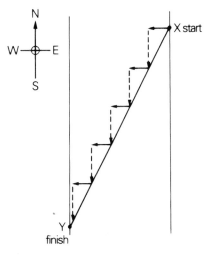

Figure 6

Figure 7

As the swimmer swims West (solid line) the current pulls him at a certain speed South (dotted line). This process takes place continuously so that the direction of motion is along XY.

The resultant velocity can be found by drawing a scale diagram, Figure 7.

Example 2

A ship is sailing due East at 5 m s^{-1}. A passenger walks due North at 2 m s^{-1}.
What is the resultant velocity of the passenger?

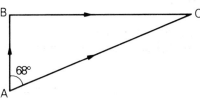

Using a scale diagram where 1 cm represents 1 m s^{-1}, the velocity of the passenger is represented by AB, a line 2 cm long, due North.
   The velocity of the ship is represented by BC, a line 5 cm long, due East.
   The resultant velocity is represented by line AC.

   length AC = 5.4 cm. This represents 5.4 m s^{-1}.

   angle BAC = 68°

The resultant velocity of the passenger is 5.4 m s^{-1} at 68° East of North.

Force as a vector

The quantities displacement, velocity and force are vector quantities and are therefore added as vectors. The combined effect of two or more vectors is called the resultant of the vectors and is their vector sum. If two forces act on an object as shown in Figure 8 the resultant can be found using a scale diagram in which the length of the line represents the magnitude of the force and the angle at which the line is drawn represents the direction. The vectors are joined head to tail as indicated, Figure 9.

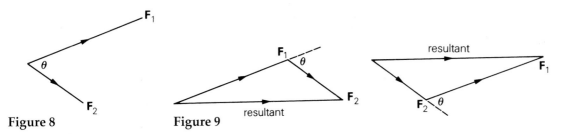

Figure 8   **Figure 9**

The same value for the magnitude and direction of the resultant is obtained irrespective of which vector is drawn first.

Example 3

Two forces of 15 N and 6 N act on an object at an angle of 80° between the directions of the forces. Find the resultant force. For the scale diagram choose 1 cm to represent a force of 2 N.

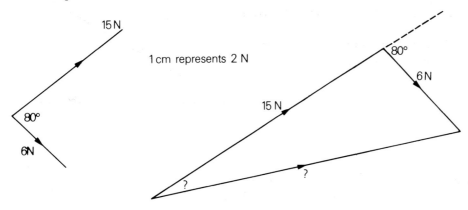

The length of the resultant vector is 8.6 cm so the resultant force is 8.6 × 2 which is 17.2 N. The angle between the resultant force and the 15 N is measured to be 20°.

Object acted upon by three forces

A brass ring is held at rest by pulling on it with three strings attached to three spring balances.

The readings of each balance are noted:

$F_1 = 12\,N$

$F_2 = 5\,N$

$F_3 = 13\,N$

Force F_1 acts at 67° to the horizontal.
Force F_2 acts at 23° to the horizontal.
Force F_3 acts vertically.

Draw a scale diagram using 1 cm to represent 2 newtons.

The vector diagram forms a triangle.

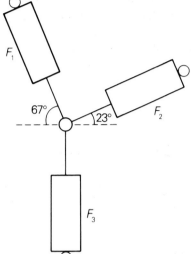

Figure 10

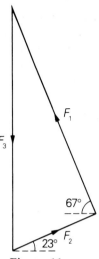

Figure 11

We can conclude that:

when an object is in equilibrium under the action of three forces, the three forces can be represented in magnitude by the three sides of a triangle.

Resolution of vectors

Two forces can be combined to give a single force called the resultant which can replace these two forces.
The reverse process is also possible, a single force being replaced by two forces called **components**. These often act at right angles to each other.

Consider a single force F acting along a line at an angle to the horizontal.

This force can be split into two components:

F_H which acts horizontally;

F_V which acts vertically.

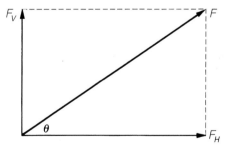

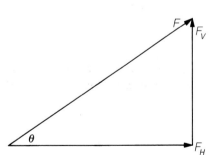

From the vector triangle

$$\frac{F_H}{F} = \cos\theta$$

and

$$\frac{F_V}{F} = \sin\theta$$

so that $F_H = F\cos\theta$
  and $F_V = F\sin\theta$

Example 4

A skier is pulled up a slope by a tow rope exerting a force of 600 N at an angle of 50° to the slope.

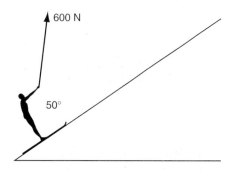

Find the components of the 600 N force acting parallel to the slope and at right angles to the slope.

force parallel $F_1 = F \cos \theta = 600 \cos 50° = 600 \times 0.64$
$\qquad\qquad = 386$

The force parallel to the slope is 386 N.

force at right angles $F_2 = F \sin \theta = 600 \sin 50°$
$\qquad\qquad\qquad\qquad = 600 \times 0.77$
$\qquad\qquad\qquad\qquad = 460$

The force acting at right angles to the slope is 460 N.

Summary

A scalar quantity has magnitude only.

A vector quantity has both a magnitude and a direction.

Velocity, displacement and force are examples of vectors. Speed and distance are examples of scalars.

The sum of two or more vectors is represented by a single vector called the **resultant**.

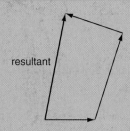

A vector V can be represented by two components, $V \sin \theta$ and $V \cos \theta$, at right angles to each other.

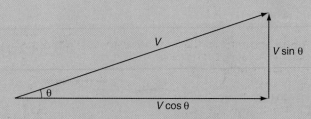

Questions

1 A person steps on the bottom step of an escalator as shown in the diagram.

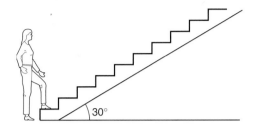

If the steps rise vertically a distance of 0.5 metre per second what is the displacement of the person after 6 seconds?

2 A ball is released at the top of a rail which is curved as shown. If the ball is released at point X what is the displacement of the ball at Y?

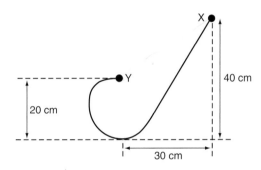

3 A ball, suspended by a string, is held at an angle of 40° to the vertical by a horizontal force F. The force in the string is 30 N.
   a) Calculate the vertical component of the force in the string.
   b) What is the weight of the ball?
   c) Determine the horizontal component of the force in the string and hence find the magnitude of the horizontal force F.

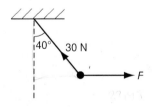

4 A runner starts at point W and runs at a constant speed to X then Y, finally ending up at Z. He takes 48 seconds.
   a) How far has he gone?
   b) What is his displacement from W when he is at Z?
   c) Find his average speed.
   d) What was his average velocity?

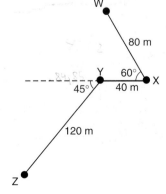

5 A boat is pulled by two forces as shown. Using a scale drawing find the magnitude and direction of the resultant of these forces.

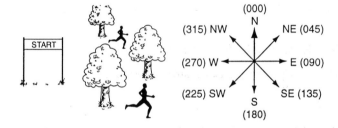

6 a) State the difference between vector and scalar quantities.
   b) In an orienteering event, competitors navigate from the start to control points around a set course.
   Two orienteers Andy and Paul, take part in a race in a flat area. Andy can run faster than Paul, but Paul is a better navigator.

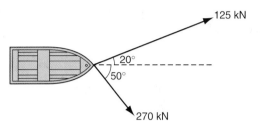

From the start, Andy runs 700m North (000) then 700m South-East (135) to arrive at the first control point. He has an average running speed of $3\,\text{m}\,\text{s}^{-1}$.
   i) By scale drawing or otherwise, find the displacement of Andy, from the starting point, when he reaches the first control point.
   ii) Calculate the average velocity of Andy between the start and the first control point.
   iii) Paul runs directly from the start to the first control point with an average running speed of $2.5\,\text{m}\,\text{s}^{-1}$.
   Determine the average velocity of Paul.
   iv) Paul leaves the starting point 5 minutes after Andy. Show by calculation who is first to arrive at this control point.

SQA

7 A barge is travelling, with a velocity of $2.0\,\text{m}\,\text{s}^{-1}$ due West, along a canal. A girl runs with a speed of $4.8\,\text{m}\,\text{s}^{-1}$, from X to Y across the deck of the barge as shown below.

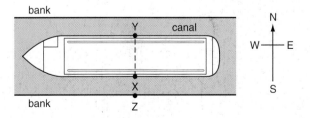

By drawing a scale diagram or otherwise, find the resultant velocity of the girl relative to someone at point Z on the bank of the canal.

SQA

8 An oil-rig has to be towed to a new operating area in the North Sea. It is towed by horizontal cables attached to two tugs as shown below.

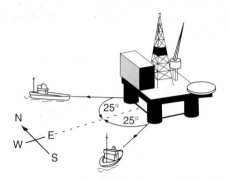

The oil-rig has a mass of 20×10^6 kg and is initially at rest.

a) **i)** If the forces applied to the oil-rig by the cables are each 1.0×10^6 N in the directions shown, what is their resultant force on the oil-rig?

ii) What is the magnitude of the acceleration of the oil-rig just as it moves from rest?

b) The cables continue to exert the same forces on the oil-rig. The acceleration of the oil-rig is continuously monitored and it is found that the acceleration decreases from its initial value. Explain the observation.

SQA

9 A water skier is being towed as shown by a boat travelling at constant speed.

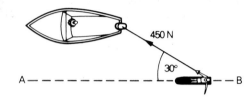

If the tension in the rope is 450 N, calculate the force acting along line AB opposing the forward motion of the skier. *SQA*

10 An acrobat is stationary at the centre of a tightrope. The angle between the rope and the horizontal is 10° as shown.

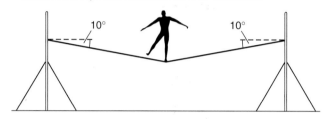

If the acrobat weighs 600 N, calculate the tension in the rope.

SQA

Topic 1.1 Test 1

1   A car follows the curved path shown. It starts at X and finishes at Y.
Determine the distance travelled by the car.
What is the displacement of the car when it arrives at Y?

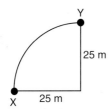

2   A runner runs from P to Q in 2 seconds at a constant speed.
Calculate his speed.
State his velocity as he passes point Q.

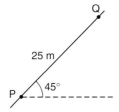

3 a)   State the difference between a vector and a scalar quantity.
   b)   The table shows a list of various quantities.
Copy the table and fill in the correct description as indicated for
the first quantity.

quantity	
time	scalar
energy	
power	
speed	
velocity	
mass	
distance	
displacement	

4 a)   A treasure hunter traces out the path shown.
Determine his final displacement from the start.

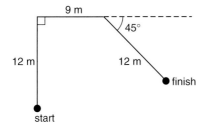

b)   A moving escalator travels at 0.8 m s⁻¹ due North.
A clockwork car is set moving due East at 0.5 m s⁻¹.
Using a scale diagram or otherwise find the velocity of the car
relative to the ground.

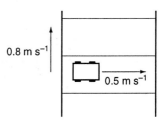

5   Three forces act on an object as shown.
Which vector diagram correctly shows the resultant *R*?

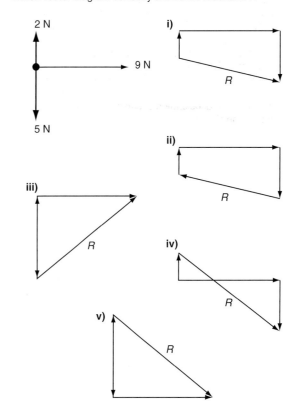

6   A ball is projected at an angle to the horizontal as shown. If the
velocity is 18 m s⁻¹ at 50° to the horizontal, find the vertical and
horizontal components of this velocity.

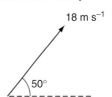

7 A crate, weighing 980 N, is suspended from the ceiling by two ropes tied as shown.
Using a scale diagram, find the forces F_1 and F_2 acting in the ropes.

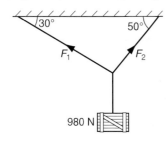

b) An orienteer ran 6 km North and then 8 km East.
He ran on level ground and it took him 2 hours.
Calculate his average speed.
What was his average velocity?

5 With the aid of a diagram explain the meaning of the **resultant** of a number of forces.

6 A sledge is pulled across a horizontal surface by a force pulling at the angle shown.
Determine the horizontal and vertical components of this force.

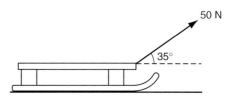

7 A weight of 60 N is suspended from the ceiling.
A horizontal force F is applied and holds the rope at an angle of 40° to the vertical.
Using a scale diagram, or otherwise, find the magnitudes of the horizontal force F and the force in the rope T.

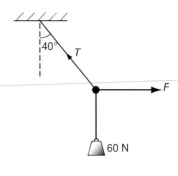

Topic 1.1 Test 2

1 A pendulum bob is suspended from the ceiling by a string which is 1.8 m long.
It is swung round from position X to position Y.
How far has the bob travelled in moving from X to Y?
What is the displacement of Y from X?

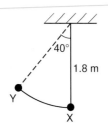

2 A runner follows the path shown starting at A and arriving at B 5 seconds later.
Determine the speed of the runner.
What is his velocity?

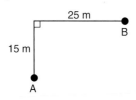

3 Write down the definitions of
a) a vector
b) a scalar
and give **three** examples of each.

4 **a)** A woman walks 500 m North, 200 m East and then 400 m due South.
What distance did she walk?
Calculate her displacement from the start.

Topic 1.1 Test 3

1 A runner runs on the perimeter of a square field.
He starts at A and runs to C.

Which of the following statement(s) is/are true?

  I At C he has travelled a distance of 80 m.
  II At C his displacement is 40 √2 m at 45° to AD.
  III At C his displacement is 80 m at 45° to AD.
i) I only
ii) II only
iii) III only
iv) I and II only
v) I and III only

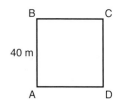

2 Two equations are given in a maths book:

$$u = \frac{\text{distance}}{\text{time}} \qquad v = \frac{\text{displacement}}{\text{time}}$$

Which letter refers to speed and which to velocity?

3 Which of the following contains vectors only?
- **i)** mass, velocity, distance
- **ii)** mass, speed, displacement
- **iii)** speed, distance, energy
- **iv)** velocity, displacement, force
- **v)** velocity, distance, power

4 a) A yacht starts at X and follows the path shown arriving at Q some time later.
What is the displacement of the yacht from the starting point?

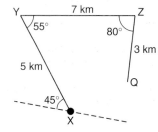

b) A conveyor belt travels at 0.5 m s⁻¹ and a box slides across it at a speed of 0.3 m s⁻¹ as shown.
Determine the velocity of the box as seen by a stationary observer.

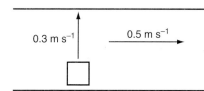

5 Pairs of forces act on a rock.
The vector triangle for each is shown.
Which diagram(s) correctly show(s) the vector for the resultant?
- **i)** I, II and III
- **ii)** II and III only
- **iii)** I only
- **iv)** II only
- **v)** III only

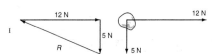

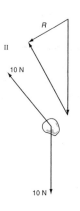

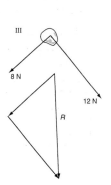

6 A skier is pulled up an incline as shown.
The tow wire exerts a force of 450 N as shown.
Determine the component of this force **at right angles to the ground**.

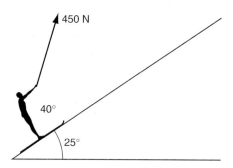

7 A car is suspended by two ropes passing over pulleys.
If the car has a weight of 15 000 N determine the forces acting in the ropes, T_1 and T_2.

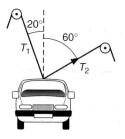

Topic 1.2
Equations of Motion

Objectives

When you have completed the work of this topic you should be able to:

1 state that the acceleration is the change in velocity per unit time;
2 describe the principles of a method for measuring acceleration;
3 draw an acceleration–time graph using information obtained from a velocity–time graph for motion with a constant acceleration;
4 use terms 'constant velocity' and 'constant acceleration' to describe motion represented in graphical or tabular form;
5 show how the following relationships can be derived from basic definitions in kinematics
   $$v = u + at \quad s = ut + \tfrac{1}{2}at^2 \quad v^2 = u^2 + 2as$$
6 carry out calculations using the above kinematic relationships.

1.2 Equations of Motion

Uniformly accelerated motion in a straight line

When an object moves with uniform acceleration in a straight line it is often necessary to predict some of the quantities involved such as displacement or the velocity attained after a given time. This is most usefully done by developing a set of equations usually known as the **equations of motion**. It is essential to remember that these are valid for **uniform** acceleration in a straight line only and cannot be used when the acceleration is variable.

The following symbols will be used:

u initial velocity s displacement t time interval
v final velocity a uniform acceleration

We shall consider motion in a straight line only, so that the vector quantities, velocity and displacement, will not have a direction quoted. When an object such as a car is moving, the changes in motion which take place over a given period of time can be displayed in the form of a graph. For example a car moving along a motorway at a steady velocity of $30\,\text{m s}^{-1}$ (70 mph) will have the velocity–time graph shown in Figure 1. Because the velocity is uniform, the displacement in each second will be the same, namely 30 metres, so that after one second the displacement will be 30 m and after two seconds 60 m. This is shown graphically in Figure 2. After t seconds the displacement will be $30 \times t$ metres.

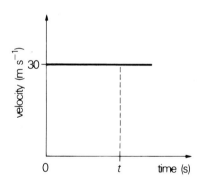

Figure 1

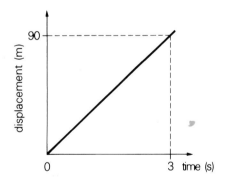

Figure 2

If however the car starts from rest and accelerates by $2\,\text{m s}^{-2}$, the velocity will be changing by $2\,\text{m s}^{-1}$ every second and the displacements in successive seconds will be continuously increasing.

A velocity–time graph of this motion, Figure 3, can be constructed as follows.

At the start the velocity will be zero.

After 1 second the velocity will be $2\,\text{m s}^{-1}$.

After 2 seconds the velocity will be $4\,\text{m s}^{-1}$.

After 3 seconds the velocity will be $6\,\text{m s}^{-1}$.

After 4 seconds the velocity will be $8\,\text{m s}^{-1}$.

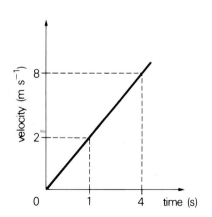

Figure 3

The acceleration can be found by calculating the gradient of the velocity-time graph. In Figure 4 the velocity is u at time t_1 and v at time t_2.

$$\text{acceleration} = \frac{\text{change of velocity}}{\text{time interval}}$$

$$a = \frac{v - u}{t_2 - t_1} = \text{gradient of graph}$$

using values from Figure 3,

$$v = 8\,\text{m s}^{-1} \text{ when } t_2 = 4\,\text{s}$$
$$u = 2\,\text{m s}^{-1} \text{ when } t_1 = 1\,\text{s}$$
$$\Rightarrow \qquad a = \frac{8 - 2}{4 - 1} = \frac{6}{3} = 2$$

The acceleration is $2\,\text{m s}^{-2}$.

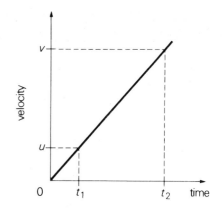

Figure 4

Displacement–time graph

The displacement–time graph associated with the motion represented in Figure 5 can be constructed in the following way.

For uniform acceleration

the average velocity is given by $\bar{v} = \dfrac{u + v}{2}$

and the displacement is given by $s = \text{average velocity} \times \text{time}$.
We can apply this to the data given in Figure 5:

displacement in first second
   initial velocity   = 0; final velocity = $2\,\text{m s}^{-1}$
   average velocity = $1\,\text{m s}^{-1}$
   displacement   = $1\,\text{m}$

displacement in second second
   initial velocity   = $2\,\text{m s}^{-1}$; final velocity = $4\,\text{m s}^{-1}$
   average velocity = $3\,\text{m s}^{-1}$
   displacement   = $3\,\text{m}$
   the total displacement after 2 seconds = $1 + 3 = 4\,\text{m}$

displacement in third second
   initial velocity   = $4\,\text{m s}^{-1}$; final velocity = $6\,\text{m s}^{-1}$
   average velocity = $5\,\text{m s}^{-1}$
   displacement   = $5\,\text{m}$
   the total displacement after 3 seconds = $4 + 5 = 9\,\text{m}$

displacement in fourth second
   initial velocity   = $6\,\text{m s}^{-1}$; final velocity = $8\,\text{m s}^{-1}$
   average velocity = $7\,\text{m s}^{-1}$
   displacement   = $7\,\text{m}$
   the total displacement from the start = $9 + 7 = 16\,\text{m}$
The displacement–time graph is shown in Figure 6.

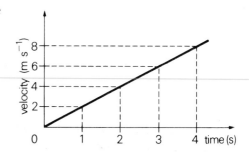

Figure 5

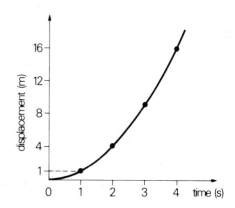

Figure 6

Velocity–time graph from displacement–time graph (constant velocity)

We can use the data from a displacement–time graph to draw the corresponding velocity–time graph.

The displacement–time graph for an object moving in a straight line is shown in Figure 7.

$$\text{average velocity} = \frac{\text{displacement}}{\text{time}}$$

$$= \text{gradient of line}$$

over first second   gradient $= \dfrac{3-0}{1-0} = 3$

over second second   gradient $= \dfrac{6-3}{2-1} = 3$

over third second   gradient $= \dfrac{9-6}{3-2} = 3$

The velocity is constant at $3\,\text{m s}^{-1}$.

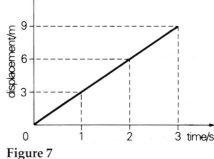

Figure 7

The graph of velocity against time is shown in Figure 8

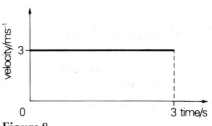

Figure 8

Velocity–time graph from displacement–time graph (constant acceleration)

A car starts from rest and the displacement varies with time as shown. The slope of this graph is continuously changing so that the gradient is not constant.

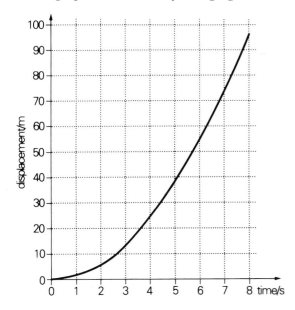

Figure 9

17

The instantaneous velocity is the gradient of the graph at any point. An estimate of the velocity at any instant can be obtained by calculating the average velocity over a short time interval.

In this case a one second interval is used, Figure 10.

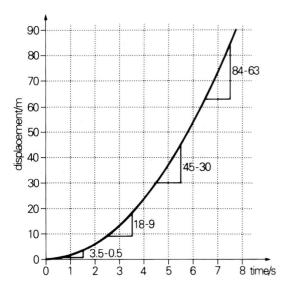

Figure 10

for $t = 1\,\text{s}$ average velocity $= \dfrac{3.5 - 0.5}{1.5 - 0.5} = 3$

for $t = 3\,\text{s}$ average velocity $= \dfrac{18 - 9}{3.5 - 2.5} = 9$

for $t = 5\,\text{s}$ average velocity $= \dfrac{45 - 30}{5.5 - 4.5} = 15$

for $t = 7\,\text{s}$ average velocity $= \dfrac{84 - 63}{7.5 - 6.5} = 21$

When these velocities are plotted, a straight line graph is obtained.

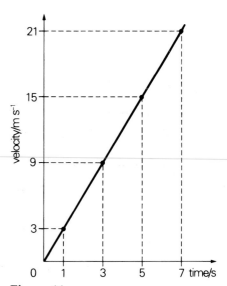

Figure 11

Acceleration–time graph from a velocity–time graph

Using the data from the velocity–time graph for the motion of the car, Figure 11, an acceleration–time graph can be constructed.

Acceleration = gradient of the velocity-time graph: $a = \dfrac{v - u}{t_2 - t_1}$

from 1 s to 3 s   acceleration $= \dfrac{9 - 3}{3 - 1} = 3$

from 3 s to 5 s   acceleration $= \dfrac{15 - 9}{5 - 3} = 3$

from 5 s to 7 s   acceleration $= \dfrac{21 - 15}{7 - 5} = 3$

In this case the acceleration is constant at $3\,\text{m s}^{-2}$. The acceleration–time graph is as shown in Figure 12.

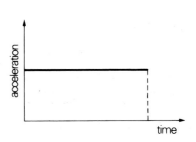

Figure 12

Starting from the displacement–time graph, the corresponding velocity–time graph was constructed. It is therefore possible, starting from the displacement–time graph, to construct the corresponding velocity–time and acceleration–time graphs for the motion of the car. These are given in Figure 13.

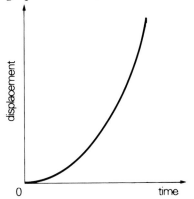 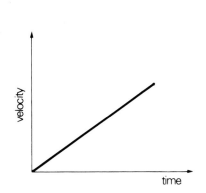 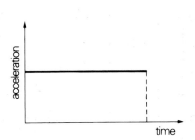

Figure 13

Example 1

The velocity of a train varies as shown.
Plot an acceleration–time graph for the motion.

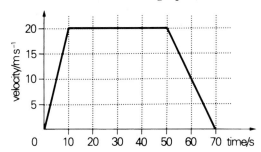

from 0 to 10 s $\quad a = \dfrac{20 - 0}{10 - 0} = +2$

from 10 to 50 s $\quad a = \dfrac{20 - 20}{50 - 10} = 0$

from 50 to 70 s $\quad a = \dfrac{0 - 20}{70 - 50} = -1$

The resulting acceleration–time graph is shown below.

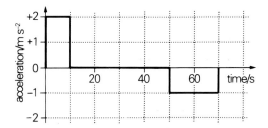

Equations of motion

Using graphical methods, we can now develop equations which can be used to analyse uniformly accelerated motion.

Figure 14 shows the velocity–time graph for a body which, initially moving at velocity u accelerates at a for time t until the final velocity is v.

final velocity = initial velocity + increase in velocity

but after a time t the increase will be at. The equation will be

$$v = u + at \qquad \ldots[1]$$

If the same graph is redrawn as in Figure 15 it can be seen that the area under the graph can be divided into a rectangle and a triangle. The total area gives the displacement.

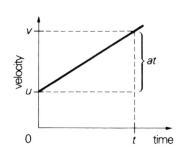

Figure 14

For the rectangle: base = $t - 0 = t$;   height = $u - 0 = u$

$\Rightarrow$ area = base × height = ut

For the triangle: base = $t - 0 = t$;   height = $v - u$,

but from equation [1], $v - u = at$

$\Rightarrow$ area = $\frac{1}{2}$ × base × height

$= \frac{1}{2} \times t \times at$

$= \frac{1}{2}at^2$

$\therefore$ total displacement = area of rectangle + area of triangle

$\Rightarrow \qquad s = ut + \frac{1}{2}at^2 \qquad \ldots[2]$

By combining equations [1] and [2], a third equation can be developed which does not involve time.

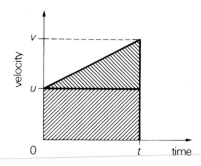

Figure 15

From equation [1], $t = \dfrac{v - u}{a}$

and substituting for t in equation [2]

$$s = u\left(\frac{v - u}{a}\right) + \frac{1}{2}a\left(\frac{v - u}{a}\right)^2$$

$$= \frac{uv - u^2}{a} + \frac{v^2 - 2uv + u^2}{2a}$$

$\Rightarrow \qquad 2as = 2uv - 2u^2 + v^2 - 2uv + u^2$

$= v^2 - u^2$

$\Rightarrow \qquad v^2 = u^2 + 2as \qquad \ldots[3]$

The acceleration term can be eliminated between equations [1] and [2] to give equation [4].

From equation [1], $a = \dfrac{v - u}{t}$

and substituting in equation [2]

$$s = ut + \frac{1}{2}at^2$$

$$= ut + \frac{1}{2}\left(\frac{v - u}{t}\right)t^2$$

$$= ut + \frac{1}{2}vt - \frac{1}{2}ut$$

$$= \frac{1}{2}ut + \frac{1}{2}vt$$

$\Rightarrow \qquad s = \left(\dfrac{u + v}{2}\right)t \qquad \ldots[4]$

The term $\left(\dfrac{u + v}{2}\right)$ is the average velocity $\bar{v}$ if acceleration is uniform.

Example 2

A ball is thrown vertically upwards at $30 \, \text{m s}^{-1}$.
The velocity–time graph is shown.
a) Construct an acceleration–time graph.
b) Calculate the displacement at one second intervals and draw the displacement–time graph.

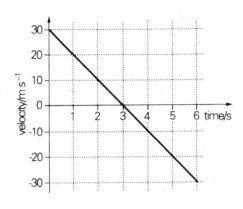

a) acceleration = gradient of velocity–time graph.

during first second $\qquad a = \dfrac{20 - 30}{1 - 0} = -10$

during third second $\qquad a = \dfrac{0 - 10}{3 - 2} = -10$

during fifth second $\qquad a = \dfrac{-20 - (-10)}{5 - 4} = -10$

The acceleration is constant at $-10 \, \text{m s}^{-2}$ and gives the graph shown.

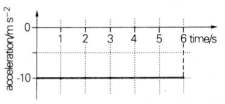

b) Using $s = ut + \frac{1}{2}at^2$, this becomes
$$s = 30t + \tfrac{1}{2}(-10)t^2$$
$$s = 30t - 5t^2$$

at $t = 1$ second $\qquad s = 30 - 5 = 25$
at $t = 2$ seconds $\qquad s = 60 - 20 = 40$
at $t = 3$ seconds $\qquad s = 90 - 45 = 45$
at $t = 4$ seconds $\qquad s = 120 - 80 = 40$
at $t = 5$ seconds $\qquad s = 150 - 125 = 25$
at $t = 6$ seconds $\qquad s = 180 - 180 = 0$

The displacement–time graph is as shown.

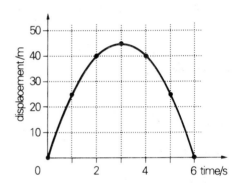

Example 3

A car starts from rest and accelerates uniformly at $3 \, \text{m s}^{-2}$.
a) How long will it take to reach a velocity of $30 \, \text{m s}^{-1}$?
b) What distance will it have travelled in this time?

a) $u = 0, \quad a = 3 \, \text{m s}^{-2}, \quad v = 30 \, \text{m s}^{-1}, \quad t = ?$
Using: $\qquad\qquad\qquad v = u + at$
$\Rightarrow \qquad\qquad\qquad 30 = 0 + 3t$
$\Rightarrow \qquad\qquad\qquad t = \frac{30}{3} = 10$

The car takes 10 seconds to reach a velocity of $30 \, \text{m s}^{-1}$.

b) $u = 0, \quad v = 30 \, \text{m s}^{-1}, \quad t = 10 \, \text{s}, \quad s = ?$

Using $\qquad s = \left(\dfrac{u + v}{2}\right)t$

$\Rightarrow \qquad s = \left(\dfrac{0 + 30}{2}\right)10$

$\qquad\qquad = 15 \times 10 = 150$

The distance travelled is 150 m.

Acceleration produced by gravity

The acceleration 'g' produced by the gravitational field of the Earth is always directed towards the centre of the Earth.

It is usual to measure displacement in a direction away from the centre of the Earth so that all vectors upwards are positive and all vectors downwards are negative.

positive vectors	negative vectors
upward displacement	downward displacement
upward velocity	downward velocity
upward acceleration	downward acceleration

In this book, the approximate value of acceleration due to gravity is always taken to be $-9.8\,\text{m s}^{-1}$.

Example 4

If a ball is dropped from a window, what is its velocity 3 seconds later?

$$u = 0, \quad a = -9.8\,\text{m s}^{-2}, \quad t = 3\,\text{s}, \quad v = ?$$

Using: $\qquad\qquad v = u + at$

$\Rightarrow \qquad\qquad v = 0 + (-9.8) \times 3 = -29.4$

The velocity of the ball 3 seconds later is 29.4 m s^{-1} downwards.
(The negative sign shows that the velocity of the ball is downwards.)

Example 5

An arrow is shot vertically upwards with a velocity of $20\,\text{m s}^{-1}$.

a)   How long will the arrow take to reach its maximum height?
b)   What is the maximum height reached by the arrow?

a)   The maximum height is reached when the velocity of the arrow is zero: the velocity then becomes negative as the arrow falls.

$$u = +20\,\text{m s}^{-1}, \quad v = 0\,\text{m s}^{-1}, \quad a = -9.8\,\text{m s}^{-2}, \quad t = ?$$

Using: $\qquad\qquad v = u + at$

$\Rightarrow \qquad\qquad 0 = 20 - 9.8 \times t$

$\Rightarrow \qquad\qquad t = \dfrac{-20}{-9.8} = 2.04$

The arrow takes 2 seconds to reach its maximum height.

b) $u = +20\,\text{m s}^{-1}, \quad v = 0\,\text{m s}^{-1}, \quad t = 2\,\text{s}$

Using: $\qquad\qquad s = \left(\dfrac{u + v}{2}\right)t$

$\Rightarrow \qquad\qquad s = \left(\dfrac{20 + 0}{2}\right) \times 2$

$\qquad\qquad\qquad = 20$

The maximum height reached is 20 metres.

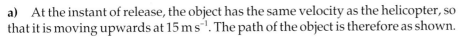

Example 6

A helicopter is climbing vertically with a velocity of $15\,\mathrm{m\,s^{-1}}$ when an object is released from it. If the object hits the ground 4 s later, find

a) the velocity of the object just as it hits the ground $v = -24.2$ downwards

b) the original height of the object. h

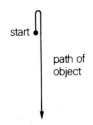

a) At the instant of release, the object has the same velocity as the helicopter, so that it is moving upwards at $15\,\mathrm{m\,s^{-1}}$. The path of the object is therefore as shown.

When the object is released: $u = +15\,\mathrm{m\,s^{-1}}$, $a = -9.8\,\mathrm{m\,s^{-2}}$, $t = 4\,\mathrm{s}$, $v = ?$

Using: $\qquad\qquad v = u + at$

$\Rightarrow \qquad\qquad v = +15 - 9.8 \times 4$

$\qquad\qquad\qquad = +15 - 39.2 = -24.2$

The velocity of the object just as it hits the ground is $24\,\mathrm{m\,s^{-1}}$ downwards.

b) To calculate the original height of the object, we must find the displacement of the object from the start.

Using: $\qquad\qquad s = ut + \tfrac{1}{2}at^2$

$\Rightarrow \qquad\qquad s = +15 \times 4 - \tfrac{1}{2} \times 9.8 \times 4^2$

$\qquad\qquad\qquad = +60 - 78.4 = -18.4$

The displacement from the starting point is 18.4 m downwards so that the original height is 18.4 m.

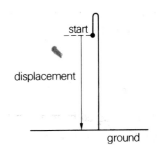

Example 7

An object is projected vertically upwards with a velocity of $40\,\mathrm{m\,s^{-1}}$.

a) Find the time taken to reach the maximum height. 4.08

b) Calculate the maximum height reached. 63.2

c) Find the time taken to fall back to the starting point.

a) At the maximum height the object stops rising so that the velocity is zero.

$u = +40\,\mathrm{m\,s^{-1}}$, $v = 0$, $a = -9.8\,\mathrm{m\,s^{-2}}$.

Using: $\qquad\qquad v = u + at$

$\Rightarrow \qquad\qquad 0 = +40 - 9.8 \times t$

$\Rightarrow \qquad\qquad -40 = -9.8t$

$\Rightarrow \qquad\qquad t = \dfrac{-40}{-9.8} = 4.08$

The time taken to reach the maximum height is 4.1 seconds.

b) The maximum height is reached after 4 s

$t = 4\,\mathrm{s}$, $u = +40\,\mathrm{m\,s^{-1}}$, $a = -9.8\,\mathrm{m\,s^{-2}}$, $s = ?$

using $s = ut + \tfrac{1}{2}at^2$

$\qquad\qquad s = 40 \times 4 - \tfrac{1}{2} \times 9.8 \times 4^2$

$\Rightarrow \qquad s = 160 - 78.4$

$\Rightarrow \qquad s = 81.6$

The maximum height is 81.6 m.

c) When the object has returned to the ground the displacement is zero.

$$s = 0, \quad u = +40\,\text{m s}^{-1}, \quad a = -9.8\,\text{m s}^{-2}, \quad t = ?$$

using $s = ut + \frac{1}{2}at^2$

$$0 = +40 \times t - \frac{1}{2} \times 9.8 \times t^2$$

$$\Rightarrow \quad 0 = 40t - 4.9t^2$$

$$4.9t^2 - 40t = 0$$

$$\Rightarrow \quad t^2 - 8.2t = 0$$

$$\Rightarrow \quad t(t - 8.2) = 0$$

$$t = 0 \text{ or } 8.2$$

The time taken to return to the starting point is 8.2 s.

Measuring acceleration

Acceleration can be measured from a multiflash photograph of a moving object. Figure 16 shows a multiflash photograph of a white marker attached to an accelerating vehicle running on a sloping linear air track. A scale showing in centimetres the actual distance travelled is given underneath. The stroboscopic light flashes every 0.1 s. The vehicle started from rest.

Figure 16

The spaces between each image are increasing, indicating that the velocity is also increasing. The average velocity during each time interval is given by

$$\text{average velocity} = \frac{\text{displacement during time interval}}{\text{time interval}}$$

In order to calculate the acceleration a table is drawn up.

distance travelled in each 0.1 s interval (m)	0.01	0.03	0.05	0.07	0.09	0.11
average velocity in each 0.1 s interval (m s^{-1})	0.10	0.30	0.50	0.70	0.90	1.10
increase in velocity during each 0.1 s interval (m s^{-1})		0.20	0.20	0.20	0.20	0.20
increase in velocity during a 1 s interval (m s^{-1})		2.00	2.00	2.00	2.00	2.00

Table 1

The acceleration is thus uniform and equal to $2\,\text{m s}^{-2}$.

If the acceleration is uniform, its value can be checked from:
$$s = ut + \tfrac{1}{2}at^2$$
where s = total displacement from the start.

From Figure 16 it can be seen that when $t = 0.6\,\text{s}$, $s = 0.36\,\text{m}$,

so that $s = 0.36$, $u = 0$, $t = 0.6\,\text{s}$, $a = ?$

$$0.36 = 0 \times 0.6 + \tfrac{1}{2}a \times 0.6^2 = 0 + \tfrac{1}{2} \times 0.36 \times a = 0.18a$$

$$\Rightarrow \quad a = \frac{0.36}{0.18} = 2$$

The acceleration is thus $2\,\text{m s}^{-2}$, confirming the result obtained from Table 1.

Example 8

A golf ball is dropped from rest and a multiflash photograph of the motion is taken at 12 flashes per second. A reproduction of the photograph is shown.

A metre stick is set up vertically and also photographed to provide the scale factor (i.e. to indicate how lengths on the photograph are related to actual distances fallen).
a)   What is the scale factor?
b)   Calculate the acceleration of the ball.

a)   In the photograph the metre stick measures 8 cm.
This means that 1 metre (100 cm) is represented by 8 cm.

The scale factor is $\dfrac{100}{8}$.

b)   The time between images is $\dfrac{1}{12}$ second.

Drawing up a table allows the acceleration to be calculated. Distances between images are taken by direct measurement from the photograph.

distance	velocity v	change of velocity v
cm	cm s^{-1}	cm s^{-1}
0.3	3.6	
0.8	9.6	6.0
1.4	16.8	7.2
1.9	22.8	6.0
2.5	30.0	7.2

$$\text{average change of velocity} = \frac{6.0 + 7.2 + 6.0 + 7.2}{4} = 6.6$$

$$\text{average acceleration} = \frac{6.6}{\frac{1}{12}} = 79\,\text{cm s}^{-2}$$

The 'real life' acceleration is given by

$$\text{calculated acceleration} \times \text{scale factor} = 79 \times \frac{100}{8} = 988\,\text{cm s}^{-2}$$

From the analysis of the photograph, the acceleration of the ball is $9.9\,\text{m s}^{-2}$.

Measuring acceleration using a computer

The acceleration can also be found using a computer with suitable accessories.

A light beam and photodiode are used to provide a light gate which operates in conjunction with a mask.

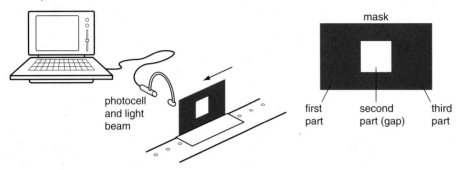

Figure 17

The light gate is connected through an interfacing device and a datalogger to the computer. Appropriate software is used which has been written to interpret the signals from the light gate. The mask is fitted to a moving object and the opaque parts of the mask cut through the light beam sending signals via the light gate.

The data used to carry out the calculation of average acceleration are as follows:

> time t_1 time for first part of the mask to cut through the light beam;
> time t_2 time for third part of the mask to cut through the light beam;
> time t period of time between t_1 and t_2
>   lengths of each section of the mask.

The software then calculates the two average velocities u_1 and u_2 for each part of the mask.

The average acceleration is then determined using

$$\text{average acceleration} = \frac{\text{change of velocity}}{\text{time}}$$

$$a = \frac{u_2 - u_1}{t}$$

It is usually possible to display t_1, t_2, u_1, u_2, t and a individually if desired.

Example 9

An experiment is carried out to find the acceleration of a moving trolley using a computer fitted with suitable equipment. By pressing the appropriate buttons information is displayed in turn on the screen:

> average velocity $u_1 = 1.428$
> average velocity $u_2 = 1.484$
> period of time t $= 0.026$

What value do these give for acceleration?

$$\text{average acceleration} \quad a = \frac{u_2 - u_1}{t} = \frac{1.484 - 1.428}{0.026}$$

$$a = \frac{0.056}{0.026} = 2.15$$

The average acceleration is 2.15 m s^{-2}.

Summary

Acceleration is given by the gradient of the velocity–time graph.

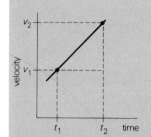

$$a = \frac{\text{change in velocity}}{\text{time}} = \frac{v_2 - v_1}{t_2 - t_1}$$

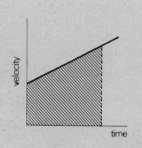

The equations of motion are:

$$v = u + at$$
$$s = ut + \tfrac{1}{2}at^2$$
$$v^2 = u^2 + 2as$$
$$s = \left(\frac{u + v}{2}\right)t$$

The distance travelled by a moving object is equal to the area under the velocity–time graph.

Graphs for motion with uniform acceleration

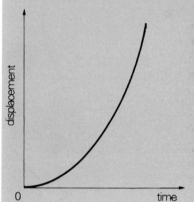

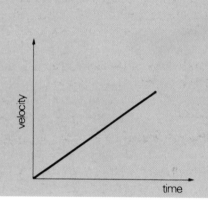

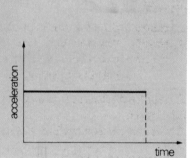

Questions

1   A car driver sees an obstacle, applies the brakes and brings his vehicle to a stop.
   The graph shows how the velocity of the vehicle changes during this time.

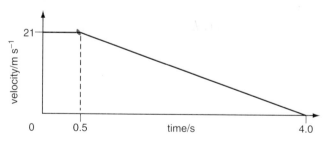

   a)   How long does the driver take to react before he starts to apply the brakes?
   b)   Draw an acceleration–time graph for the 4 seconds of the motion.
   c)   What is the total stopping distance?

2   An object is initially at rest but experiences the acceleration shown in the graph for 3 seconds.

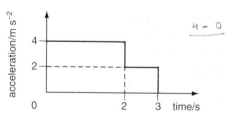

   a)   Calculate the speed of the object after 3 seconds.
   b)   How far has the object travelled?
   c)   Determine the average speed of the object over the 3 second period.

3   A motion sensor linked to a computer with suitable software is used to determine the velocity of a ball which is dropped from rest towards the ground.
   The computer displays the results which are printed in the table overleaf.

time t s	speed v $\mathrm{m\,s^{-1}}$
0	0
0.2	–2
0.4	–4
0.6	–6
0.8	–8
1.0	–10
1.2	+5
1.4	+3
1.6	+1
1.8	–1
2.0	–3

a) Plot a graph of v against t and use it to find the height from which the ball was dropped.
b) Draw an acceleration–time graph for the motion.
c) Determine the height of the ball 2 seconds after it was first dropped.

4 The acceleration of a car varies as shown.

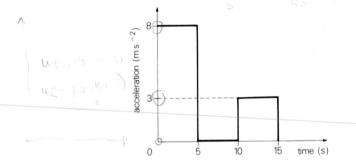

If the initial velocity is zero, draw a speed–time graph. How far did the car travel during the period 10 s to 15 s?

5 A helicopter is rising vertically at $8\,\mathrm{m\,s^{-1}}$. An object is released from it and falls. The object hits the ground 3 s later.
a) What is the velocity of the object as it hits the ground?
b) Determine the height of the object when it was released.

6 An artificial hare travels along a straight section of track at a constant speed of $14\,\mathrm{m\,s^{-1}}$.

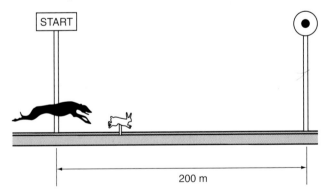

200 m

A dog with a reaction time of 0.4 s is released at the instant the hare passes the starting line. The dog accelerates at a constant rate for

2.5 s and reaches a speed of $15\,\mathrm{m\,s^{-1}}$. This speed is maintained for 7.5 s, after which the dog begins to decelerate at a rate of $0.5\,\mathrm{m\,s^{-2}}$ until it has covered 200 m.
a) Calculate the distance the dog has run, up to the instant at which it starts to decelerate.
b) Calculate:
   i) the speed of the dog at the 200 m mark;
   ii) the time the dog takes to cover this distance.
c) Using square-ruled paper, draw an accurate acceleration–time graph for the motion of the dog from the time of release until it covers 200 m.
d) Explain whether or not the dog catches the hare before the 200 m mark.

SQA

7 In a 'handicap' sprint race, sprinters P and Q both start the race at the same time but from different starting lines on the track. The handicapping is such that both sprinters reach the line XY, as shown below, at the same time.

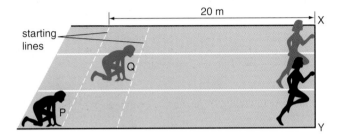

Sprinter P has a constant acceleration of $1.6\,\mathrm{m\,s^{-2}}$ from the start line to the line XY. Sprinter Q has a constant acceleration of $1.2\,\mathrm{m\,s^{-2}}$ from the start line to XY.
a) Calculate the time taken by the sprinters to reach line XY.
b) Find the speed of **each** sprinter at this line.
c) What is the distance, in metres, between the starting lines for sprinters P and Q?

SQA

8 The velocity of a trolley on a slope can be investigated using a computer and a sensor as shown below.

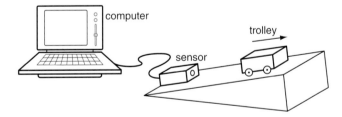

The sensor emits ultrasound pulses which are reflected from the trolley. The computer measures the time between emitted and reflected pulses and uses this information to calculate the velocity at regular times.
In an investigation, the trolley is given a sharp push **up** the slope and then released. The graph on the next page shows the resulting velocity–time graph as displayed on the screen.

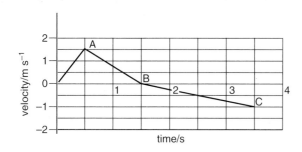

Point A on the graph corresponds to the instant at which the trolley is released.
  a)   At what time is the trolley at its maximum displacement from the sensor? You must justify your answer.
  b)   On the square-ruled paper provided, draw the corresponding acceleration–time graph of the motion.
  c)   Draw a diagram to show the forces acting on the trolley as it moves **up** the slope after the push is removed. Show only forces or components of forces acting parallel to the slope.
  d)   Explain, in terms of the forces acting on the trolley, why the magnitude of the acceleration from A to B differs from the magnitude of the acceleration from B to C.

SQA

9   The velocity–time graph shown below is for an object moving with constant acceleration a.

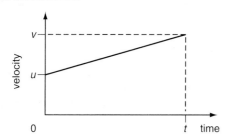

Show that during the time interval *t* the object moves through a displacement *s* given by

$$s = ut + \tfrac{1}{2} at^2$$

SQA

10   The manufacturers of tennis balls require that the balls meet a given standard. When dropped from a certain height on to a test surface, the balls must rebound to within a limited range of heights.
The ideal ball is one which, when dropped from rest from a height of 3.15 m, rebounds to a height of 1.75 m as shown below.

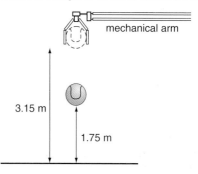

  a)   Assuming air resistance is negligible, calculate:
    i) the speed of an ideal ball just before contact with the ground;
    ii) the speed of this ball just after contact with the ground.
  b)   When a ball is tested six times, the rebound heights are measured to be
        1.71 m, 1.78 m, 1.72 m, 1.76 m, 1.73 m, 1.74 m.
    Calculate:
    i) the mean value of the height of the bounce;
    ii) the random error in this value.

SQA

Topic 1.2 Test 1

1   The velocity of an object changes as shown in the diagram. Write down the expression used to find the acceleration of the object.

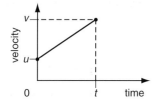

2   An experiment is carried out to determine the acceleration of a trolley running down an inclined slope.
A card attached to the trolley passes through two light beams. This activates the timers which record the time taken to pass through the beam.
The beams are separated by a distance of 0.5 m.
List the measurements that you should take and indicate how you would use them to calculate the acceleration.

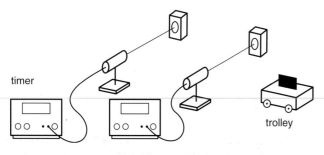

3   A trolley moves in a straight line and the velocity is as shown in the graph.
Draw an acceleration–time graph for the motion during this 4 second period.

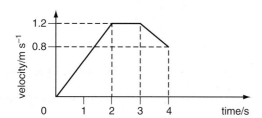

4   The speed of a car moving in a straight line is shown in the graph. Describe the motion of the car for each section of the graph between P and T.

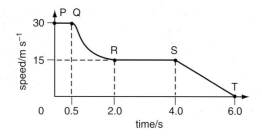

5   a)   An object moving with a speed u slows down to a speed of v in a time t.
This is shown in the graph.
Use this graph to derive the equation

$$v = u - at$$

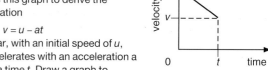

b)   A car, with an initial speed of u, accelerates with an acceleration a for a time t. Draw a graph to illustrate this motion and use it to derive the equation

$$s = ut + \tfrac{1}{2}at^2$$

where s = displacement.

c)   Combining the two equations from parts a) and b), show that the displacement can be given by

$$s = \frac{v^2 - u^2}{2a}$$

6   a)   A motion sensor is used with a computer to plot the speed of a ball which runs down an inclined slope.
Calculate the acceleration of the ball during the first 2 seconds of the motion.

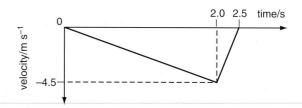

b)   A train accelerates from rest and travels 72 m in 8 seconds. Determine the acceleration assuming that it is constant.

c)   A vehicle, travelling at 18 m s^{-1}, accelerates uniformly at 0.8 m s^{-2} until it reaches a speed of 22 m s^{-1}.
How far does it travel in this time?

Topic 1.2 Test 2

1   A car has an initial speed of u but accelerates uniformly reaching a speed of v after t seconds. Write down the expression for the acceleration.

2   A multiflash photograph is reproduced in the diagram below. It shows the position of a marker attached to a moving trolley.

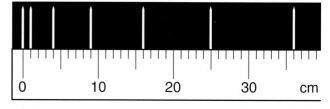

Describe how this would have been taken and explain how the acceleration could be calculated.
State any other information which would be needed.

3 The velocity–time graph for a bouncing ball is shown. Draw the corresponding acceleration–time graph.

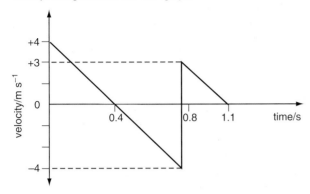

4 The diagram shows the speed–time graph for a car. Describe the motion of the car during each section of the graph.

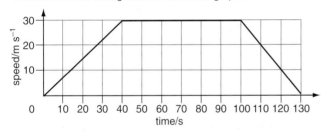

5 a) When an object changes speed the acceleration is given by

$$a = \frac{v - u}{t}$$

Re-arrange this to give an expression for the final velocity.

b) The distance travelled by an accelerating object is given by

$$s = \tfrac{1}{2}(v + u)t$$

Combine this with a suitable equation to derive the equation

$$s = ut + \tfrac{1}{2}at^2$$

c) The graph shows how the speed of an object varies.

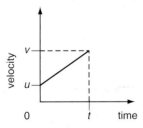

Using the fact that the distance travelled is given by the area of the graph and that the acceleration is given by

$$a = \frac{v - u}{t}$$

show that $v^2 = u + 2as$.

6 a) A car accelerates uniformly at 2 m s^{-2} for 7 seconds starting from a speed of 12 m s^{-1}.
It then travels with a constant speed for 5 seconds. How far has it gone in this 12 second period?

b) A ball is thrown vertically upwards at 14 m s^{-1} from a window. Find the displacement of the ball 4 seconds later.

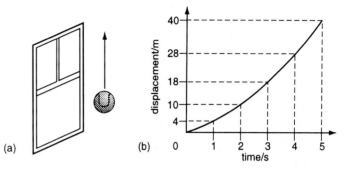

(a)   (b)

c) The displacement–time graph shows the motion of a bicycle which accelerates uniformly from rest in a straight line. Determine the acceleration of the cyclist.

Topic 1.2 Test 3

1 The speed of a car changes as shown in the graph. What quantity does the gradient of the graph represent?

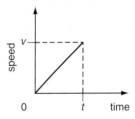

2 It is desired to estimate the acceleration of a trolley as it runs slowly down a slope.
The trolley is fitted with a card which cuts through a light beam and switch attached to an electronic timer.
A digital stopwatch is also available.
Describe how you would carry out the experiment and indicate how the acceleration would be calculated.

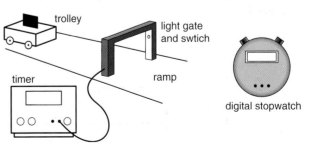

3   A motion sensor is used to record the speed of a moving object and the computer plots a graph which is reproduced in the diagram.

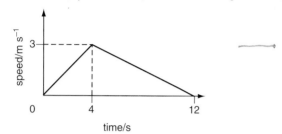

Draw the corresponding acceleration–time graph.

4   The motion of a trolley is shown in the velocity–time graph. Describe the motion during each section of the graph.

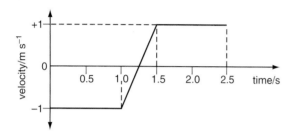

5   In this question the following symbols are used:

u = initial velocity v = final velocity
t = time d = distance
a = acceleration

a)   The speed of an object changes as shown in the graph.

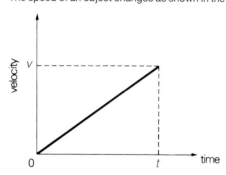

Using this graph, derive an expression for the final velocity of the object.

b)   Given that $d = \frac{1}{2}(v + u) \times \left(\dfrac{v - u}{a} \right)$
show that $d = ut + \frac{1}{2}at^2$

c)   Re-arrange the equation in part b) to show that
$$v^2 = u^2 + 2ad$$

6 **a)**   A ball is dropped from rest from a height of 3.5 m.
What is the speed of the ball as it hits the ground?
b)   A van accelerates uniformly from rest and travels a distance of 72 m in 8.0 seconds.
Calculate the acceleration of the van.
c)   An arrow is fired vertically upwards with a speed of 18 m s⁻¹.
How long will it take to reach the maximum height?

Topic 1.3
Newton's Second Law, Energy and Power

Objectives

When you have completed the work of this topic you should be able to:

1 define the newton;
2 carry out calculations using the relationship $F = ma$ in situations where resolution of forces is not required;
3 use free body diagrams to analyse the forces on an object;
4 carry out calculations involving work done, potential energy, kinetic energy and power.

1.3 Newton's Second Law, Energy and Power

Dynamics

When a force acts on an object, it can produce a change in velocity either by changing its speed or by changing its direction. A force can also produce a change of shape. A change of velocity will only take place if the forces acting on the object fail to balance out. When the forces do balance, the object does not change its velocity. If the object is at rest, it remains at rest. If the object is moving, it continues to do so with the same speed and direction.

Figure 1 shows a multiflash photograph of a straw marker attached to a vehicle moving along a horizontal linear air track. In this case friction is negligible so that the net horizontal force is virtually zero. The distances between the images of the marker are equal, indicating a constant horizontal velocity.

Figure 1

An object can be moving at a steady speed but can change direction because of a resultant force. This is illustrated in Figure 2 which shows a multiflash photograph of a frictionless puck being whirled at constant speed in a circle. The attached string exerts a force which continually changes the direction of travel of the puck so that it travels in a circle rather than in a straight line.

Figure 2   **Figure 3**

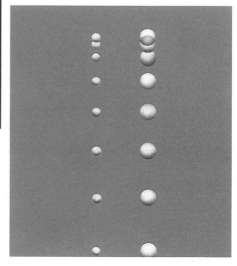

Figure 4

If the string breaks (Figure 3) the puck shoots off at a tangent to the circular path. The equal spacing between the images indicates constant speed. Newton summarized these observations in his First Law which can be formally stated:

> 'An object will remain at rest or will continue to move in a straight line at constant speed unless it is acted upon by a net or unbalanced force.'

Every object near the surface of the Earth accelerates downwards. In Figure 4, the spacing between the images increases, showing that the ball is accelerating. This acceleration is caused by the unbalanced force acting on the ball.

It can be shown experimentally that the acceleration a of an object is
  a) directly proportional to the applied force F if the mass is constant,

$$a \propto F$$

and b) inversely proportional to the mass m if the applied force is constant,

$$a \propto 1/m$$

Combining these results, we get $a \propto \dfrac{F}{m}$

$$F \propto ma$$

This can be written $F = kma$

One newton is defined as the unbalanced force which gives an acceleration of $1\,\mathrm{m\,s^{-2}}$ to a mass of 1 kg.
  Hence, if $m = 1\,\mathrm{kg}$ and $a = 1\,\mathrm{m\,s^{-2}}$, then $F = 1\,\mathrm{N}$.
  Using this in the equation $F = kma$, we find that $k = 1$ and we can write:

$$F = ma$$

This is a form of **Newton's Second Law**.

Example 1

A trolley with a marker attached is pulled by a stretched elastic cord the extension of which is kept constant. A multiflash photograph is taken at a flash rate of 10 Hz.
  If the mass of the trolley is 0.8 kg, find the unbalanced force acting on the trolley. The distances travelled by the marker in the time interval of 0.1 s are shown in the diagram.

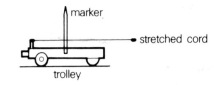

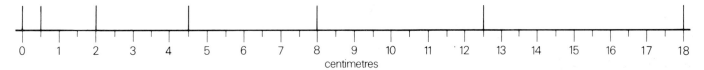

The acceleration can be found by constructing a table:

Distance moved in successive 0.1 s intervals	0.005 m	0.015 m	0.025 m	0.035 m	0.045 m	0.055 m
Time interval	0.1 s	0.1 s	0.1 s	0.1 s	0.1 s	0.1 s
Average speed in each 0.1 s interval ($\mathrm{m\,s^{-1}}$)	0.05	0.15	0.25	0.35	0.45	0.55
Increase in speed between successive 0.1 s intervals ($\mathrm{m\,s^{-1}}$)		0.10	0.10	0.10	0.10	0.10
Increase in speed between successive 1 s intervals ($\mathrm{m\,s^{-1}}$)		1.00	1.00	1.00	1.00	1.00
Acceleration ($\mathrm{m\,s^{-2}}$)		1.00	1.00	1.00	1.00	1.00

Table 1

From the table we can see that the acceleration is uniform and equal to $1\,\mathrm{m\,s^{-2}}$. The unbalanced force F acting on the trolley is given by

$$F = ma$$
$$= 0.8 \times 1 = 0.8$$

The unbalanced force acting on the trolley is 0.8 N.

Example 2

An unbalanced force of 25 N acts on a mass of 5 kg.
What is the acceleration produced?

Using $F = ma$

$$25 = 5 \times a \implies a = \frac{25}{5} = 5$$

The acceleration produced is $5\,\mathrm{m\,s^{-2}}$.

Example 3

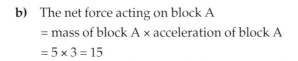

A net force of 24 N acts on two blocks A and B.

a) What is the acceleration of each block?
b) What is the net force acting on block A?

a)   The blocks will move together so that

total mass = 5 + 3 = 8 kg

the acceleration a is given by $a = \dfrac{F}{m} = \dfrac{24}{8} = 3$

The acceleration of each block is $3\,\mathrm{m\,s^{-2}}$.

b)   The net force acting on block A

= mass of block A × acceleration of block A

= 5 × 3 = 15

The net force acting on block A is 15 N.

Example 4

A person of mass 75 kg enters a lift. He presses the starting button and the lift
descends with an acceleration of $1\,\mathrm{m\,s^{-2}}$. The lift then descends at a steady speed
before coming to rest with a deceleration of $1\,\mathrm{m\,s^{-2}}$.

a)   What is the force exerted on the person by the floor when the lift is
stationary?
b)   What is the force exerted by the floor on the person when the lift is
accelerating?
c)   Calculate the force exerted by the floor when the lift is decelerating.

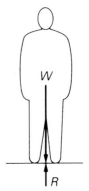

a)   The weight W of the person is given by

$W = mg = 75 \times -9.8 = -735$

This weight of 735 N acts downward.
If R is the reaction force exerted by the floor

$R + W = ma$

But when the lift is stationary,

$$a = 0$$
$$\implies R - 735 = 0$$
$$R = 735$$

The force exerted by the floor is 735 N acting upwards.

W = force exerted on the floor by the person
R = force exerted on the person by the floor

b)   When the lift accelerates downwards $a = -1\,\mathrm{m\,s^{-2}}$

and $R + W = ma$

$$\implies R - 735 = 75 \times (-1)$$
$$R - 735 = -75$$
$$\implies R = -75 + 735 = 660$$

The force is 660 N acting upwards.

c) The lift is moving downwards but is decelerating. This indicates that there must be an unbalanced force acting upwards. The acceleration is thus directed upwards opposing the downward motion.

In this case $a = +1\,\text{m s}^{-2}$

$$R + W = ma$$
$$\Rightarrow \quad R - 735 = 75 \times 1$$
$$R - 735 = 75$$
$$\Rightarrow \qquad R = 75 + 735$$
$$R = 810$$

The force is 810 N and acts upwards.

Example 5

A mass of 0.05 kg is suspended inside a lift. The lift starts from rest, accelerates upwards at $0.4\,\text{m s}^{-2}$, moves upwards at a steady speed of $0.6\,\text{m s}^{-1}$ and then decelerates at $0.4\,\text{m s}^{-2}$. Find the readings of the spring balance at each stage of the motion.

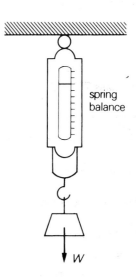

spring balance

W

The upward force R is provided by the spring in the balance and the equation relating the forces will be

$$R + W = ma$$

In each stage the magnitude of the weight will be the same and is given by

$$W = mg = 0.05 \times -9.8 = -0.49$$

The weight is 0.49 N acting downwards.

Stage 1: the lift at rest

$$R + W = ma \qquad a = 0$$
$$m = 0.05\,\text{kg}$$
$$W = -0.49\,\text{N}$$
$$R - 0.49 = 0.05 \times 0$$
$$R = 0.49$$

The reading on the balance is 0.49 N.

Stage 2: lift accelerating upwards

$$R + W = ma \qquad a = +0.4\,\text{m s}^{-2}$$
$$m = 0.05\,\text{kg}$$
$$W = -0.49\,\text{N}$$
$$R - 0.49 = 0.05 \times 0.4$$
$$R - 0.49 = 0.02$$
$$R \quad = 0.02 + 0.49$$
$$R \quad = 0.51$$

The balance reads 0.51 N.

Stage 3: lift moving at uniform velocity

$$R + W = ma \qquad a = 0$$
$$m = 0.05\,\text{kg}$$
$$W = -0.49\,\text{N}$$
$$R - 0.49 = 0.05 \times 0$$
$$R - 0.49 = 0$$
$$R = 0.49$$

The balance reading is 0.49 N.

Stage 4: lift decelerating

$$R + W = ma \qquad a = -0.4\,\text{m s}^{-2}$$
$$m = 0.05\,\text{kg}$$
$$W = -0.49\,\text{N}$$
$$R - 0.49 = 0.05 \times (-0.4)$$
$$R - 0.49 = -0.02$$
$$R \quad = -0.02 + 0.49$$
$$R \quad = 0.47$$

The reading on the balance is 0.47 N.

Free body diagram

When an object, sometimes referred to as a body, is in equilibrium under the action of two or more forces (i.e. there is no resultant force) the forces can be analysed using a vector diagram.

In order to construct the vector diagram it is useful to draw a free body diagram. This is done by considering one point in the system at a time and isolating the forces acting on it.

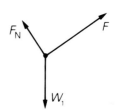

Figure 5

The following illustrate the method.

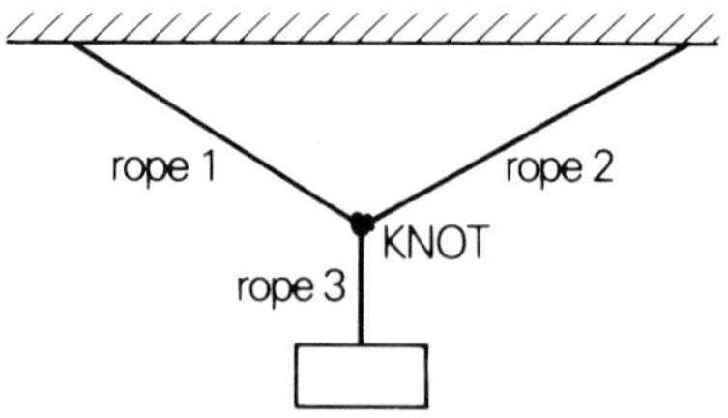

1. Block suspended by three ropes, Figure 5.
    Here we can draw free body diagrams for two chosen points in the system.

    a) Free body diagram for the knot, Figure 6.

    b) Free body diagram for the block, Figure 7.

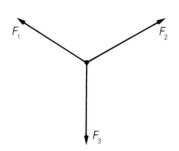

Figure 6

F_1 = force exerted by rope 1 on the knot
F_2 = force exerted by rope 2 on the knot
F_3 = force exerted by rope 3 on the knot

Figure 7

F_3 = force exerted by rope 3 on the block
W = force of gravity acting on the block

2. Block resting on a frictionless slope, Figure 8.

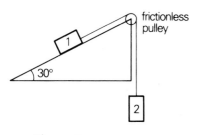

Figure 8

a) Free body diagram for mass 2, Figure 9.

Figure 9

F = force exerted by rope on mass 2
W_2 = force of gravity acting on mass 2

b) Free body diagram for mass 1, Figure 10.

Figure 10

F = force exerted by rope on mass 1
W_1 = force of gravity acting on mass 1
F_N = force of slope, acting at right angles to surface, on mass 1

Example 6

Two masses, $m_1 = 1.5$ kg and $m_2 = 2.0$ kg, are attached to a string passing over a pulley.
The masses are held in position and, when released, the larger mass accelerates downwards and the smaller mass accelerates upwards. The force acting in the string is T and friction is negligible.
Draw free body diagrams for each mass and calculate the acceleration of the masses.

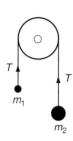

Free body diagrams

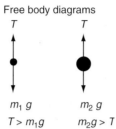

The weights of the masses are m_1g and m_2g and they act downwards.
Let the acceleration of the masses be a.
Applying Newton's Second Law:

net force = mass × acceleration

for m_1 $T - m_1g = m_1 \times a$
for m_2 $m_2g - T = m_2 \times a$

Putting numerical values into these equations gives

for m_1 $T - 1.5 \times 9.8 = 1.5 \times a$
for m_2 $2.0 \times 9.8 - T = 2.0 \times a$

Adding these two equations removes T and gives

$\Rightarrow$ $2.0 \times 9.8 - 1.5 \times 9.8 = (-2.0)a$
$\Rightarrow$ $19.6 - 14.7 = 3.5a$
$\Rightarrow$ $4.9 = 3.5a$
$\Rightarrow$ $3.5a = 4.9$
$\Rightarrow$ $a = \dfrac{4.7}{3.5} = 1.4$

The acceleration of the masses is 1.4 m s^{-2}.

Work done

When a force acts on an object it transfers energy to the object.
The work done is defined by:

work done = force × displacement along the line of action of the force

$W = F \times s$

where

W = work in joules
F = force in newtons
s = displacement in metres

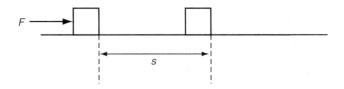

Example 7

A crate is pulled 2 m across a horizontal floor against a constant friction force of 24 N. Calculate the work done.

$$W = F \times s$$
$$= 24 \times 2 = 48$$

The work done is 48 N.

Gravitational potential energy

When an object is raised upwards against the force of gravity it gains potential energy E_p:

E_p = work done against the force of gravity

= weight × vertical displacement

= $m\,g\,h$

where

m = mass in kg

g = acceleration of gravity

   = $9.8\,\mathrm{m\,s^{-2}}$

h = height in metres.

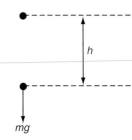

Example 8

A box, mass 50 kg, is raised through a vertical height of 3 m. How much potential energy is gained?

$$E_p = m\,g\,h = 50 \times 9.8 \times 3 = 1470$$

The potential energy gained is 1470 J.

Kinetic energy

When an object is moving it possesses kinetic energy. The kinetic energy E_k is given by:

$E_k = \tfrac{1}{2}\,m\,v^2$ where E_k = kinetic energy in joules

m = mass in kilogrammes

v = speed in $\mathrm{m\,s^{-1}}$.

Example 9

A constant force acts on an object, mass 3 kg, causing it to increase in speed from $8\,\mathrm{m\,s^{-1}}$ to $20\,\mathrm{m\,s^{-1}}$. Calculate the force if the distance over which it acts is 14 m.

Since the speed increases there is a gain of kinetic energy.

energy transferred = gain in kinetic energy

$$F \times s = \tfrac{1}{2}mv^2 - \tfrac{1}{2}mu^2$$
$$F \times 14 = \tfrac{1}{2} \times 3 \times 400 \ - \tfrac{1}{2} \times 3 \times 64$$
$$F \times 14 = \ 600 - 96 \ = 504$$
$$F = \ 504/14 \ = 36$$

The force acting on the object is 36 N.

Interconversion of potential and kinetic energy

When an object which has gravitational potential energy falls it gathers speed and gains kinetic energy. When this interconversion of energy takes place either:

i)   friction is negligible and can be ignored; or

ii) friction is present and some energy is converted to heat.

i)   Friction is negligible and can be ignored.

A pendulum bob, mass m, is pulled sideways, rising a vertical height h.

At X the bob has gravitational potential energy and when released it gains kinetic energy as it falls, reaching a maximum speed of v when it passes through point Y.

At X, gravitational potential energy $= mgh$
At Y, kinetic energy $= \frac{1}{2} m v^2$

In this case air resistance is negligible and can be ignored.
gain of kinetic energy = loss of potential energy

$$\frac{1}{2} m v^2 = mgh$$

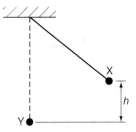

Figure 13

Example 10

A pendulum bob is raised through a vertical height of 0.10 m and then released. What is the maximum speed of the bob if air resistance can be ignored?

gain of kinetic energy = loss of potential energy

$$\frac{1}{2} m v^2 = mgh$$

$$\Rightarrow \qquad v = \sqrt{2gh} = \sqrt{2 \times 9.8 \times 0.10} = \sqrt{1.96}$$

$$\Rightarrow \qquad v = 1.4$$

The maximum speed of the bob is 1.4 m s^{-1}.

ii)   Friction is present and some energy is converted into heat

A block of wood, mass m, is released on a slope from a height h. It slides down the slope a distance of d.
There is a constant force of friction F between the block and the slope.
The speed of the block at the bottom of the slope is v.

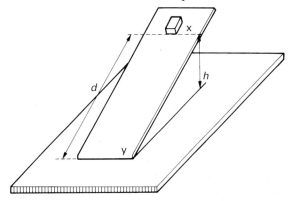

Figure 14

gravitational potential energy lost by the block in falling from X to Y $= mgh$
kinetic energy gained by the block in falling from X to Y $= \frac{1}{2}mv^2$
energy converted into heat = work done against friction
work done against friction = force × distance $= F \times d$

$$\begin{pmatrix} \text{loss of potential} \\ \text{energy} \end{pmatrix} = \begin{pmatrix} \text{gain of kinetic} \\ \text{energy} \end{pmatrix} + \begin{pmatrix} \text{work done} \\ \text{against friction} \end{pmatrix}$$

$$mgh \qquad = \qquad \frac{1}{2}mv^2 \qquad + \qquad Fd$$

Example 11

A girl, mass 25 kg, climbs to the top of a slide which is 2 m above the ground.

She slides down to the bottom, having travelled 5 m down the slide, reaching a speed of 2 m s^{-1} at the bottom, which is at a level 2 m below the starting point.

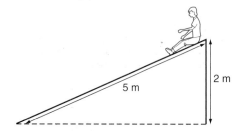

a)   Find the gravitational potential energy gained by the girl at the starting point when she has climbed up to the top of the slide.

b)   When her speed is 2 m s^{-1} what is her kinetic energy?

c)   How much work is done overcoming friction?

d)   Determine the average force of friction acting on the girl as she slides 5 m down the slope.

a) $E_p = mgh = 25 \times 9.8 \times 2 = 490$

   Potential energy gained is 490 joules.

b) $E_k = \frac{1}{2} mv^2 = \frac{1}{2} \times 25 \times 2^2 = 50$

   Kinetic energy of the girl is 50 joules.

c)   work done $= E_p - E_k = 490 - 50 = 440$

   Work done against friction is 440 joules.

d)   work done = force × distance = $F \times d = 440$

$$F \times d = 440$$
$$F \times 5 = 440$$
$$F = \frac{440}{5} = 88$$

   The average force of friction acting on the girl is 88 newtons.

Power

Power is defined as the rate of transfer of energy.

$$\text{power} = \frac{\text{work done}}{\text{time}}$$

Power is measured in watts where 1 watt = 1 joule per second but

$$\text{work done} = \text{force} \times \text{distance}$$

$$\text{therefore power} = \frac{\text{force} \times \text{distance}}{\text{time}} = \text{force} \times \frac{\text{distance}}{\text{time}}$$

$$\Rightarrow \quad \text{power} = \text{force} \times \text{velocity}$$

Example 12

A car, travelling at a steady speed of 20 m s^{-1}, experiences a friction and air resistance force of 450 N. How much power is required to overcome this force?

power = force × velocity = $450 \times 20 = 9000$

The power required is 9000 watts (9 kW).

Summary

A net force of 1 newton will produce an acceleration of 1 m s^{-2} when applied to a mass of 1 kg.

Newton's Second Law can be expressed by the equation

$F = ma$

Work done = force × displacement = $F \times s$

$\text{Power} = \dfrac{\text{work done}}{\text{time}}$

Power = force × velocity = $F \times v$

Kinetic energy $E_k = \frac{1}{2} mv^2$

Gravitational
potential energy $E_p = mgh$

Questions

1   Two blocks are pushed from rest a distance of 12 m across a horizontal surface.

The blocks accelerate from rest with an acceleration of 3 m s^{-2}.
   a)   What friction force acts on the blocks?
   b)   Calculate the unbalanced force which Y exerts on X.
   c)   How much work has been done by the 30 N force?
   d)   What is the work done against friction?
   e)   Calculate the combined kinetic energy of both blocks after they have travelled 12 m.
   f)   When the 30 N force is removed both blocks slow down because of the friction force. How far will the blocks travel before coming to rest?

2   A trolley, mass 0.8 kg, runs from rest down a ramp. It travels 2 m along the ramp, dropping a vertical distance of 0.5 m. The speed at the bottom of the ramp is 2 m s^{-1}

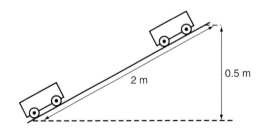

   a)   How much potential energy is lost?
   b)   What is the kinetic energy of the trolley at the bottom of the ramp?
   c)   How much work is done against friction as the trolley runs down the ramp?
   d)   Calculate the force of friction.

3   A car, mass 1800 kg, travels at a constant speed of 20 m s^{-1} against a constant air resistance force of 400 N.
   a)   What power is required to keep the car moving?
   b)   How much kinetic energy has the car?
   c)   Assuming a horizontal surface and a constant retarding force of 400 N, how far will the car travel before it stops?

4   Two masses, X = 1 kg and Y = 2 kg, are attached to a string which passes over a smooth pulley.
   Both masses are supported and then released.
   Mass X accelerates upwards and mass Y accelerates downwards.

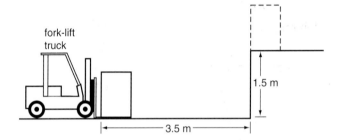

Draw free body diagrams for X and Y and hence find the value of the acceleration.

5   A fork-lift truck raises a box vertically, then moves 3.5 m across the floor of a warehouse and deposits the box on a platform 1.5 m high.

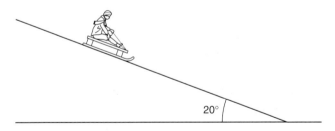

Calculate the displacement of the box from the starting position.

6   A child on a sledge slides down a slope which is at an angle of 20° to the horizontal as shown below.

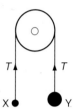

The combined weight of the child and the sledge is 400 N. The frictional force acting on the sledge and child at the start of the slide is 20.0 N.
   a)   i)   Calculate the component of the combined weight of the child and sledge down the slope.
        ii) Calculate the initial acceleration of the sledge and child.
   b)   The child decides to start the slide from further up the slope. Explain whether or not this has any effect on the initial acceleration.
   c)   During the slide, the sledge does not continue to accelerate but reaches a constant speed. Explain why this happens.

SQA

7 A lunar landing craft descends vertically towards the surface of the Moon with a constant speed of 2.0 m s⁻¹. The craft and crew have a total mass of 15 000 kg.
Assume that the gravitational field strength on the Moon is 1.6 N kg⁻¹.

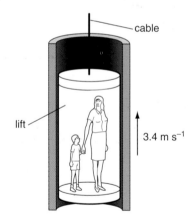

a) During the first part of the descent the upward thrust of the rocket engine is 24 000 N.
Show that this results in the craft moving with a constant speed.
b) The upward thrust of the engine is increased to 25 500 N for the last 18 seconds of the descent.
  i) Calculate the deceleration of the craft during this time.
  ii) What is the speed of the craft just before it lands?
  iii) How far is the craft above the surface of the Moon when the engine thrust is increased to 25 500 N?

SQA

8 A lift of total mass 2000 kg, including passengers, is travelling upwards in a tall building. At a certain instant, the speed of the lift is 3.4 m s⁻¹ and the cable supporting the lift exerts an upward force of 17 000 N.

Find:
a) the acceleration of the lift;
b) how long it will take to stop from this instant, assuming the acceleration remains constant.

SQA

9 A liquid-fuelled rocket is taking off vertically upwards.

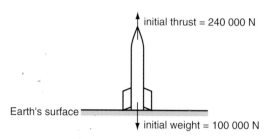

a) What is the initial acceleration of the rocket?
b) Assuming that the burning fuel provides a constant thrust, explain what would happen to the acceleration as the rocket rises.

SQA

10 In an experiment, a block of mass 1.00 kg is released from rest from a point A, 2.00 m up a slope as shown in the diagram. The block slides down to the point B at the bottom of the slope where its speed is measured. This is repeated several times, the block being released from the same point A each time but with the slope adjusted so that the initial height h is different on each occasion.

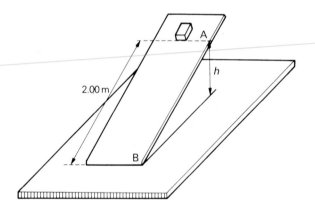

The speeds of the block for four different initial heights are shown in the table.

Height h (m)	0.60	1.00	1.40	1.80
Speed at B (m s⁻¹)	2.50	3.85	4.90	5.80
Potential energy at A (J)				
Kinetic energy at B (J)				

a) **i)** Copy the table and complete it to show the potential energy of the block at A and the kinetic energy of the block at B.
  ii) Account for the difference between the potential energy at A and the corresponding kinetic energy at B.
b) Calculate the average frictional force acting on the block during the experiment when h = 1.00 m.
c) **i)** Plot a graph of the kinetic energy at B against the initial height h.
  ii) Use this graph to find a value for the initial height h which makes the slope friction-compensated for this block.

SQA

Topic 1.3 Test 1

1 Define the newton.

2 Two blocks are pushed across a horizontal, frictionless surface. Determine the acceleration of each block. What force does block Y exert on block X?

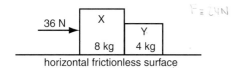

3 A block rests on an inclined plane, held in place by a friction force. Draw a free body diagram to show the forces acting on the block.

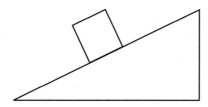

4 a) A car, total mass of 1800 kg, accelerates from rest to a speed of 20 m s⁻¹. It travels a distance of 60 m during this process. Calculate the net average force acting on the car during this time.

b) A steel ball is released from a height of 4.5 m. If the mass of the ball is 0.05 kg how much potential energy does the ball lose during this fall?

c) Determine the speed of the ball in b) just as it hits the ground.

d) A motor cyclist travels at a constant speed of 15 m s⁻¹ against a constant air resistance of 120 N. What power is used overcoming this force?

3 Two unequal weights are suspended from a pulley. W_2 is greater than W_1 and the tension in the string is T. Draw free body diagrams for:

a) W_1;   **b)** W_2;   **c)** the pulley.

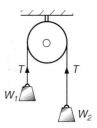

4 a) A force of 500 N acts on an object pushing it a distance of 60 m. Calculate the work done by the force.

b) A pendulum bob has a mass of 0.12 kg. How much potential energy does it gain when it is lifted to a height which is 0.15 m above the starting point?

c) A vehicle, moving at 15 m s⁻¹, possesses 180 kJ of kinetic energy. What kinetic energy will it have when the speed is 25 m s⁻¹?

d) A shopper, mass 70 kg, steps on to an escalator and arrives at the next floor after 18 seconds. How much power is used to take her to the next floor?

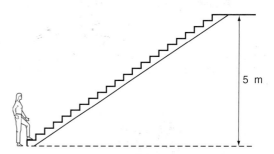

Topic 1.3 Test 2

1 When an object accelerates the acceleration is given by

$$a = \frac{\text{force}}{\text{mass}}$$

If the acceleration is measured in metres per second squared and the mass in kilogrammes, what unit is used to measure force?

2 A 24 N force pulls two blocks across a surface as shown. What is the unbalanced force acting on block A? If the 24 N force acts for 2 seconds and is then removed, calculate the speed of block B 5 seconds after the start, assuming that it starts from rest. (The surface is frictionless and horizontal).

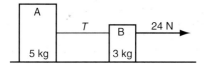

Topic 1.3 Test 3

1 Which of the following is equivalent to the newton?

i) J s⁻¹
ii) kg m s⁻¹
iii) kg s⁻²
iv) kg m s⁻²
v) J m⁻¹ s⁻²

2 A car accelerates a caravan with an acceleration of 1.5 m s⁻². If the mass of the car is 1600 kg and the mass of the caravan is 1800 kg what force does the caravan exert on the car?

Unit 1   Mechanics and properties of matter

3   A crate is pulled across a rough horizontal floor by a rope which is at an angle of 30° to the floor. Draw a free body diagram to show the forces acting on the crate.

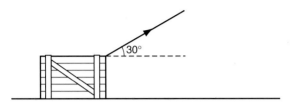

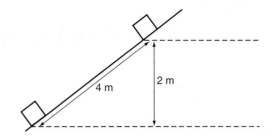

4   A box slides down a slope.
It starts from rest and, after travelling 4 m, is moving with a speed of 5 m s⁻¹.
The mass of the box is 12 kg.

a)   Calculate the potential energy lost.
b)   How much kinetic energy was gained?
c)   Determine the work done against friction and hence find the friction force.
d)   An invalid stair-lift raises an 820 N person through a vertical height of 1.8 m and takes 8 seconds. How much power is needed to do this?

Topic 1.4
Momentum and Impulse

Objectives

When you have completed the work of this topic you should be able to:

1 state that momentum is the product of mass and velocity;
2 state that the law of conservation of linear momentum can be applied to the interaction of two objects moving in one dimension, in the absence of net external forces;
3 state that an elastic collision is one in which both momentum and kinetic energy are conserved;
4 state that an inelastic collision is one in which only momentum is conserved;
5 carry out calculations concerned with collisions in which the objects move in only one dimension;
6 carry out calculations concerned with explosions in one dimension;
7 apply the law of conservation of momentum to the interaction of two objects moving in one dimension to show that:
   a) the changes in momentum of each object are equal in size and opposite in direction,
   b) the forces acting on each object are equal in size and opposite in direction;
8 state that impulse = force × time;
9 state that impulse = change of momentum;
10 carry out calculations using the relationship impulse = change of momentum.

1.4 Momentum and Impulse

Momentum and collisions

This section is concerned with objects which collide.
In a collision between a vehicle and a wall, the total amount of damage can perhaps indicate which physical quantities are important.

Consider the following.

Figure 1 Mini moving slowly

Figure 1 Mini moving slowly   **Figure 2** Mini moving fast

Figure 3 Bus moving slowly   **Figure 4** Bus moving fast

The mass of an object and the speed at which it is travelling affect the amount of damage; it can be concluded that:

  'the greater the mass and the greater the speed at which it is travelling the more damage it would cause'.

Having identified mass and velocity as important factors in collisions, experiments can be carried out using colliding trolleys and measurements can be made of mass and velocity. These experiments can investigate the pattern of motion after the collision.

  It is useful to use letters to indicate the mass of the moving objects and the velocities before and after the collision.

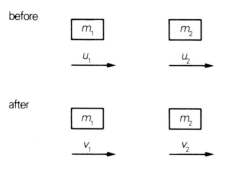

Figure 5

Collision experiments

Experiment 1
The arrangement used is shown in Figure 6.

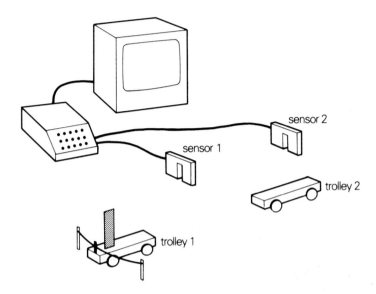

Figure 6

Trolley 1 is catapulted towards trolley 2 which is stationary. When they collide they stick together which means that they both move with the same common velocity. The velocities of the trolleys are obtained photo-electrically and analysed by the computer.

When the marker interrupts the light beam in sensor 1, a pulse is sent to the computer.

The computer calculates the velocity u_1 of trolley 1 before the collision. On collision, the trolleys stick together and the marker interrupts the light beam in sensor 2.

The computer calculates the velocity v_1 of the trolleys after the collision; v_2 is the same as v_1.

Masses can be added to each trolley to change its mass. A set of results is given in Tables 1 and 2.

mass of trolley 1	velocity of trolley 1		mass of trolley 2	velocity of trolley 2		
m_1 kg	u_1 m s^{-1}	m_1u_1 kg m s^{-1}	m_2 kg	u_2 m s^{-1}	m_2u_2 kg m s^{-1}	$m_1u_1 + m_2u_2$ kg m s^{-1}
0.8	1.2	1.0	0.8	0	0	1.0
1.7	0.9	1.5	0.8	0	0	1.5
0.8	0.7	0.6	1.3	0	0	0.6
1.3	1.1	1.4	1.5	0	0	1.4

Table 1 Before the collision

mass of trolley 1	velocity of trolley 1		mass of trolley 2	velocity of trolley 2		
m_1 kg	v_1 m s^{-1}	m_1v_1 kg m s^{-1}	m_2 kg	v_2 m s^{-1}	m_2v_2 kg m s^{-1}	$m_1v_1 + m_2v_2$ kg m s^{-1}
0.8	0.6	0.5	0.8	0.6	0.5	1.0
1.7	0.6	1.0	0.8	0.6	0.5	1.5
0.8	0.3	0.2	1.3	0.3	0.4	0.6
1.3	0.5	0.7	1.5	0.5	0.8	1.5

Table 2 After the collision

From the results it can be seen that the following relationship is confirmed.

$$m_1u_1 + m_2u_2 = m_1v_1 + m_2v_2$$

Example 1

Two identical vehicles collide on a linear air track, Figure 7. The left-hand vehicle approaches at a constant velocity. The right-hand vehicle is stationary, but after the collision both vehicles travel to the right with the same constant velocity.

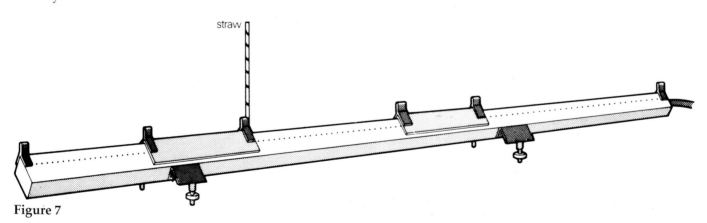

Figure 7

The diagram below is a representation of the stroboscopic photograph of the straw; the spacing is one-sixth full size and the flash rate is 10 Hz.

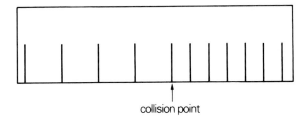

collision point

The mass of each vehicle is 0.2 kg.
Show that the product (mass × velocity) is the same before and after the collision.

flash rate = 10 per second
time interval = 0.1 second

From the photograph,
space between images before collision = 1 cm
actual distance = 6 × 1 = 6 cm

$$\text{velocity of vehicle before collision} = \frac{\text{distance}}{\text{time}} = \frac{6}{0.1} = 60$$
$$= 0.60 \, \text{m s}^{-1}$$

Space between images after collision = 0.5 cm
actual distance = 6 × 0.5 = 3 cm

$$\text{velocity of vehicles after collision} = \frac{\text{distance}}{\text{time}} = \frac{3}{0.1} = 30$$
$$= 0.30 \, \text{m s}^{-1}$$

total mass after collision = 0.2 + 0.2 = 0.4 kg
(mass × velocity) after = 0.4 × 0.3 = 0.12 kg m s^{-1}
(mass × velocity) before = 0.2 × 0.6 = 0.12 kg m s^{-1}

The quantity (mass × velocity) is the same before and after the collision.

Experiment 2
In this experiment the vehicles do not stick together after the collision but move separately. Vehicles floating on a linear air track can be used to investigate such a collision, Figure 8.

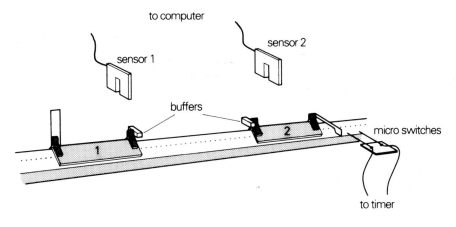

Figure 8

Figure 9

Vehicle 1 is catapulted towards vehicle 2 which is initially stationary. Both vehicles are fitted with rubber buffers so that they move off separately after impact.

Two or more vehicles can be clamped together in order to obtain different masses, Figure 9.

The marker on vehicle 1 interrupts the light beam of sensor 1 and a pulse is sent to the computer which calculates the velocity u_1 of vehicle 1 before the collision. After the collision the marker cuts the light beam of sensor 2 and the computer calculates the velocity v_1 of vehicle 1 after the collision.

In order to separate velocities of the vehicles after the collision the velocity of vehicle 2 is obtained in a different way. A light metal arm is attached to vehicle 2. This metal arm pushes against two thin rods which are connected to two microswitches which are connected to an electronic timer, Figure 10.

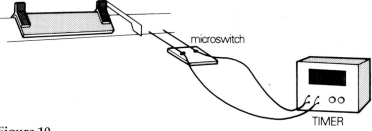

Figure 10

The first switch starts the timer and the second switch stops the timer. The distance between the rods is 0.1 metre so that the speed v_2 of vehicle 2 after the collision is given by

$$v_2 = \frac{0.1}{\text{time registered on the timer}}$$

Since vehicle 2 is stationary at the start, its velocity v_1 before the collision is zero.

A set of results is given in Tables 3 and 4.

m_1 kg	u_1 m s^{-1}	$m_1 u_1$ kg m s^{-1}	m_2 kg	u_2 m s^{-1}	$m_2 u_2$ kg m s^{-1}	$m_1 u_1 + m_2 u_2$ kg m s^{-1}
0.2	1.8	0.4	0.2	0	0	0.4
0.2	2.0	0.4	0.4	0	0	0.4
0.2	1.8	0.4	0.5	0	0	0.4
0.4	1.5	0.6	0.6	0	0	0.6
0.4	2.1	0.8	0.5	0	0	0.8

Table 3 Before the collision

m_1 kg	v_1 m s^{-1}	$m_1 v_1$ kg m s^{-1}	m_2 kg	v_2 m s^{-1}	$m_2 v_2$ kg m s^{-1}	$m_1 v_1 + m_2 v_2$ kg m s^{-1}
0.2	0.5	0.1	0.2	1.3	0.3	0.4
0.2	0.3	0.1	0.4	0.8	0.3	0.4
0.2	0.4	0.1	0.5	0.6	0.3	0.4
0.4	0.5	0.2	0.6	0.7	0.4	0.6
0.4	0.8	0.3	0.5	1.0	0.5	0.8

Table 4 After the collision

Investigation of the results from both experiments on collisions shows that the product (mass × velocity) has a special significance; (mass × velocity) is called **momentum**. For all objects involved in a collision, an equation can be used to describe the relationship between the values of the product (mass × velocity).

$$m_1u_1 + m_2u_2 = m_1v_1 + m_2v_2$$

This relationship is known as **the conservation of linear momentum** and can be written as

(total momentum before the collision) = (total momentum after the collision)

Example 2

A car moving at $30\,\text{m s}^{-1}$ collides head-on with a small van which is stationary. The vehicles lock together. If the car has a mass of 900 kg and the van has a mass of 1200 kg, determine the common velocity of the vehicles after the collision.

By the principle of conservation of linear momentum:

$$m_1u_1 + m_2u_2 = m_1v_1 + m_2v_2$$

(momentum of car before collision) = (momentum of car plus van after collision)

$$900 \times 30 = (900 + 1200) \times v$$

$$v = \frac{900 \times 30}{2100} = 13$$

The velocity is 13 m s^{-1} after the collision.

Example 3

A trolley, mass 1 kg, moving at $1.2\,\text{m s}^{-1}$ collides with a stationary trolley, mass 1 kg.

After the collision the first trolley slows down to $0.5\,\text{m s}^{-1}$ and the other trolley moves off with velocity v_2.

Calculate the value of this velocity.

By conservation of linear momentum

$$m_1u_1 + m_2u_2 = m_1v_1 + m_2v_2$$

$$1 \times 1.2 + 1 \times 0 = 1 \times 0.5 + 1 \times v_2$$

$$v_2 = \frac{1.2 - 0.5}{1} = 0.7$$

The trolley moves off with a velocity of 0.7 m s^{-1}.

Kinetic energy and collisions

In all collisions momentum is conserved.

Some of the kinetic energy is converted into heat which is generated during the impact.

This can be illustrated by calculating kinetic energies for the experimental results previously obtained in the last section.

Results from experiment 1

total kinetic energy before $\frac{1}{2}m_1u^2$ (joules)	total kinetic energy after $\frac{1}{2}(m_1 + m_2)v^2$ (joules)
0.6	0.3
0.7	0.5
0.2	0.1
0.8	0.4

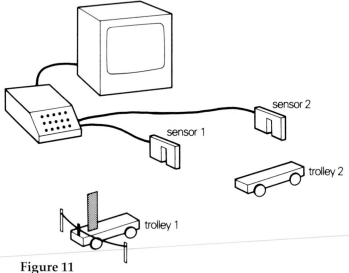

Figure 11

Results from experiment 2

total kinetic energy before $\frac{1}{2}m_1u_1^2 + 0$ (joules)	total kinetic energy after $\frac{1}{2}m_1v_1^2 + \frac{1}{2}m_2v_2^2$ (joules)
0.32	0.03 + 0.17 = 0.20
0.40	0.01 + 0.13 = 0.14
0.32	0.02 + 0.09 = 0.11
0.45	0.05 + 0.15 = 0.20
0.88	0.13 + 0.25 = 0.38

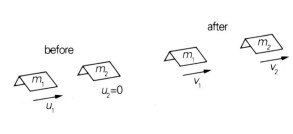

Figure 12

Collisions such as these in which there is a loss of kinetic energy are called **inelastic** collisions.

Example 4

A van, mass 1200 kg, is travelling at $30\,\mathrm{m\,s^{-1}}$ when it collides with a stationary car, mass 800 kg.

If both vehicles lock together after the collision calculate the common velocity of the vehicles immediately after the accident and determine the loss of kinetic energy.

Let the velocity after the collision be v.

By conservation of momentum

$$m_1u_1 + m_2u_2 = m_1v_1 + m_2v_2$$
$$1200 \times 30 = (1200 + 800) \times v$$
$$v = \frac{1200 \times 30}{2000} = 18$$

The velocity after the collision is $18\,\text{m s}^{-1}$.

kinetic energy before $= \frac{1}{2} \times 1200 \times 30^2 = 540\,\text{kJ}$

kinetic energy after $\quad = \frac{1}{2} \times 2000 \times 18^2 = 324\,\text{kJ}$

There is a loss of kinetic energy of 216 kJ.

Elastic collisions

In an **elastic** collision, there is *no* loss of kinetic energy. In practice, collisions are never perfectly elastic, but such a collision is approximated when two hard objects such as curling stones collide.

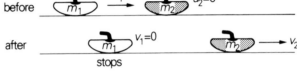

As in all collisions, momentum is conserved:

$$m_1u_1 + m_2u_2 = m_1v_1 + m_2v_2$$

and because $u_2 = 0$ and $v_1 = 0$,

$$m_1u_1 = m_2v_2$$

Since the collision is elastic, kinetic energy is also conserved: $\frac{1}{2}m_1u_1^2 = \frac{1}{2}m_2v_2^2$

Figure 13

In the actual collision, the first curling stone does not stop immediately because the collision is not fully elastic, and the second curling stone moves off with a velocity slightly smaller than u_1.

Example 5

A single white snooker ball is hit towards a row of red balls lying along the cushion. Assuming an elastic collision, show that
a) one red shoots off the end of the row with the same velocity as that of the white before the collision,
b) it is impossible for the white ball and the red balls to move off together with a common velocity.

a) By conservation of momentum: $m_1u_1 + m_2u_2 = m_1v_1 + m_2v_2$

If the red ball has the same velocity v as the white, and the mass of each ball is m:

$$mv = mv$$

kinetic energy of white ball $= \frac{1}{2}mv^2$

kinetic energy of red ball $\quad = \frac{1}{2}mv^2$

Kinetic energy is conserved.

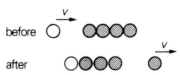

b) By conservation of momentum: $m_1u_1 + m_2u_2 = m_1v_1 + m_2v_2$

If the common velocity is v: $\qquad m_1u_1 + 0 = m_1v + m_2v$

and the mass of each ball is m: $\qquad mu_1 = mv + 4mv$

$$v = \tfrac{1}{5}u_1$$

kinetic energy before $= \frac{1}{2}mu_1^2$

kinetic energy after $\quad = \frac{1}{2} \times (5m) \times (\tfrac{1}{5}u_1)^2$

$\qquad\qquad\qquad\quad = \tfrac{1}{5}(\tfrac{1}{2}mu_1^2)$

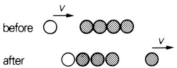

There is a loss of kinetic energy so that for an elastic collision, this is impossible.

Explosions

Explosions can be investigated by using two trolleys, one with a spring-loaded plunger, standing close to each other on a horizontal surface. When released, the plunger forces the trolleys apart, Figure 14.

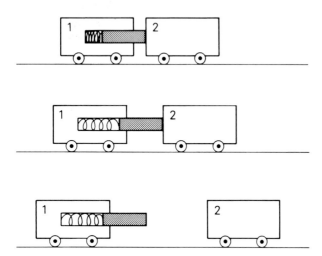

Figure 14

The mass of trolley 1, which is fitted with the plunger, remains unaltered but the mass of trolley 2 is varied by adding known masses to it.

The magnitude of the momentum of each trolley is calculated and entered in Table 5.

mass of trolley 1 is m_1; v_1 is velocity of trolley 1 after the explosion
mass of trolley 2 is m_2; v_2 is velocity of trolley 2 after the explosion

m_1 kg	v_1 m s^{-1}	$m_1 \times v_1$ kg m s^{-1}	m_2 kg	v_2 m s^{-1}	$m_2 \times v_2$ kg m s^{-1}
1	− 0.90	− 0.90	1	0.88	0.88
1	− 1.05	− 1.05	2	0.53	1.06
1	− 1.15	− 1.15	3	0.39	1.17
1	− 1.30	− 1.30	4	0.33	1.32

Table 5

Within the limits of the experiment, the momentum values for trolley 1 and trolley 2 have the same magnitude.

Before the explosion, both trolleys are stationary so that the momentum of each is zero.

If we take the direction of motion of each trolley into account so that one direction is taken to be positive and the other as negative, momentum will be conserved.

Taking motion to the right as positive and motion to the left as negative:

$$m_1v_1 + m_2v_2 = 0$$

It can be concluded from this that momentum is a vector quantity.

Example 6

A girl and her brother are on an ice rink. They push each other apart. Calculate the speed of the girl if the boy moves off at $0.6\,\text{m s}^{-1}$.

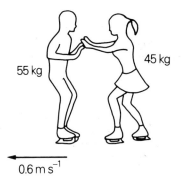

By conservation of momentum:

$$m_1v_1 + m_2v_2 = 0$$
$$-45 \times v_1 + 55 \times 0.6 = 0$$
$$v_1 = \frac{55 \times 0.6}{45}$$
$$= 0.7$$

The girl moves off with a speed of $0.7\,\text{m s}^{-1}$.

Impulse

Suppose that an object, mass m, is acted upon by a net force F for a time t which causes the velocity to change from u to v.

By Newton's Second Law $F = ma$

but the acceleration $a = \dfrac{v - u}{t}$

and substituting for a in the first equation we get

$$F = \frac{m(v - u)}{t}$$
$$= \frac{mv - mu}{t}$$

but mv = final momentum
and mu = initial momentum
so that $(mv - mu)$ is the change in momentum. It follows that

$$\text{net force} = \frac{\text{change in momentum}}{\text{time during which force acts}}$$

and this can be written

force × time during which it acts = change of momentum

$$Ft = mv - mu$$

The product Ft is called the impulse of the force and the unit of impulse is the newton-second which is the same as the unit of momentum, kg m s^{-1}.

Forces which act over short time intervals are, in general, not constant. A typical variation of force with time is shown in Figure 15. In such a case the impulse is given by the area under the graph, which is indicated by the shading. Thus the change in momentum produced equals the area under the force-time graph.

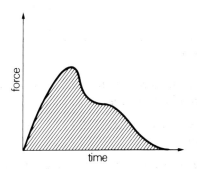

Figure 15

Often the exact variation of the force is not known and the average force $\overline{F}$ is used so that the equation becomes

$$\overline{F}t = mv - mu$$

where $\overline{F}$ = average force acting during the time interval.

Example 7

A billiard cue hits a stationary ball, mass 0.2 kg, which is at rest. The ball moves off with a velocity of $3 \, m \, s^{-1}$ and the time of contact between the ball and the cue is 0.015 s. Calculate the average force exerted by the cue on the ball.

$$\overline{F} = \frac{mv - mu}{t}$$

where $v = 3 \, m \, s^{-1}$
$u = 0$
$m = 0.2 \, kg$
$t = 0.015 \, s$

$$\overline{F} = \frac{0.2 \times 3 - 0.2 \times 0}{0.015}$$

$$= \frac{0.6}{0.015}$$

$$= 40$$

The force exerted by the cue is 40 N.

Newton's Third Law

Newton's Third Law states

'To every action force, there is an equal and opposite reaction force'.

This could be demonstrated using the equipment shown in Figure 16.

A spring-loaded trolley is placed close to but not touching another trolley on a horizontal surface. The metal plunger of trolley A and the metal edge of trolley B are connected to the start terminals of an electronic timer using long thin wire. When the plunger is triggered, it makes contact with the edge of trolley B and the electronic timer records the contact time. Each trolley shoots off and the card attached to it cuts a light beam causing the electric clock to operate. This allows the velocity of each trolley to be calculated.

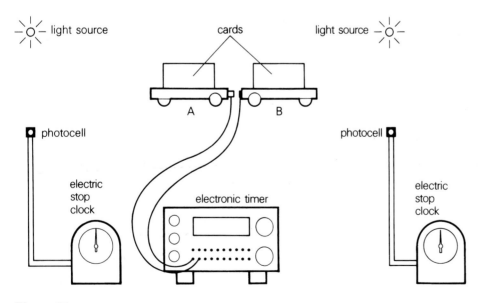

Figure 16

The following results were obtained.

trolley A

length of card	0.1 m
time on clock	0.32 s
mass m_A	1.20 kg
time of contact	0.05 s

$$\text{speed of A} = \frac{\text{length of card}}{\text{time on clock}}$$

$$= \frac{0.1}{0.32}$$

$$= 0.31 \text{ m s}^{-1}$$

trolley B

length of card	0.1 m
time on clock	0.25 s
mass m_B	0.90 kg
time of contact	0.05 s

$$\text{speed of B} = \frac{\text{length of card}}{\text{time on clock}}$$

$$= \frac{0.1}{0.25}$$

$$= 0.40 \text{ m s}^{-1}$$

We can use these results and the law of conservation of momentum to calculate the average force exerted on each trolley.

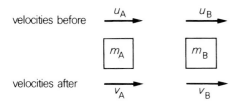

velocities before u_A u_B

m_A m_B

velocities after v_A v_B

Figure 17

From the results:

$$u_A = 0 \qquad\qquad u_B = 0$$
$$v_A = -0.31 \text{ m s}^{-1} \qquad\qquad v_B = 0.40 \text{ m s}^{-1}$$

To calculate the average force we use: $$\overline{F} = \frac{mv - mu}{t}$$

$$\overline{F}_A = \frac{m_A v_A - m_A u_A}{t} \qquad\qquad \overline{F}_B = \frac{m_B v_B - m_B u_B}{t}$$

$$= \frac{1.20 \times (-0.31) - 0}{0.05} \qquad\qquad = \frac{0.90 \times 0.40 - 0}{0.05}$$

$$= -\frac{0.37}{0.05} \qquad\qquad = \frac{0.36}{0.05}$$

$$= -7.4 \qquad\qquad = 7.2$$

$$\overline{F}_A \text{ is } -7.4 \text{ N} \qquad\qquad \overline{F}_B \text{ is } 7.2 \text{ N}$$

We can see that, within the limits of experimental error

$$\overline{F}_A = -\overline{F}_B \qquad\qquad \text{thus confirming Newton's Third Law.}$$

The average force acting on each trolley will be 7.3 N.

Example 8

Two trolleys A (mass 1 kg) and B (mass 3 kg) are attached with an elastic cord and pulled apart by a distance of 1 m on a horizontal surface.

They are released simultaneously and collide at point P. Find the displacements s_A and s_B.

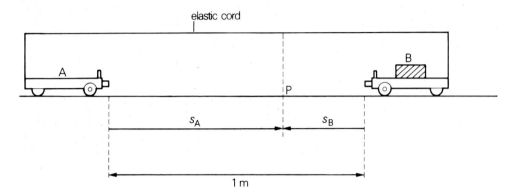

Because of Newton's Third Law, the average force $\overline{F}_A$ exerted on trolley A by the elastic cord has the same magnitude as the average force $\overline{F}_B$ exerted on trolley B by the elastic cord, but it will act in the opposite direction.

$$\overline{F}_A = -\overline{F}_B$$

The work done on trolley A by the cord $= \overline{F}_A s_A$.

This will provide the trolley with kinetic energy given by $\frac{1}{2} m_A v_A^2$ where v_A = velocity of A just before impact

$$\overline{F}_A s_A = \frac{1}{2} m_A v_A^2$$

In the same way $\overline{F}_B s_B = \frac{1}{2} m_B v_B^2$

but $m_A = 1$ kg and $m_B = 3$ kg $\qquad \Rightarrow \qquad \overline{F}_A s_A = \frac{1}{2} v_A^2 \quad \dots [1]$

$$\Rightarrow \qquad \overline{F}_B s_B = \frac{3}{2} v_B^2 \quad \dots [2]$$

The initial momentum is zero and since there is no external force acting on the whole system, the momentum just before impact is also zero.

$$m_A v_A + m_B v_B = 0$$

$$m_A v_A = -m_B v_B \qquad \Rightarrow \qquad v_A = -3 v_B$$

If we divide the energy equations [1] and [2] and substitue $-3v_B$ for v_A we have

$$\frac{\overline{F}_B s_B}{\overline{F}_A s_A} = \frac{\frac{3}{2} v_B^2}{\frac{1}{2} v_A^2}$$

$$\frac{\overline{F}_B s_B}{\overline{F}_A s_A} = \frac{3 v_B^2}{v_A^2} \qquad \Rightarrow \qquad \frac{-\overline{F}_A s_B}{\overline{F}_A s_A} = \frac{3 v_B^2}{(-3 v_B)^2}$$

$$\frac{-s_B}{s_A} = \frac{3 v_B^2}{9 v_B^2} \qquad \Rightarrow \qquad \frac{-s_B}{s_A} = \frac{1}{3}$$

$$s_A = -3 s_B$$

The total distance between the trolleys at the start is 1 m.

The magnitude of s_A must be 0.75 m and of s_B must be 0.25 m.

If we wish to indicate the vector direction of the displacements, we can write

$$s_A = +0.75 \text{ m and } s_B = -0.25 \text{ m}$$

Summary

Momentum = mass × velocity

During collisions and explosions momentum is conserved.

In an *inelastic* collision momentum only is conserved.

In an *elastic* collision momentum and kinetic energy are both conserved.

The net force acting on an object is equal to the rate of change of momentum.

$$F = \frac{mv - mu}{t}$$

Impulse = force × time over which it acts (units N s)
Impulse = change of momentum

For variable forces the impulse is equal to the area under the force–time graph.

Impulse = change of momentum

Questions

1 Car A is moving at 6 m s⁻¹ when car B, which is moving much faster, hits it and the bumpers lock.
Both cars move off together at 10 m s⁻¹.

mass of A = 1100 kg
mass of B = 1500 kg

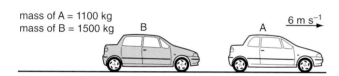

a) What is the speed of car B just before the collision?
b) Calculate the combined kinetic energy of the cars immediately after the collision.
c) If the cars slide to a halt after going a distance of 25 m determine the average retarding force acting on the cars.

2 In a computer simulation of a collision, vehicle A collides with a stationary vehicle B and rebounds at 0.6 m s⁻¹. The impact time is 0.02 s.

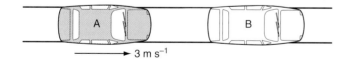

vehicle A mass = 4 kg
velocity before = +3 m s⁻¹
velocity after = – 0.6 m s⁻¹
vehicle B mass = 6 kg
velocity before = zero

a) What is the speed of vehicle B after the collision?
b) Show that the collision is elastic.
c) What is the impulse exerted on vehicle B during the collision?
d) Calculate the average force causing B to move off from rest.
e) What is the average force bringing vehicle A to a stop?

3 A vehicle on a linear air track has a mass of 80 g. It is catapulted by an elastic cord which is pulled back a short distance. When released the vehicle moves off at 0.4 m s⁻¹ after being in contact with the cord for 0.045 s.
a) Calculate the momentum of the trolley.
b) What is the average force exerted by the cord?
c) Estimate the original potential energy stored in the stretched cord.

SQA

4 A rocket is on a launch vehicle resting on a linear air track. When the rocket is lit it shoots off and the vehicle recoils.

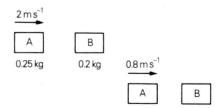

If the recoil velocity of the vehicle is 0.8 m s⁻¹ and the mass of the vehicle is 0.3 kg calculate the impulse exerted on the vehicle by the rocket. If the rocket takes 0.25 seconds to leave the vehicle find the average force exerted on the vehicle.

SQA

5 Two vehicles on a linear air track collide.
Vehicle A approaches vehicle B with a speed of 2 m s⁻¹ while vehicle B is at rest.
After the collision vehicle A is moving with speed 0.8 m s⁻¹.

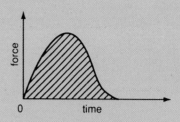

Calculate:
a) the velocity of vehicle B;
b) the loss of kinetic energy during the collision.

SQA

6 During a test on car safety, two cars as shown below are crashed together on a test track.

car A   car B

18.0 m s⁻¹   10.8 m s⁻¹

a) Car A, which has a mass of 1200 kg and is moving at 18.0 ms⁻¹, approaches car B, which has a mass of 1000 kg and is moving at 10.8 m s⁻¹, in the opposite direction.
The cars collide head on, lock together and move off in the direction of car A.
   i) Calculate the speed of the cars immediately after the collision.
   ii) Show by calculation that this collision is inelastic.
b) During a second safety test, a dummy in a car is used to demonstrate the effects of a collision.
During the collision, the head of the dummy strikes the dash board at 20 m s⁻¹ as shown below and comes to rest in 0.02 s. The mass of the head is 5 kg.

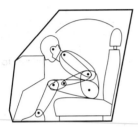

   i) Calculate the average force exerted by the dashboard on the head of the dummy during the collision.
   ii) If the contact area between the head and the dashboard is 5 × 10⁻⁴ m², calculate the pressure which this force produces on the head of the dummy.
   iii) The test on the dummy is repeated with an airbag which inflates during the collision. During the collision, the head of the dummy again travels forward at 20 m s⁻¹ and is brought to rest by the airbag.

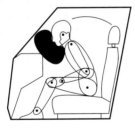

Explain why there is less risk of damage to the head of the dummy when the airbag is used.

SQA

7 A student uses a linear air track to investigate collisions. In one experiment a vehicle, mass 0.50 kg, moves along and rebounds from a metal spring mounted at one end of the level track as shown.

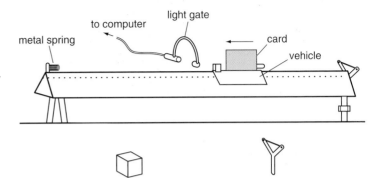

to computer

light gate

metal spring

card

vehicle

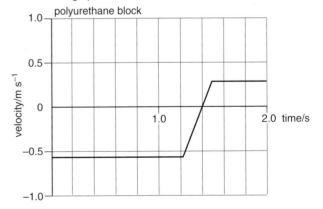

block of polyurethane foam   rubber band catapult

By using a light gate connected to a computer, she obtains values for the speed of the vehicle before and after it collides with the spring.
She then repeats the procedure, replacing the metal spring first with the block of polyurethane foam and then with the rubber band catapult. She records the results of each experiment in a table shown below.

	Metal spring	Polyurethane block	Rubber band
Speed before collision/m s⁻¹	0.55	0.55	0.55
Speed after collision/m s⁻¹	0.49	0.33	0.43
Kinetic energy before collision/J	0.076	0.076	0.076
Kinetic energy after collision/J	0.060		

a) Calculate the values of kinetic energy to complete the last row of the table.
b) For which experiment is the collision most nearly elastic? You must justify your answer.
c) Describe a method she could use to give the vehicle the same initial speed each time.
d) In order to analyse a collision in more detail, she now uses a motion sensor. This enables the computer to display a velocity–time graph of motion.

polyurethane block

(velocity/m s⁻¹ vs time/s graph, with values 1.0, 0.5, 0, −0.5, −1.0 on vertical axis and 1.0, 2.0 on horizontal axis)

   i) Use information from this graph to calculate the average force exerted by the polyurethane block on the vehicle, mass 0.50 kg, during the time that they are in contact.
   ii) Describe the motion of the vehicle during the time that it is in contact with the polyurethane block.

SQA

8 The velocity–time graph for one bounce of a ball is obtained using a motion sensor connected to a computer as shown.

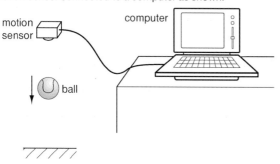

The ball is dropped from a position below the motion sensor and measurements start at the same instant as the ball is released. The graph obtained is shown below.

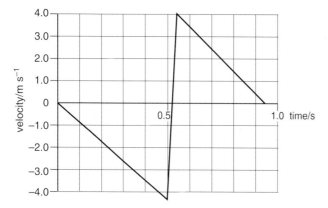

a) Calculate the acceleration of the falling ball.
b) The ball loses 1.7 joules of kinetic energy during the bounce, Show that the mass of the ball is 0.80 kg.
c) The momemtum of the ball is changed by the bounce. What is the magnitude of this change?
d) The ball is in contact with the ground for 50 milliseconds, Calculate the magnitude of the average force exerted by the ball on the ground during the bounce.

SQA

9 A stationary golf ball of mass 0.05 kg is hit by a putter as shown below.

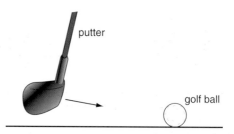

The ball moves off with an initial velocity of 2.0 m s⁻¹. The time of contact between the putter and ball is measured electronically to be 0.060 s.
a) Calculate the average force exerted by the putter on the golf ball.
b) Sketch a possible force–time graph for the impact of the putter with the golf ball.

SQA

10 a) State the law of conservation of linear momentum as it applies to a collision between two objects.
b) Two cars travelling in the same direction, skid on a patch of smooth, level ice. Car A, of mass 1400 kg, skids straight into the back of car B, of mass 1000 kg. The two cars become entangled after the impact and continue to move in the same straight line.

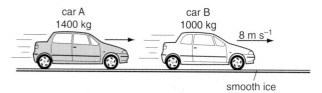

Immediately before the impact, car B is moving with a speed of 8 m s⁻¹. Immediately after the impact, both cars are moving with a speed of 15 m s⁻¹.
i) Calculate the speed of car A just before the collision takes place.
ii) After the collision, the cars leave the patch of ice and continue skidding along the road. They come to rest in a distance of 20 metres after leaving the ice. Calculate the average frictional force acting on the cars as they come to rest.
iii) State what happens to the kinetic energy of the cars after they leave the ice.

SQA

Unit 1 Mechanics and properties of matter

Topic 1.4 Test 1

1 A trolley moves due North with a speed of v.
The mass of the trolley is m.
Write down the expression for the momentum of the trolley.

2 An experiment is carried out on a linear air track.
A vehicle is fired towards a stationary vehicle. After the collision the vehicles bounce apart with the speeds shown.

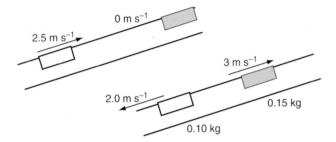

Which conservation law is illustrated by these results?
Show how the results verify the law.

3 Explain what is meant by an **elastic** collision.

4 A trolley, mass 0.8 kg, hits an identical trolley which is stationary with a speed of 2.4 m s^{-1}.
Both trolleys stick together and move off at 1.2 m s^{-1}.
Show that this is an inelastic collision.

5 A vehicle on a linear air track collides with a stationary vehicle and sticks to it.
The two vehicles move off with a speed of 0.2 m s^{-1}.
What is the speed of the moving vehicle before the collision?

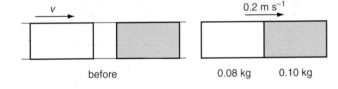

6 Two vehicles are exploded part.
They move off with the speeds shown in the diagram. What is the mass of the vehicle which moves at a speed of 3 m s^{-1}?

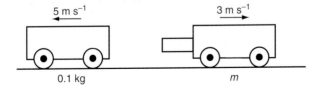

7 A vehicle A is travelling at 4 m s^{-1}. It hits a stationary vehicle and rebounds at 2 m s^{-1}. Vehicle B, mass 0.15 kg, goes to the right with a speed of 4 m s^{-1}.

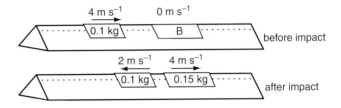

a) Using the results, compare the momenta of both vehicles before and after the collision.

b) Using the expression

force = rate of change of momentum

compare the forces acting on each vehicle during the collision if the impact lasted for 0.05 seconds.

8 Define **impulse** and state the unit in which it is measured.

9 The product force × time over which it acts is equivalent to which of the following?
  i) change of kinetic energy
  ii) acceleration × mass
  iii) change of momentum
  iv) power/time
  v) change of velocity / mass

10 A ball, mass 0.25 kg, is hit with a hammer and shoots off with a speed of 3.0 m s^{-1}.
Calculate the average force exerted on the ball if the contact time is 0.055 s.

Topic 1.4 Test 2

1 Define momentum and state the units in which it is measured.
2 A vehicle on a linear air track is catapulted towards a stationary vehicle.
When it collides with the other vehicle it sticks to it and they both have a speed of 2 m s^{-1}.
What quantity is conserved during this sequence of events?

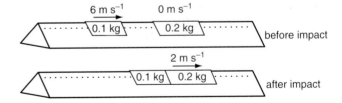

3 Using the results from the collision in question 2 show that the collision was **not** elastic.

4 Which type of collision **did** take place in question 2?

5   A vehicle on a linear air track hits a stationary vehicle and rebounds with a speed of 2 m s⁻¹.
Determine the speed of the other vehicle after the collision.

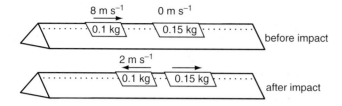

6   Two trolleys are exploded apart on a horizontal surface. If the 1.2 kg trolley moves with a speed of 0.5 m s⁻¹ calculate the speed of the other trolley.

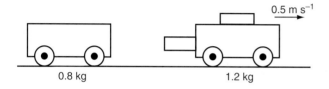

7   Two trolleys are exploded apart on a horizontal surface. The masses and speeds of each trolley are shown in the diagram.

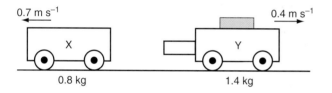

a)   Show that the change in momentum of X is equal and opposite to the change in momentum of Y.
b)   Compare the forces acting on X and Y during the explosion if the time of contact during the explosion is 60 milliseconds.
Use the expression

force = rate of change of momentum

8   A force acts on a stationary object for a short time. The product force × time over which it acts gives which physical quantity?

9   Newton's Second Law can be stated

'the net force acting on a body is equal to the rate of change of momentum'.

What quantity is equal to the 'change of momentum'?

10   An object, mass 2 kg, is travelling at a speed of 3 m s⁻¹ when the force shown in the graph is applied to it.
Find the speed of the object after 3 seconds.

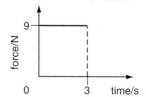

Topic 1.4 Test 3

1   An object, mass m, moving where the acceleration of gravity is g with a speed of v will have momentum equal to which of the following?
  i) mgv
  ii) $\frac{1}{2}mg/v$
  iii) m/v
  iv) $\frac{1}{2}mv^2$
  v) mv

2   When a collision takes place between two objects which quantity is conserved?

3   When an elastic collision takes place, which of the following is true?

  I   Kinetic energy only is conserved.
  II   Momentum and kinetic energy are both conserved.
  III   Momentum is conserved, kinetic energy is lost.

  i) I only
  ii) II only
  iii) III only
  iv) I and II
  v) II and III

4   In an inelastic collision between two objects in which there is no net external force which quantity is conserved and which is lost?

5   A vehicle, mass 0.150 kg, moving to the right at 1.8 m s⁻¹, hits a stationary vehicle, mass 0.100 kg which moves off to the right with a speed of 2.3 m s⁻¹. Calculate the speed of the larger vehicle after the collision.

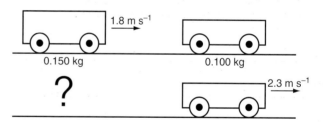

6   The diagram shows an explosion on a horizontal surface. The masses and the speed of one of the trolleys is given. Calculate the speed of the larger trolley.

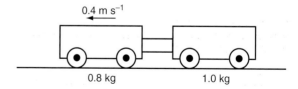

Which trolley has gained the greater kinetic energy?

7 A van, moving at 18 m s⁻¹, collides head-on with a stationary car. Calculate the common velocity of both vehicles which lock together during the collision.

 mass of van = 2000 kg   mass of car = 1500 kg

What is the change of momentum of the van during the collision? How does this compare with the change in momentum of the car? The van exerts a force of 80 kN on the car during the collision. What force does the car exert on the van?

8 A force of F acts on a stationary mass m for t seconds, giving it a speed of v.
Which expression gives the impulse of this force?

 i) Fv
 ii) Ft/m
 iii) F/t
 iv) Ft
 v) mv/t

9 A lorry, mass 15 000 kg, is travelling at 25 m s⁻¹ when brakes are applied slowing the speed to 15 m s⁻¹ after 5 seconds. Calculate the impulse acting on the lorry.

10 A force sensor is attached to a croquet mallet and the computer plots out an approximate graph of the force against time. This is reproduced in the diagram.
What is the impulse applied to the ball?
If the mass of the ball is 0.45 kg, determine its speed.

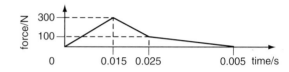

Topic 1.5
Density and Pressure

Objectives

When you have completed the work of this topic you should be able to:

1 state that density is mass per unit volume;
2 carry out calculations involving density, mass and volume;
3 describe the principles of a method for measuring the density of air;
4 state and explain the relative magnitudes of the densities of solids, liquids and gases;
5 state that pressure is force per unit area, when the force acts normal to the surface;
6 state that one pascal is one newton per square metre;
7 carry out calculations involving pressure, force and area;
8 state that the pressure at a point in a fluid at rest is given by $h\rho g$;
9 carry out calculations involving pressure, density and depth;
10 explain buoyancy force (upthrust) in terms of the pressure difference between the top and bottom of an object.

1.5 Density and Pressure

Motion of particles

In the investigation of the properties of gases it is normal to measure the three quantities, pressure, temperature and volume. The changes in these quantities can be explained in terms of the motion of particles. This chapter will consider the results for experiments on gases, and describe matter in terms of particles.

Pressure

Like the word 'work', pressure has many meanings in everyday use. For example, we talk of the pressure of exams, or pressure being exerted by the Government. In physics however, pressure is defined in terms of two other quantities, force and area. The following example illustrates the effects of different pressures.

When you stand in soft snow you sink into it. This is because your weight is acting over a small area, the area of your feet. However, if you wear snow shoes you find that you can walk over the snow without sinking in, Figure 1.

Your weight has not changed but has simply been spread over a much larger area by the snow shoes.

Without snow shoes a force is exerted on a small area and so the force on unit area is large. In this case we say that the **pressure** is large and so you sink into the snow. When wearing snow shoes, the same force is exerted over a much larger area and so the force on unit area is much smaller. We say that the pressure is smaller and so this time you do not sink. To be more exact, we define pressure as follows,

$$\text{pressure} = \frac{\text{force acting at right angles to an area}}{\text{area}}$$

i.e. $\quad p = \dfrac{F}{A}$

where $\quad p$ = pressure, F = force, A = area.

Figure 1 Soldier using snow shoes

Units

As the SI unit of force is the newton (N) and the SI unit of area is the square metre (m^2) it follows that the unit of pressure is the newton per square metre, written as $N\,m^{-2}$. This unit has been named the pascal (Pa) after Blaise Pascal, a Frenchman who did many experiments involving gas and liquid pressures.

$$1\,Pa = 1\,N\,m^{-2}$$

However the pascal is a very small unit and so we will often use the kilopascal (kPa) where $1000\,Pa = 1\,kPa$.

Example 1

Calculate the pressure produced by a force of 50 N acting down on a metal sheet of area 0.01 m^2.

$$p = \frac{F}{A}$$

$$p = \frac{50}{0.01}$$

$$p = 5000$$

The pressure produced is 5000 Pa.

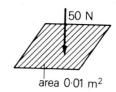

Example 2

A person, weight 750 N, stands on snowshoes each of which has an area of 0.2 m². Calculate the pressure on the snow.

$$\text{pressure} \quad = \quad \frac{\text{force}}{\text{area}} \quad = \quad \frac{750}{2 \times 0.2} \quad = \quad 1875 \text{ pascals}$$

The pressure on the snow is 1875 Pa.

The Bourdon pressure gauge

In the experiments discussed in this chapter we shall use a Bourdon pressure gauge to measure gas pressures. Figure 2 shows front and rear views of the pressure gauge.

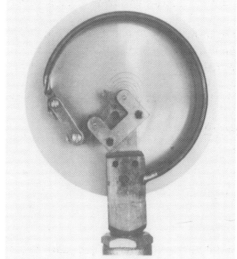

Figure 2 Bourdon pressure gauge

Figure 3

This pressure gauge works on the same principle as the familiar party-tooter often found in Christmas crackers, Figure 3. The harder you blow into the party-tooter, the more the paper tube uncurls. The Bourdon gauge consists of a hollow curved metal tube. An increase in pressure in the tube causes it to uncurl and a system of cogwheels makes a pointer move round a scale. A decrease in pressure results in the pointer moving in the opposite direction. In some Bourdon gauges, although the gauge is not connected to anything, the pointer is not at zero. This is because the air around us exerts a pressure which we call **atmospheric pressure**. The value of atmospheric pressure changes from day to day but is approximately 1×10^5 Pa or 100 kPa. The gauge in Figure 2 is indicating the atmospheric pressure.

The Bourdon gauge has many uses in industry, for example on gas cylinders, pumps and boilers. Figure 4 shows a type of Bourdon gauge which can be seen on many car dashboards. It is used to measure the oil pressure in the engine.

Figure 4 Oil pressure gauge

Checking the calibration

Using the apparatus shown in Figure 5 the pressure of a gas can be changed by applying a force on a piston in a syringe.

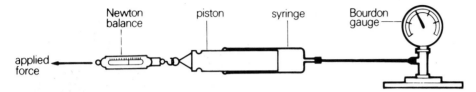

Figure 5 Calibration of Bourdon gauge

If we measure the force and the area of the piston we can calculate the change in pressure from the equation $p = \dfrac{F}{A}$. If the calibration of the gauge is correct, the change in pressure recorded by the gauge should equal our calculated pressure change.

Typical results from this experiment are shown below:

Original pressure reading on gauge	$p_1 = 102\ 000\ Pa$
Final pressure reading on gauge	$p_2 = 72\ 000\ Pa$
Change in pressure recorded by gauge	$(p_1 - p_2) = 30\ 000\ Pa$
Force applied to piston	$F = 30\ N$
Radius of piston	$r = 0.018\ m$
Area of circular piston	$(A = \pi r^2) = 0.001\ m^2$
Calculated pressure change	$F/A = 30\ 000\ Pa$

These results show that the pressure change calculated from F/A agrees with that recorded by the gauge. We have therefore checked that the calibration of the Bourdon gauge is correct.

Density

When a solid melts, there is very little change in volume. However, when a liquid is changed to a gas, there is a large increase in volume.

Two experiments can provide us with an estimate of the change in volume when a liquid changes to a gas and when a solid changes to a gas.

Liquid to gas

The plunger of a calibrated syringe is pushed to the bottom to exclude all air and the nozzle is sealed with a rubber cap, Figure 6. A small measured volume of water is then injected through the rubber seal by means of a hypodermic syringe.

The large calibrated syringe is then immersed in a beaker of salt solution which is boiling at a temperature just above 100°C. The sample of water turns into steam which pushes back the plunger. The volume of steam produced is read off the scale of the syringe. It is found that the water produces a volume of steam that is about 1600 times greater than the volume of water.

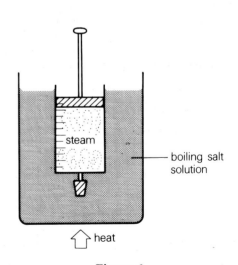

Figure 6

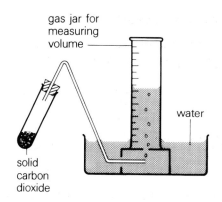

Solid to gas

A small test tube containing about 1 cm³ of solid carbon dioxide is connected by tubing to an inverted gas jar, Figure 7. The gas jar is calibrated for measuring volume and is initially filled with water. As the solid carbon dioxide vaporizes, it is collected in the gas jar. It is found that the volume of gas produced is about 800 times greater than the volume of solid.

Results from experiments such as these indicate that the volume occupied by particles of a gas is of the order of one thousand times greater than when in the liquid or solid state.

Figure 7

Density

Although the volume of the particles has increased on heating, the mass of the particles, whether in the gaseous or the liquid state, has remained unchanged. If we take equal volumes of the liquid and of the gas, their mass would be very different.

The mass per unit volume of a substance is called its **density** ρ.

density $\quad \rho = \dfrac{\text{mass}}{\text{volume}} = \dfrac{m}{V}$

The SI units for density are $kg\,m^{-3}$.

Example 3

A block of metal has the measurements shown.

The mass of metal is found to be 540 g.

Calculate the density of the metal.

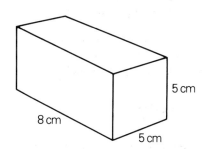

$$\text{volume} = 5 \times 5 \times 8 = 200\,cm^3 = 2 \times 10^{-4}\,m^3$$
$$\text{mass} = 540\,g = 0.540\,kg$$
$$\text{density} = \frac{\text{mass}}{\text{volume}} = \frac{0.54}{2 \times 10^{-4}} = 2700$$

The density of the metal is 2700 kg m⁻³.

Example 4

An experiment is carried out to find the density of a liquid.

An empty beaker is placed on a balance. The mass of the empty beaker is noted. 25 cm³ of liquid is measured accurately using a pipette. This is poured into the beaker and the new mass is noted.

Calculate the density of the liquid from the results.

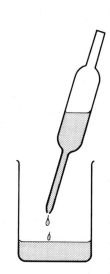

mass of empty beaker = 95.6 g
mass of beaker + liquid = 115.7 g
volume of liquid = 25 cm³.

$$\text{mass of liquid} = 115.7 - 95.6 = 20.1\,g = 0.02\,kg$$
$$\text{volume of liquid} = 25\,cm^3 = 2.5 \times 10^{-5}\,m^3$$
$$\text{density} = \frac{\text{mass}}{\text{volume}} = \frac{0.02}{2.5 \times 10^{-5}} = 800$$

The density of the liquid is 800 kg m⁻³.

Density of air

The density of air is very low but it can be determined if a sensitive balance is available.

A strong glass flask is fitted with a stopper, glass tube and rubber tube with clip attached. This is fitted to a vacuum pump and the air is withdrawn. The clip is closed and the empty flask is weighed. The clip is opened and air at atmospheric pressure enters the flask.

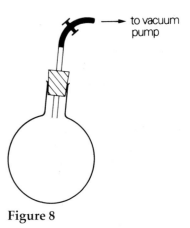

Figure 8

The flask full of air is weighed. Typical results are given below.

mass of empty flask   = 186.1 g

mass of flask full of air   = 186.8 g

volume of flask   = 500 cm³

mass of air   = 186.8 − 186.1 = 0.7 g = 0.7×10^{-3} kg

volume of air = 500 cm³ = 5×10^{-4} m³.

density $= \dfrac{\text{mass}}{\text{volume}} = \dfrac{0.7 \times 10^{-3}}{5 \times 10^{-4}}$

$= 1.4$

The density of air at room temperature and atmospheric pressure is 1.4 kg m⁻³.

This method gives a reasonable estimate of the density of air but is not entirely satisfactory because the flask may contain water vapour which will give a false result.

In general, solids and liquids do expand a little when heated: the same mass will then occupy a slightly larger volume, and the density will be smaller. An accurate value of the density should also state the temperature at which it was measured.

A change in temperature or in pressure can produce a large change in the volume of gas. The value of a gas density must state the temperature and the pressure at which it was measured. The conditions chosen are usually a temperature of 0°C and a pressure of 1.01×10^{5} Pa: this is known as **Standard Temperature and Pressure** (s.t.p.).

Table 1 shows the densities of some solids, liquids and gases.

Example 5

A sample of oxygen with a density of 1.43 kg m⁻³ at s.t.p. occupies a volume of 5.00×10^{-3} m³ at s.t.p. What is the mass of the sample?

$$\rho = \frac{m}{V} \qquad\qquad \rho = 1.43 \text{ kg m}^{-3}$$
$$V = 5.00 \times 10^{-3} \text{ m}^3$$

$$\Rightarrow \quad 1.43 = \frac{m}{5.00 \times 10^{-3}}$$

$$\Rightarrow \quad m = 1.43 \times 5.00 \times 10^{-3}$$

$$\Rightarrow \quad m = 7.15 \times 10^{-3}$$

The mass of the sample is 7.15×10^{-3} kg.

gases	density at s.t.p. (kg m⁻³)
hydrogen	0.09
helium	0.18
nitrogen	1.25
air	1.29
oxygen	1.43
carbon dioxide	1.98

solids and liquids	density at 20°C (kg m⁻³ × 10³)
cork	0.25
olive oil	0.92
water	1.00
naphthalene	1.15
perspex	1.19
glycerol	1.26
aluminium	2.70
glass	3.00
iron	7.86
silver	10.50
lead	11.40
mercury	13.60
gold	19.30

Table 1 Densities

Spacing of particles

Figure 9 shows a model of the structure of a liquid in which it is assumed that the particles are spherical. This shows that when the particles are closely packed together, the spacing d is equal to the particle diameter d_o. If the liquid is compressed, this is resisted by a repulsion force between the particles. If the particles are pulled apart, this is resisted by an attraction force between the particles.

As we saw earlier, the change in volume which takes place when a sample of liquid changes into a gas is by a factor of the order of 1000 times. To estimate the change in spacing which will take place, it is assumed that each particle is enclosed in a cubical box, Figure 10. The sides of the box have a length equal to the particle diameter d_o. The volume is therefore d_o^3

When the liquid becomes a gas, the size of the particles does not change but they become more widely spaced and the volume occupied by one particle will be 1000 times greater than the original volume.

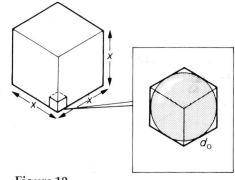

surface of liquid

$d = d_o$

Figure 9

The new volume is $1000\,d_o^3$ which can be represented by a cube of side x, Figure 10. In this case the new volume will be x^3.

$$x^3 = 1000\,d_o^3$$
$$\Rightarrow x = \sqrt[3]{1000\,d_o^3}$$
$$\Rightarrow x = 10\,d_o$$
$$\Rightarrow x = 10\,d \quad \text{since } d = d_o$$

Thus in a gas the particle spacing is about 10 times greater than that of the liquid, Figure 11.

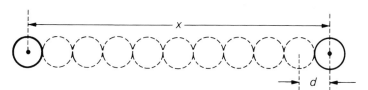

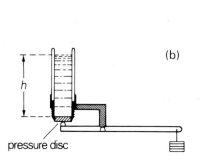

Figure 10

Figure 11

Pressure in a liquid

The French scientist Blaise Pascal (1623–1662) investigated the pressure in a liquid.

Figure 12(a) shows a set of vessels known as Pascal's vases. These are used to show that the depth of water determines the pressure exerted on the pressure disc and not the amount of water in each case.

A disc is held firmly in place by a lever at the end of which weights can be added, Figure 12(b).

The parallel-sided vessel is used first. Water is poured into the vessel until at a particular height h, the water

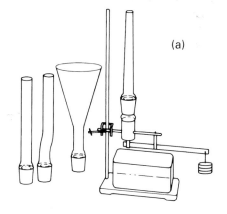

(a)

(b)

pressure disc

Figure 12

starts to drip out. This shows the downward force on the disc from the liquid is just sufficient to overcome the upward force on the disc from the lever system.

The experiment is repeated with different shapes of vase. In each case the height of water which causes the water to drip out is the same regardless of the shape of the vessel.

This shows that the pressure is determined by the depth of the liquid, and not by the shape of the vessel.

The pressure at any depth acts equally in all directions

This can be illustrated by stretching a thin rubber membrane over a thistle funnel. This is then connected to a sensitive Bourdon gauge which registers any change in pressure.

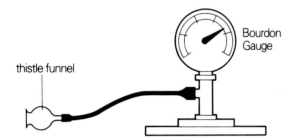

Figure 13

The funnel is then placed at a given depth in water and set at various angles. In each case the pressure reading is the same, indicating that at a given depth the pressure of the liquid acts equally in all directions.

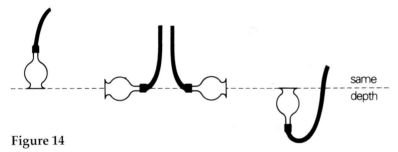

Figure 14

The pressure in a given liquid increases with depth

The relationship between depth and pressure can be investigated by floating a flat-bottomed tube loaded with lead shot in water, Figure 3.24.

A scale fitted inside the tube allows the depth to be measured.

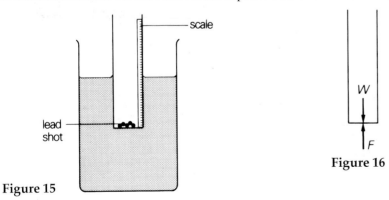

Figure 15

Figure 16

When the tube floats, the pressure of the liquid on the base of the tube supports it. If the weight of the tube plus lead shot is W and the area of the base is A, the tube floats so that the upward force acting on it balances the weight.

$W = F$ where the upward force is F (Figure 16).

The upward force acts over an area A so that the pressure acting upwards on the base of the tube is given by

$$p = \frac{F}{A}$$

but $F = W$

$$\Rightarrow \quad p = \frac{W}{A}$$

This pressure is provided by the liquid.

If the tube is made heavier by adding lead shot, it will sink to a greater depth where the liquid pressure is greater.

The experiment is carried out by adding lead shot until the tube floats with a specified depth below the surface.

i)   The tube is weighed.
ii) It is loaded with more lead shot until it sinks to the next depth.
iii) It is weighed again.

This process is repeated and a set of results is given in Table 2.

depth h (m)	total weight of tube W (N)
0.07	0.21
0.08	0.23
0.09	0.26
0.10	0.29
0.11	0.32
0.12	0.35

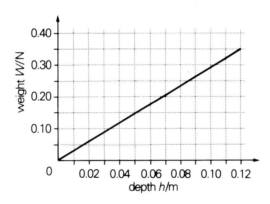

Table 2   **Figure 17**

When the results are plotted a straight line graph passing through the origin is obtained, Figure 17.

The graph shows that the weight of the tube W is directly proportional to the depth h.

As previously shown, the pressure of the liquid p is directly proportional to the weight W:

$$p \propto h$$

It can be concluded that the pressure is directly proportional to the depth.

A manometer containing water can be connected to a gas tap. The greater pressure on the right–hand side forces the water up on the left–hand side. The difference in level h indicates the difference in pressure between each side of the U-tube, Figure 18.

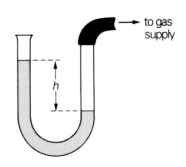

Figure 18

The pressure at a given depth depends on the density of the liquid

To illustrate the effect which the density of the liquid has on the pressure, a flat-bottomed tube is floated in the liquid.

Lead shot is added until the depth achieved is some constant value, for example 8 cm.

The weight of lead shot is noted and as previously demonstrated this weight W is directly proportional to the pressure of the liquid.

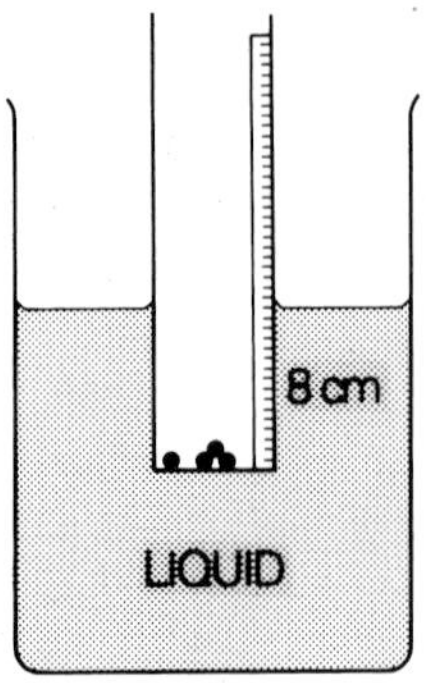

The tube is floated in water to a depth of 8 cm and the weight noted.

i)   The tube is cleaned and dried and then floated in another liquid.
ii) Lead shot is added until the tube sinks to a depth of 8 cm in the liquid.
iii) The weight of lead shot plus tube is noted.
iv) This is repeated for liquids of known density.

Figure 19

A set of results is given in Table 3.

liquid	density ρ $(kg\,m^{-3})$	weight W (N)
glycerol	1260	0.32
vinegar	1050	0.26
water	1000	0.25
olive oil	920	0.23
turpentine	870	0.22
ethanol	800	0.20

Table 3

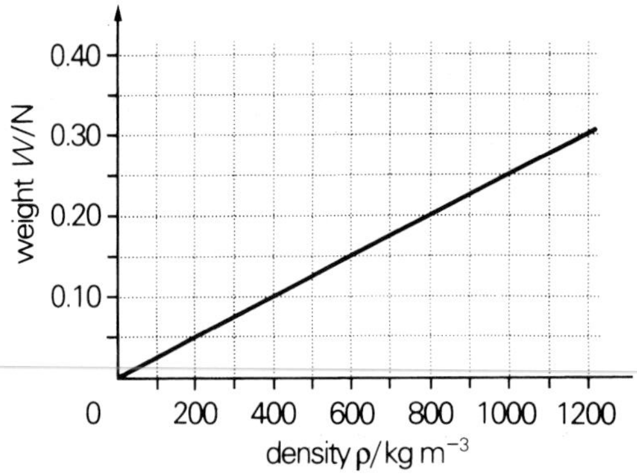

Figure 20

A graph of W plotted against ρ gives a straight line graph through the origin, Figure 20.

This shows that

$$W \propto \rho$$

and since the upward force acting on the base F is equal to W

$$F \propto \rho$$

but the pressure p of the liquid

$$p = \frac{F}{A}$$

so that $p \propto \rho$

It can be concluded that the pressure is directly proportional to the density of the liquid.

Combining these two results gives the equation

$p = kh\rho$ where h = depth below the surface
ρ = density of the liquid
k = a constant.

Calculation of pressure in a liquid

To obtain an expression for the pressure of a liquid at any depth in a liquid consider a cylindrical column of liquid as shown in Figure 21.

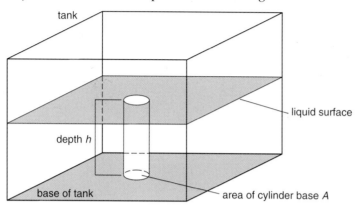

Figure 21

The pressure acting on the base of this column is due to the weight of the column pressing downwards on the base. The area of the base is A and the depth is h.

$$\text{volume of cylinder} = \text{area of base} \times \text{height}$$
$$= Ah$$

$$\text{mass of liquid} = \text{volume} \times \text{density}$$
$$= Ah\rho$$

$$\text{weight of liquid} = \text{mass} \times \text{gravitational field strength}$$
$$= Ah\rho g$$

$$\text{pressure} = \text{force}/\text{area}$$
$$= Ah\rho g / A$$
$$= h\rho g$$

Example 6

A liquid has a density of 800 kg m^{-3}.
Calculate the pressure due to this liquid at a depth of 6 metres.

$$\text{pressure} = h\rho g \qquad \begin{aligned} h &= 6\,\text{m} \\ \rho &= 800\,\text{kg m}^{-3} \\ g &= 9.8\,\text{N kg}^{-1} \end{aligned}$$

$$= 6 \times 800 \times 9.8$$
$$= 4.7 \times 10^{4}$$

The pressure is 4.7×10^{4} Pa.

Buoyancy

When an object is hung at the end of a spring balance, Figure 22, the weight W exerts a downward force which is supported by the upward force T of the spring.

As the object is lowered into a liquid, the spring balance reading decreases, giving a minimum reading when the object is totally immersed, Figure 23.

The reduction of the balance reading is due to the buoyant force F_B or upthrust which is exerted on the object by the liquid. It is this buoyant force which produces buoyancy or 'floating power'. The forces acting on the immersed object are balanced, so that

$T = W - F_B$ where T = force exerted by the spring
W = weight of the object
F_B = buoyant force due to the liquid.

If an object is less dense than a liquid, it will float and displace only a small volume of the liquid. The buoyancy force will be equal to the weight of the object, and to the weight of the liquid displaced, Figure 24:

$F_B = W$

Materials with a density close to, but less than, the density of a liquid will still float but with much more of their volume submerged. The buoyancy force again equals the weight of the object, Figure 24(b).

An object which has a density greater than that of the liquid will sink into the liquid. In this case, the buoyant force is less than the weight of the object – by how much depends on the densities of the object and of the liquid.

For most purposes, an object which has a density greater than that of a liquid will sink in that liquid.

For a floating object that is pushed below the surface with a force P, Figure 25, the forces acting on the object are balanced:

$P = F_B - W$

If the force P is now removed, the buoyant force F_B pushes the object up to the surface because this force is greater than the weight W of the object. The object rises and floats on the surface.

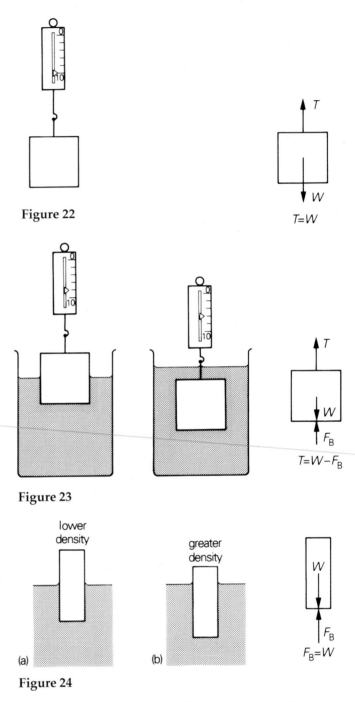

Figure 22

$T = W$

Figure 23

$T = W - F_B$

lower density

greater density

(a)   (b)

$F_B = W$

Figure 24

$P = F_B - W$

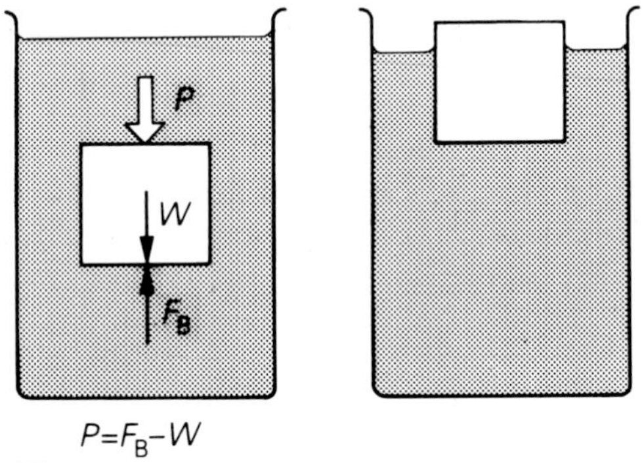

Figure 25

Calculation of buoyancy force

The buoyancy force or upthrust arises because there is a difference in pressure between the top of the object and the bottom of the object.

Consider an object in the form of a cube supported under the surface of a liquid as shown in Figure 26.

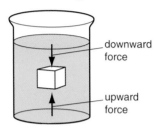 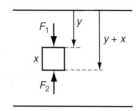

Figure 26

$$\text{depth of top face of cube} = y$$
$$\text{depth of bottom face of cube} = y + x$$
$$\text{area of each face of cube} = x^2$$
$$\text{density of the liquid} = \rho$$

$$\text{pressure acting on the top face} = y\rho g$$
$$\text{force acting on the top face} = \text{pressure} \times \text{area}$$
$$F_1 = y\rho g x^2$$
$$\text{pressure acting on the bottom face} = (y + x)\rho g$$
$$\text{force acting on the bottom face} = \text{pressure} \times \text{area}$$
$$F_2 = (y + x)\,\rho g x^2$$
$$= y\rho g x^2 + g\rho x^3$$

$$\text{buoyancy force} = F_2 - F_1$$
$$= y\rho g x^2 + g\rho x^3 - y\rho g x^2$$
$$= g\rho x^3$$

When the object is lowered into the liquid it displaces a volume of liquid equal to its own volume.

$$\text{volume of displaced liquid} = x^3$$
$$\text{mass of displaced liquid} = \text{density} \times \text{volume}$$
$$= \rho x^3$$
$$\text{weight of the displaced liquid} = \text{mass} \times \text{gravitational field strength}$$
$$= \rho x^3 g$$

This is exactly the same as the expression for the buoyancy force acting on the object.

Thus:

$$\text{buoyancy force (upthrust)} = \text{weight of liquid displaced}$$

This relationship was first discovered over two thousand years ago by a Greek mathematician and is usually named after him. It is referred to as **Archimedes' Principle**.

Example 7

A cube of side 5 cm has a weight of 3.5 N in air.
It is lowered into water until it is completely submerged.
If the density of the water is 1000 kg m^{-3} what will be its weight in water?

$$\text{volume of displaced water} = \text{volume of the cube}$$
$$\text{mass of water displaced} = \text{density} \times \text{volume}$$
$$\text{weight of water displaced} = \text{mass} \times \text{gravitational field strength}$$
$$= 1000 \times 0.05^3 \times 9.8$$
$$= 1.2$$
$$\text{upthrust due to the liquid} = 1.2$$
$$\text{weight in water} = \text{weight in air - upthrust}$$
$$= 3.5 - 1.2 = 2.3$$

The weight of the cube in water is 2.3 N.

Example 8

A tank contains water to a depth of 0.5 m.
A wooden cube of side 0.06 m is held 0.2 m below the surface
by a vertical string attached to the bottom of the tank.
Determine the force exerted on the cube by the string.
(density of cube material 600 kg m^{-3}
density of water 1000 kg m^{-3}).

The density of the cube is less than the density of water so that the cube would
float on the surface if it were not held in place by the string.

$$\text{the force exerted by the string} = \text{upthrust due to the water} - \text{weight of the cube}$$

$$
\begin{aligned}
\text{upthrust due to the water} &= \text{weight of water displaced by the cube} \\
&= \text{volume of water displaced} \times \text{density} \times g \\
&= \text{volume of the cube} \times \text{density} \times g \\
&= 0.06^3 \times 1000 \times 9.8 = 2.12 \text{ N}
\end{aligned}
$$

$$
\begin{aligned}
\text{weight of cube} &= \text{volume of cube} \times \text{density} \times g \\
& 0.06^3 \times 600 \times 9.8 = 1.27 \text{ N}
\end{aligned}
$$

$$
\begin{aligned}
\text{but the force exerted by the string} &= \text{upthrust - weight} \\
&= 2.12 - 1.27 \\
&= 0.85
\end{aligned}
$$

The force exerted by the string on the cube is 0.85 N.

Hydrometer

The proportion of an object which is immersed depends on the density of the liquid in which it floats. The same object will float to a greater depth in a liquid of density $800 \, kg \, m^{-3}$ than it would in a liquid density $1000 \, kg \, m^{-3}$. This fact is used in the **hydrometer**. A glass tube with a loaded bulb at one end floats in a liquid and its scale indicates the density. The hydrometer will sink further in liquids of lower density and the scale can be calibrated.

In the photograph, Figure 27, a hydrometer floats in a liquid with a density less than that of water.

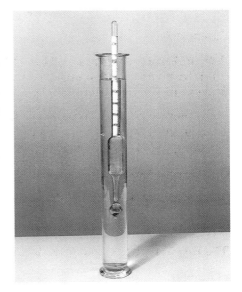

Figure 27

Hot air balloon

When an object floats in a fluid (liquid or gas) it experiences an upthrust.

A hot air balloon, floating in air makes use of this, Figure 28. A burner raises the temperature of the air inside the balloon making it less dense than the surrounding air.

The denser air outside the balloon produces an upthrust which lifts the balloon upwards.

Figure 28

Submarines

Ships float because a large part of the inner volume is air making the average density less than the density of water.

In a submarine, ballast tanks are fitted. These can be filled with water or with air. When on the surface the tanks are mainly full of air.

In order to dive, the tanks are filled with water. The weight of the submarine is now greater than the upthrust and the submarine sinks.

Figure 29

Figure 30

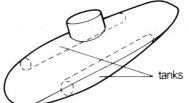

tanks

Summary

Density = $\dfrac{\text{mass}}{\text{volume}}$

The density of a solid or liquid substance is approximately 1000 times the density it would have as a gas.

pressure = $\dfrac{\text{force acting at right angles to an area}}{\text{area over which the force acts}}$

1 pascal = 1 newton per square metre ($1\,\text{N m}^{-2}$)

The pressure p due to a liquid of density p at a depth h is given by

$p = h\rho g$

where
- h = depth
- ρ = density
- g = acceleration due to gravity.

Buoyancy force is the net upward force acting on an object submerged or floating in a fluid (liquid or gas).

Archimedes' Principle states that the upthrust (the buoyancy force) acting on an object, in a fluid, is equal to the weight of the fluid displaced.

Questions

1 A spring balance is used to measure the weight of a cube of metal. It reads 9.2 N when the cube is in air.

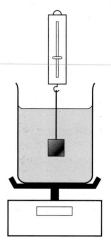

A beaker containing water is placed on an electronic balance which gives a reading of 17.5 N.
The cube is lowered into the water until it is fully submerged.
The spring balance now reads 8.1 N.
  a) What is the reading on the electronic balance?
  b) If the density of the metal of the cube is $8.5 \times 10^3\,\text{kg m}^{-3}$ calculate the volume of the cube.

2 A block of wood measuring 5 cm × 5 cm × 20 cm floats in water submerged to a depth of 3 cm.

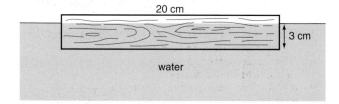

20 cm

3 cm

water

The density of the wood is $600\,\text{kg m}^{-3}$.
  a) What is the mass of the block?

  b) What is the weight of the block?
  c) Calculate the pressure acting on the bottom surface of the wood and hence determine the buoyancy force.
  d) A mass of 100 g is laid on the top surface of the wood. Determine the depth to which the wood will now sink.

3 A syringe has a piston with cross-section area $2\,\text{cm}^2$. The piston is pushed with a force of 12 N. Calculate the pressure.

4 A tank contains 1000 kg of water. If the base of the tank has an area of $20\,\text{m}^2$, calculate the pressure exerted by the water on the base.

5 An elephant exerts a force of 5000 N by pressing his foot on the ground. If the area of his foot is $0.02\,\text{m}^2$, calculate the pressure exerted by his foot.

6 A crane is used to lower a concrete block of mass $5.0 \times 10^3\,\text{kg}$ into the sea.

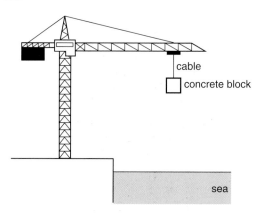

cable

concrete block

sea

  a) The crane lowers the block towards the sea at a constant speed.
  Calculate the tension in the cable supporting the block.
  b) The crane lowers the block into the sea. The block is held stationary just below the surface of the sea as shown in the diagram.

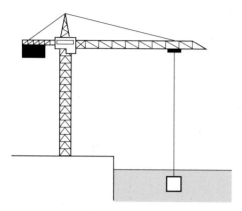

The tension in the cable is now 2.9×10^4 N.

   i) Calculate the size of the buoyancy force acting on the block.

   ii) Explain how this buoyancy force is produced.

c) The block is now lowered to a greater depth.
What effect, if any, does this have on the tension on the cable?
Justify your answer.

SQA

7 A hot air balloon, of total mass 500 kg, is held stationary by a single vertical rope.

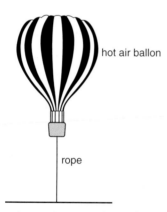

   i) Draw a sketch of the balloon. On your sketch, mark and label all the forces acting on the balloon.

   ii) When the rope is released, the balloon initially accelerates vertically upwards at $1.5 \, \text{m s}^{-2}$. Find the magnitude of the buoyancy force.

   iii) Calculate the tension in the rope **before** it is released.

b) An identical balloon is moored using two ropes, each of which makes an angle of 25° to the vertical, as shown below.

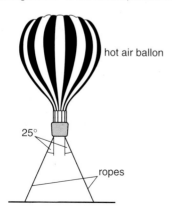

By using a scale diagram, or otherwise, calculate the tension in each rope.

   c) During a flight, when a hot air balloon is travelling vertically upwards with constant velocity, some hot air is released. This allows cooler air to enter through the bottom of the balloon. Describe **and** explain the effect of this on the motion of the balloon. You may assume that the volume of the ballon does not change.

SQA

8 The apparatus in the diagram below may be used to measure the density of air.

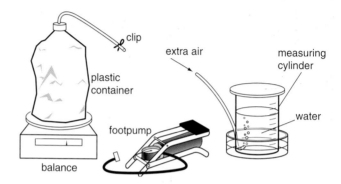

Using the footpump, extra air is pumped into the container. This extra air is released into the measuring cylinder as shown above and its volume measured.

The following measurements are recorded.

Mass of container full of air   = 362.00 g
mass of container with extra air = 363.86 g
volume of air released   = 1687.00 cm³

What value do these results give for air in kg m⁻³?

SQA

9 A mooring buoy is tethered to the sea bed by a rope which is too short. The buoy floats under the water at high tide. The weight of the buoy is 50 N.

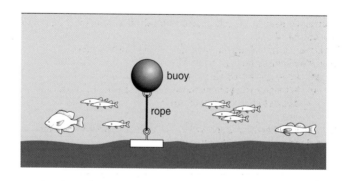

a)   **i)** Draw a labelled diagram to show all the forces acting on the buoy in the vertical direction.

     ii) The tension in the rope is 1200 N.
Calculate the buoyancy force.

b) The rope now snaps and the buoy starts to rise.
What is the size of the buoyancy force on the buoy when it is just below the surface of the water?

SQA

10   A sonar detector, of mass 6 kg, is used for monitoring the presence
of dolphins, It is attached by a vertical cable to the sea bed so that
the detector is held below the surface of the sea

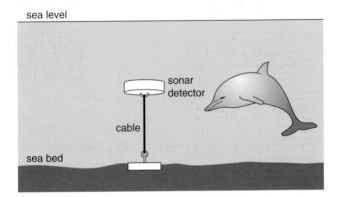

a)   Explain the cause of the buoyancy force on the detector.
b)   Draw a diagram showing the buoyancy force and the other
forces acting on the detector.
c)   If the buoyancy force has a value of 31 500 N, what is the value
of the tension in the cable attached to the sea bed?
d)   The detector is now used at the same depth in fresh water.
How would this effect the value of the buoyancy force?
Justify your answer.

Topic 1.5 Test 1

1 Write down the expression for density of a material in terms of its mass and its volume.

2 The density of glycerin is $1.25 \times 10^3 \, kg \, m^{-3}$. What volume is occupied by 0.25 kg?

3 A plastic container holding about 2 litres of air at atmospheric pressure is fitted with a valve so that extra air can be pumped into it using a foot pump. Describe how this could be used to determine the density of air.
State any additional apparatus required and indicate how the results would be used.

4 a) For any element the density of the liquid state is approximately 1000 times the density it has as a gas.
Explain why this should be so by considering the spacing of the molecules in each state.

b) Solid carbon dioxide changes into a gas when placed in surroundings at 20°C.
Approximately what volume of vapour is produced by one cubic centimetre of solid carbon dioxide?

5 A force F pushes vertically downwards on an area A. What expression gives the pressure due to the force?

6 The pascal has the same units as which of the following?
  i) N
  ii) $N \, m^{-1}$
  iii) $N \, m^{-2}$
  iv) N m
  v) $N \, m^2$

7 A metal cylinder, weight 9.8 N, has a cross-sectional area of 2.8×10^{-3} square metres.
What pressure does it exert if it rests on a horizontal table top?

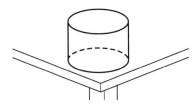

8 The pressure at any point in a liquid is directly proportional to the density of the liquid and directly proportional to the depth below the surface of the liquid.
What formula would allow the actual pressure at a point to be calculated?

9 A measuring cylinder contains methanol which has a density of $800 \, kg \, m^{-3}$.
Determine the pressure exerted by the methanol 18 cm below the surface.

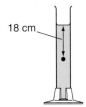
18 cm

10 A cube of metal, measuring $0.05 \times 0.05 \times 0.05$ m is weighed in air and then in water.
The density of the metal is $2700 \, kg \, m^{-3}$.

  weight in air = 3.3 N
  weight in water = 2.1 N

What is the difference in liquid pressure acting on the top and bottom of the cube?

Topic 1.5 Test 2

1 Which of the following gives the density of a substance?
  i) $\dfrac{weight}{volume}$
  ii) mass × volume
  iii) $\dfrac{mass}{volume}$
  iv) weight × volume
  v) $\dfrac{volume}{mass}$

2 A gas has a density of $1.4 \, kg \, m^{-3}$.
Calculate the volume of 4 kg of this gas.

3 Briefly describe how the density of a sample of air could be estimated.
Sketch the apparatus used, list the measurements taken and show the calculations involved.

4 a) If $10 \, cm^3$ of water evaporates completely, approximately how much water vapour would be produced?

b) The spacing of the molecules in the solid state is about one tenth of the spacing in the gaseous state.
Explain what this information indicates about the relative densities of solids and gases.

5 Explain what is meant by the pressure exerted by a force.

6 Which of the following has the same unit as newtons per square metre?
  i) pascal
  ii) kelvin
  iii) $kg \, m \, s^{-1}$
  iv) joule per metre
  v) millibars

7 Air is enclosed in a cylinder which has an area of cross-section of $2 \, cm^2$.

The piston is pulled to the right until the pressure inside the cylinder is 50 kPa while the outside pressure is 100 kPa.
What is the magnitude of the force F?

8   A cylinder contains a liquid of density ρ.
A point X is h metres below the surface and d metres above the bottom of the cylinder.
Which of the following will give the pressure, exerted by the liquid, at point X?

i) $\rho g d$
ii) $\rho g h$
iii) ρh
iv) ρd
v) $\rho h/g$

9   Oil is pumped up a pipe from below the sea bed.
If the density of oil is 830 kg m^{-3} and the column of oil is 2500 m long what is the pressure at the bottom of the pipe?

10   A cube is immersed, at a depth h, under the surface of a liquid as shown in the diagram.
The area of a side of the cube is A and the length of one side is x.
The density of the liquid is ρ.
Derive an expression for the buoyancy force acting on the base of the cube.

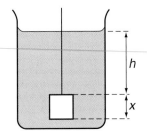

Topic 1.5 Test 3

1   State the meaning of density and give the units in which it is measured.

2   Perspex has a density of 1.2×10^3 kg m^{-3}. What is the volume of 120 g of perspex?

3   A light metal flask has a volume of 250 cm^3.
Describe how you would use this to estimate the density of air at atmospheric pressure. State any additional apparatus required and explain how the results are used to calculate the final answer.

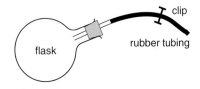

4   When a sample of water is completely changed into steam the volume expands to about 1500 times the volume of the water. Discuss how the density of steam compares with that of water.

5   A box of weight W rests on a horizontal surface. The area of contact between the box and the surface is A.
Which of the following is the pressure exerted by the box on the surface? (The acceleration of gravity is g.)

i) $\dfrac{W}{A}$
ii) $W \times A$
iii) $\dfrac{Wg}{A}$
iv) WgA
v) $\dfrac{W}{gA}$

6   A pressure of 1 kPa is the same as which of the following?

i) 1 kg cm^{-2}
ii) 1 kN cm^{-2}
iii) 100 N m^{-2}
iv) 1 kN m^{-2}
v) 10 kg m^{-2}

7   A board measures 1.8 m × 0.4 m and rests on a horizontal surface. It has a weight of 80 N.
A person, weight 720 N, stands on the board. What is the pressure exerted on the surface?

8   What expression would be used to calculate the pressure at a point under the surface of a liquid?

9   Two glass tubes contain different liquids A and B.
density of A = 800 kg m^{-3}
density of B = 1200 kg m^{-3}
Calculate the pressure due to liquid A at a depth of 0.6 m.
At what depth in liquid B would the pressure be the same?

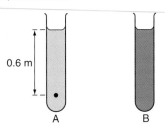

10   A cylinder, length 0.15 m, area of base 1.2×10^{-3} m^2, weighs 14.4 N in air.
The cylinder is lowered into water so that its top surface is at a depth of 0.4 m.
Determine the pressure acting on the top surface and the pressure acting on the bottom surface and hence calculate the buoyancy force.
What is the apparent weight of the cylinder in water?

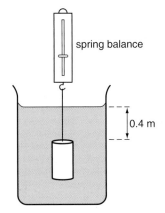

Topic 1.6
Gas Laws

Objectives

When you have completed the work of this topic you should be able to:

1 describe how the kinetic model accounts for the pressure of a gas;
2 state that the pressure of a fixed mass of gas at constant temperature is inversely proportional to its volume;
3 state that the pressure of a fixed mass of gas at constant volume is directly proportional to its temperature measured in kelvin (K);
4 state that the volume of a fixed mass of gas at constant pressure is directly proportional to its temperature measured in kelvin (K);
5 carry out calculations to convert °C to K and vice versa;
6 carry out calculations involving pressure, volume and temperature of a fixed mass of gas using the general gas equation;
7 explain what is meant by absolute zero of temperature;
8 explain the pressure–volume, pressure–temperature and volume–temperature laws qualitatively in terms of a kinetic model.

1.6 Gas Laws

Kinetic Theory

The basic assumption of the Kinetic Theory is that all matter consists of particles which are in constant motion at any temperature above absolute zero. Air particles cannot be seen as they are extremely small. However, evidence for their motion was discovered in 1827 by Robert Brown.

Brownian motion

Robert Brown, a Scottish botanist, carried out an experiment which showed that when tiny pollen grains suspended in water are viewed under a microscope they are seen to be in constant motion. At first it was thought that this motion was a form of life but further experiments with non-living particles showed that the motion was always present.

In the laboratory we can look at the Brownian motion of smoke particles using the apparatus shown in Figure 1.

Light from the lamp is focused by the glass rod on the glass cell. A dropper filled with smoke from smouldering string is used to fill the glass cell and a glass cover will then seal the cell. When the microscope is correctly adjusted, the smoke which consists of tiny specks of ash can be seen reflecting the light from the lamp. The smoke particles are seen to move jerkily through short distances in many different directions. The first accurate explanation of this Brownian motion was given by Albert Einstein in 1905. According to the Kinetic Theory, the air particles surrounding a speck of ash are moving randomly and colliding with it. Although a speck of ash is much larger than the air particles, it is small enough to be affected by collisions with them. These randomly occurring collisions produce unbalanced forces which cause the speck of ash to move. The air particles are moving in all directions so that the collisions come from all directions. The motion of a speck of ash is therefore random, i.e. it moves, but not in any particular direction, Figure 2.

According to the Kinetic Theory, at a higher temperature the air particles have more kinetic energy and so are moving faster. This means that at higher temperatures the collisions are more violent and so the specks of ash are jostled around faster.

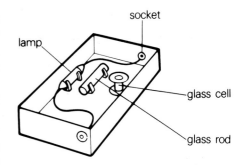

Figure 1 Brownian motion apparatus

Behaviour of gases

Robert Boyle investigated the relationship between the pressure p and the volume V for a fixed mass of gas at constant temperature. The apparatus shown in Figure 3 can be used for this investigation. The results when plotted give Figure 4. If $1/V$ is plotted against p, the straight line graph in Figure 5 is obtained.

Figure 2 Random motion of specks of ash

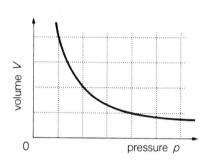

Figure 4

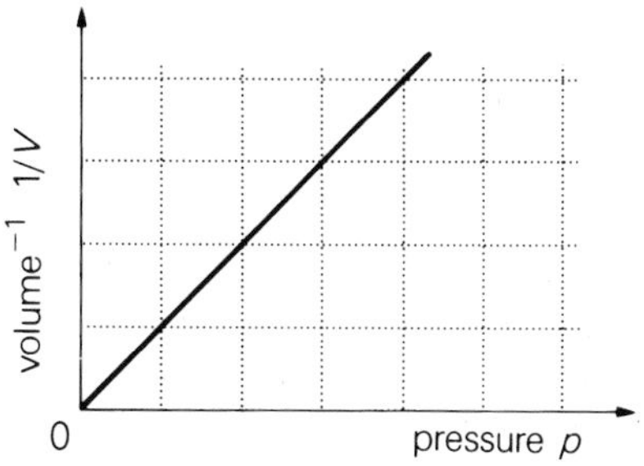

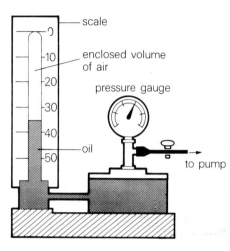

Figure 5

Figure 3 Boyle's Law apparatus

This illustrates that

$$p \propto \frac{1}{V} \quad \text{(mass and temperature constant)}$$

$$pV = \text{constant (mass and temperature constant)}$$

This is known as **Boyle's Law** which can be written

$$p_1 V_1 = p_2 V_2 \quad \text{where } V_1 \text{ is the volume at pressure } p_1$$
$$\text{and } V_2 \text{ is the volume at pressure } p_2$$

Example 1

A cylinder contains $0.2\,\text{m}^3$ of oxygen at a pressure of $3 \times 10^5\,\text{Pa}$. What volume will this oxygen occupy at a pressure of $1 \times 10^5\,\text{Pa}$ if the temperature is unchanged?

$$p_1 V_1 = p_2 V_2 \qquad V_1 = 0.2\,\text{m}^3; \qquad V_2 = \text{final volume}$$
$$p_1 = 3 \times 10^5\,\text{Pa}; \qquad p_2 = 1 \times 10^5\,\text{Pa}$$

$$\Rightarrow 3 \times 10^5 \times 0.2 = 1 \times 10^5 \times V_2$$
$$\Rightarrow \qquad V_2 = \frac{3 \times 10^5 \times 0.2}{1 \times 10^5}$$
$$\Rightarrow \qquad V_2 = 0.6$$

The new volume will be $0.6\,\text{m}^3$.

The pressure exerted by a gas is caused by the bombardment of the sides of the container by the gas molecules. If the temperature is increased, the kinetic energy of the molecules will also increase and the pressure will be greater because of more frequent collisions by particles colliding with greater energy.

The relationship between pressure and temperature can be investigated by heating a fixed mass of gas at constant volume over a range of temperatures, Figure 6, and measuring the corresponding pressures.

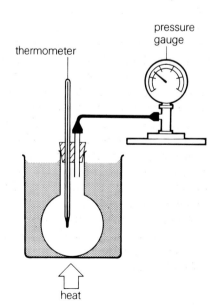

Figure 6

A graph of the results from such an experiment is shown in Figure 7. If the experiment is repeated with fewer molecules in the flask, a different set of results is obtained. When the results of both experiments are plotted and the lines extended backwards, they both intersect the temperature axis at –273°C, Figure 8.

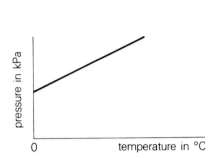

Figure 7

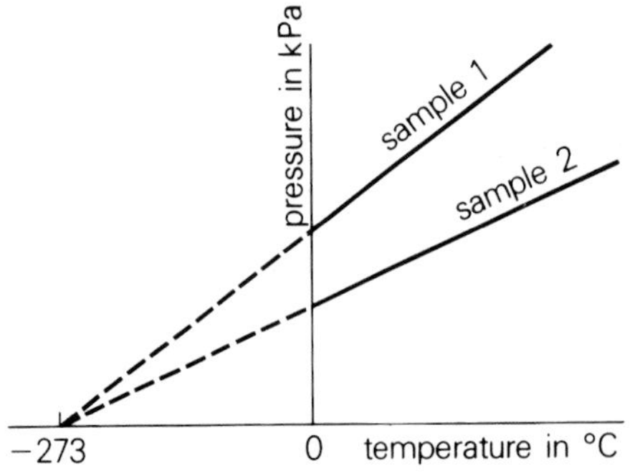

Figure 8

In general this is true for any graph of pressure against temperature for a fixed mass of gas.

The temperature –273°C is known as absolute zero and is the starting point for the absolute temperature scale.

It is also, theoretically, the lowest temperature which can be attained by any substance. It is taken to be the lowest temperature at which the particles of a material have lost all their thermal energy.

The unit of measurement of the absolute scale is the kelvin (K) and when pressure is plotted against temperature the pressure line passes through the origin, Figure 9.

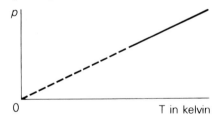

Figure 9

This means that

$p \propto T$ (mass and volume constant)   where T is
the absolute temperature
measured in kelvin

$\Rightarrow \quad \dfrac{p}{T} = $ constant

This is known as the **Pressure Law.**

$\dfrac{p}{T} = $ constant

$\Rightarrow \quad \dfrac{p_1}{T_1} = \dfrac{p_2}{T_2}$ where p_1 is the pressure at absolute temperature T_1
and p_2 is the pressure at absolute temperature T_2

To convert a celsius reading into kelvin, 273 is added to the degrees Celsius reading.

kelvin = degrees Celsius + 273

Note that a temperature change of one kelvin is the same as a temperature change of one degree Celsius.

Example 2

A sample of gas has a volume of $50\,cm^3$ and a pressure of $120\,kPa$ at room temperature of $20°C$.

If the volume is constant what is the pressure at a temperature of $70°C$?

$$\frac{p_1}{T_1} = \frac{p_2}{T_2}$$

$p_1 = 120\,kPa \qquad p_2 = ?$

$T_1 = 20 + 273 = 293\,K$

$T_2 = 70 + 273 = 343\,K$

$$p_2 = \frac{120 \times 343}{293} = 140$$

The final pressure is 140 kPa.

Volume and temperature

If the pressure acting on a fixed mass of gas is kept constant the volume of the gas will increase when the temperature is raised.

If the original volume is V_1 when the temperature is T_1 and it expands to V_2 when the temperature is T_2, the relationship between these is given by the expression

$$\frac{V_1}{T_1} = \frac{V_2}{T_2}$$

where T_1 and T_2 are the temperatures measured on the absolute scale, i.e. in kelvin.

This relationship is usually called **Charles's Law** which can be stated formally as

'The volume of a fixed mass of an ideal gas is directly proportional to the absolute temperature provided the pressure remains constant.'

Example 3

A sample of gas has a volume of 5 litres at $20°C$. The temperature is raised to $100°C$. What is the new volume?

$$\frac{V_1}{T_1} = \frac{V_2}{T_2}$$

$V_1 = 5\,litres$

$T_1 = 20 + 273 = 293\,K$

$T_2 = 100 + 273 = 373\,K$

$$\frac{5}{293} = \frac{V_2}{373}$$

$$V_2 = 5 \times \frac{373}{293} = 6.4$$

The new volume is 6.4 litres.

Example 4

An experiment is carried out to investigate the expansion of air when the temperature is raised but the pressure is constant.

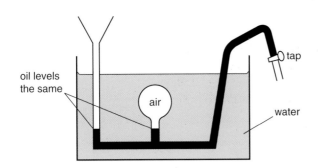

When placed in melting ice at 0°C the volume is 27.3 cm^3. The apparatus containing the air is now put into boiling water at 100°C.

a)   What is the new volume?
b)   What is the increase in volume?
c)   Calculate the fractional increase in volume for each degree rise in temperature.

a) $\dfrac{V_1}{T_1} = \dfrac{V_2}{T_2}$

$$V_1 = 27.3 \text{ cm}^3$$
$$T_1 = 0 + 273 = 273 \text{ K}$$
$$T_2 = 100 + 273 = 373 \text{ K}$$

$$V_2 = 27.3 \times \frac{373}{273} = 37.3$$

The new volume is 37.3 cm^3.

b)   increase in volume $= V_2 - V_1 = 37.3 - 27.3 = 10.0 \text{ cm}^3$

The increase in volume is 10.0 cm^2.

c)   fractional increase $= \dfrac{\text{increase in volume}}{\text{original volume}} = \dfrac{10}{27.3}$

$\dfrac{\text{fractional increase}}{\text{per degree Celsius rise}} = \dfrac{10}{27.3 \times 100} = \dfrac{10}{2730}$

The fractional increase in volume is 1/273 for each degree rise in temperature.

Combined gas equation

Having done three experiments in which either the volume, pressure or temperature of a fixed mass of gas was kept constant, we will now consider how these quantities are related when all three are allowed to vary. Suppose that we repeated the third experiment (p and V varying), at *different* temperatures. Typical results are shown in Table 1.

p	100	125	250	100	125	250
V	50	40	20	45.5	47	24.9
T (K)	300	300	300	273	353	373
$\dfrac{p \times V}{T}$	16.67	16.67	16.67	16.67	16.64	16.69

Table 1

It is clear from Table 1 that the quantity $p \times V/T$ is approximately constant,

i.e. $\dfrac{p \times V}{T}$ = constant (for a fixed mass of gas)

This equation is usually called the **Combined Gas Equation**, and is obeyed very well by most gases over a wide range of temperatures and pressures.

According to the Combined Gas Equation, if a fixed mass of gas has initial values of pressure, volume, and kelvin temperature given by p_1, V_1 and T_1, and these values change to p_2, V_2 and T_2, then

$\dfrac{p_1 \times V_1}{T_1} = \dfrac{p_2 \times V_2}{T_2}$ (for a fixed mass of gas)

Note that if the volume is held constant in the above equation, i.e. $V_1 = V_2$, then the equation simplifies to,

$\dfrac{p_1}{T_1} = \dfrac{p_2}{T_2}$ (constant volume and mass)

which is a statement of the Pressure Law. Similarly, if the pressure is constant the equation reduces to Charles's Law, and if the temperature is constant it reduces to Boyle's Law. Thus the Combined Gas Equation includes the three gas laws.

Example 5

A weather balloon contains $3\,m^3$ of helium at a pressure of 100 kPa and a temperature of 27°C. If the pressure is doubled and the temperature changes to 127°C, what will be the new volume of the balloon?

$p_1 = 100 \times 10^3\,Pa$; $p_2 = 200 \times 10^3\,Pa$; $T_1 = 27\,°C = 300\,K$;
$T_2 = 127\,°C = 400\,K$; $V_1 = 3\,m^3$; new volume = V_2

using $\dfrac{p_1 \times V_1}{T_1} = \dfrac{p_2 \times V_2}{T_2}$

$\Rightarrow \dfrac{100 \times 10^3 \times 3}{300} = \dfrac{200 \times 10^3 \times V_2}{400}$

$\Rightarrow \dfrac{3}{3} = \dfrac{2 \times V_2}{4}$ (cancelling and dividing both sides by 10^3)

$\Rightarrow 1 = \dfrac{V_2}{2}$

$\Rightarrow 2 = V_2$

The new volume of the balloon is $2\,m^3$.

Explanations based on Kinetic Theory

Although the Kinetic Theory has its limitations, it is useful because it provides an explanation of many properties of gases.

Pressure Law: $p \propto T$ (at constant V)
Consider a fixed volume of gas at temperature T and pressure p. If the temperature of the gas increases, this means that the kinetic energy and therefore the speed of the particles must increase. As the volume is constant, this will lead to an increased gas pressure because the particles will be colliding more violently and more frequently with the container walls.

i.e. as T increases, p increases.

Charles's Law: $V \propto T$ (at constant p)
Consider a volume V of gas at temperature T. If the temperature of the gas increases, this means that the kinetic energy and therefore the speed of the gas particles must increase. If the volume were to remain the same, this would produce an increased gas pressure because the particles would be colliding more violently and more frequently with the container walls. Therefore if the

pressure is to remain constant, the volume of the gas must increase to spread the increased force over a larger area.

i.e. as T increases, V increases.

Boyle's Law: $p \propto 1/V$ (at constant T)

Consider a volume V of gas at pressure p. If the volume is reduced without change in temperature, the particles will collide more frequently with the container walls. This will produce a larger force. Also the area of the container walls has been reduced and both the increased force and reduced area will lead to an increase in the gas pressure,

i.e. as V decreases, p increases.

Summary

Kinetic theory assumes that gas pressure is due to the number of collisions per second which a large number of molecules make with the sides of the container. The three Gas Laws can be summarized as below:

where p = gas pressure, V = volume, T = kelvin temperature and m = mass of gas.

Pressure Law   (constant V and m)

$$p \propto T$$

$$\Rightarrow \frac{p_1}{T_1} = \frac{p_2}{T_2}$$

Charles's Law   (constant p and m)

$$\Rightarrow V \propto T$$

$$\Rightarrow \frac{V_1}{T_1} = \frac{V_2}{T_2}$$

Boyle's Law   (constant T and m)

$$p \propto \frac{1}{V}$$

$$\Rightarrow p_1 \times V_1 = p_2 \times V_2$$

The Combined Gas Equation (for constant m) relates all three of the other variables.

$$\frac{p \times V}{T} = \text{constant}$$

$$\Rightarrow \frac{p_1 \times V_1}{T_1} = \frac{p_2 \times V_2}{T_2}$$

Absolute temperature scale

K		°C		
(kelvin)	=	(degrees Celsius)	+	273

Absolute zero is the theoretical lowest temperature at which particles of a material have lost all their thermal energy.

Questions

1 Two containers filled with air are connected by a tube fitted with a tap T_1. The first container P has a pressure gauge attached and the second container Q is connected to a vacuum pump via a pipe with a tap, T_2 attached.

Tap T_1 is closed, tap T_2 is open and the vacuum pump is used to evacuate container Q. Tap T_2 is now closed.

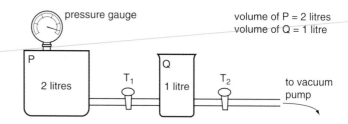

The pressure in P is 120 kPa and the pressure in Q is zero.
Tap T_1 is now opened and air flows into container Q. Assuming no temperature change, calculate the new pressure in P and Q.
How does the density of the air in container P compare with its original density?

2 A sealed flask is fitted with a pressure gauge. It is placed in boiling oxygen at −183°C and the gauge reads 45 kPa.
What pressure would you expect when the flask is placed in melting ice at zero degrees Celsius?

3 In an experiment the temperature of a fixed mass of gas is kept constant. The pressure is altered and various readings of pressure and volume are taken. These are listed in the table

pressure (kPa)	101	116	122	135	180	210	250
volume (cm³)	45	39	37	34	25	22	18

Plot a graph of pressure against volume.
What is the relationship between pressure and volume?

4 The pressure of air in a car tyre is 2.5×10^5 Pa at a temperature of 27°C. After a motorway journey the pressure has risen to 3.0×10^5 Pa. Assuming that the volume of the tyre has not changed,
   a) Calculate the resulting temperature of the air in the tyre.
   b) Explain the change in pressure in terms of the motion of the air particles in the tyre.

5 I Change the following Celsius temperatures into kelvin temperatures:
   a) –273°C,   **b)** –150°C,   **c)** 500°C.
  II Change the following kelvin temperatures into Celsius temperatures:
   a) 0 K,   **b)** 272 K,   **c)** 500 K.

6 A water rocket consists of a plastic bottle, partly filled with water. Air is pumped in through the water as shown in Figure 1. When the pressure inside the bottle is sufficiently high, water is forced out at the nozzle and the rocket accelerates vertically upwards as shown in Figure 2.

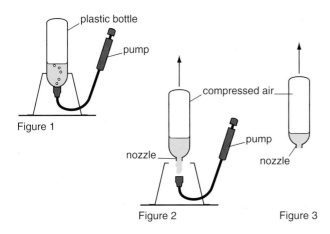

Figure 1

Figure 2   Figure 3

  a) **i)** At take-off, the volume of air in the bottle is 750 cm³ at a pressure of 1.76×10^5 Pa.
        Figure 3 shows the rocket at a later stage in its flight, when the volume of the air in the bottle has increased to 900 cm³.
        Calculate the new pressure of the compressed air at this later stage in its flight.
    ii) The area of the water surface which is in contact with the compressed air in the bottle is 5.0×10^{-3} m².
        Calculate the force exerted on the water by the compressed air at the new pressure.
  b) Explain fully why the rocket rises as the water is forced out at the nozzle.

                                              SQA

7 A pupil uses the apparatus shown in the diagram to investigate the relationship between the pressure and the temperature of a fixed mass of gas at constant volume.

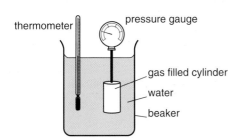

The cylinder is fully immersed in a beaker of water and the water is slowly heated.
You may assume that the volume of the cylinder does not change as the temperature of the water changes.
  a) Explain why the cylinder must be fully immersed in the beaker of water.
  b) The pressure of the gas in the cylinder is 100 kPa when the gas is at a temperature of 17°C.
        Calculate the pressure of the gas in the cylinder when the temperature of the gas is 75°C.
  c) The base of the cylinder has an area of 0.001 m².
        What is the force exerted by the gas on the base when the temperature of the gas is 75°C?
  d) What happens to the density of the gas in the cylinder as the temperature increases from 17°C to 75°C? Justify your answer.

                                              SQA

8 A pupil uses the apparatus below to investigate properties of a sample of gas.

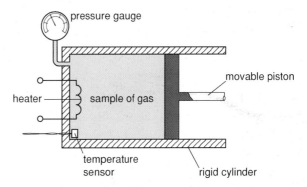

The volume of the sample of gas can be changed by moving the piston. The temperature of the sample of gas can be increased by using the heater.
At the start, the pressure of the gas is 400 kPa and its volume is 1000 cm³.
During the investigation, the pressure and volume of the gas change as indicated by sections AB and BC on the graph below.

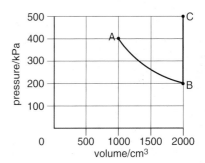

During section AB, the temperature of the gas is constant at 300 K.
  a) **Calculate** the volume of the gas when its pressure is 250 kPa during stage AB.
  b) State what happens to the pressure, volume and temperature of the gas over the section of the graph which starts at B and finishes at C.
  c) What is the temperature of the gas, in kelvin, corresponding to point C on the graph?

                                              SQA

9   The apparatus shown below can be used as a type of thermometer.
It consists of a bulb containing helium gas, the pressure of which
can be monitored.
The volume of the bulb is considered to be constant over the range
of temperature measured by the thermometer.

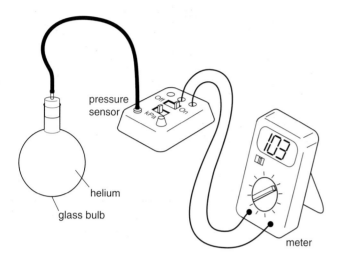

The following results for the temperature and pressure of the gas were
obtained while calibrating the thermometer.

Pressure (kPa)	89	96	103	110	117
Temperature (°C)	−20	0	20	40	60
Temperature (K)					

a)   i) Copy the above table. Complete the table, giving the
temperature in kelvin.
ii) Use the data from your completed table to establish the
relationship between the pressure and temperature of the
gas.
iii) Explain this change of pressure with temperature in terms of
the movement of the helium molecules.
b)   When the bulb is immersed in a sample of liquid nitrogen, the
meter gives a reading of 24 kPa for the pressure of the helium
gas.
Find the temperature of the liquid nitrogen sample.

SQA

10   The following diagram, taken from a physics textbook, shows the
effect of increasing the force on a compression spring.

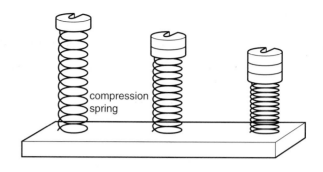

compression
spring

This type of spring is used in the design of a safety device for a gas
cylinder.

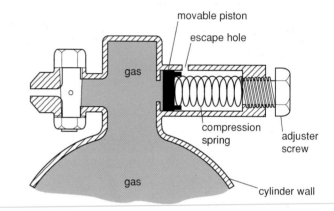

a)   The pressure of the gas in the cylinder is 5.0×10^5 Pa at a
temperature of 20°C. The area of the piston is 2.5×10^{-4} m^2.
i) What is the size of the force exerted by the gas on the
piston?
ii) Explain how the device operates if the gas pressure in the
cylinder exceeds a safety limit.
b)   The safety limit is set at a pressure of 9.0×10^5 Pa.
At what temperature would this limit be reached by the gas
described in part a)?
Assume that any increase in volume of the gas in the cylinder
can be neglected.
c)   The adjuster is screwed inwards.
What would be the effect on the value of the pressure safety
limit? Justify your answer.

SQA

Topic 1.6   Test 1

1 The 'kinetic model' assumes that a gas consists of a large number of tiny particles.
Using this model explain how a gas enclosed in a container exerts a pressure on the walls.

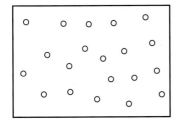

2 An experiment is carried out to investigate how the volume of a fixed mass of gas changes when the pressure is altered. The temperature is kept constant.
The graph shows the results obtained.

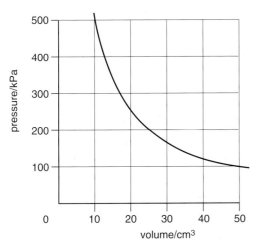

State the relationship between volume and pressure which these results illustrate.

3 A sample of air is contained in a cylinder with a close fitting piston attached. The piston is free to move up or down.
The initial volume is V_1.
The temperature is increased from T_1 to T_2 and the air expands to a new volume of V_2.
State the relationship between V_1, V_2, T_1 and T_2 for this expansion.

atmosphere

piston

4 A sample of air is enclosed in a flask which is placed in melting ice and then in oil which is heated. The pressure at various temperatures is noted and when the results are plotted a straight line graph is obtained. What is the relationship between pressure and temperature?

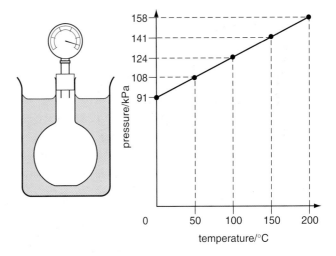

5 a) Convert 120°C to kelvin.
b) Express 90 K in degrees Celsius.
c) Energy is transferred to a cylinder of metal and the temperature rises from 20°C to 100°C. What is the temperature **rise** in kelvin?

6 Air is trapped in a cylinder by a movable piston.

heating coil

The volume of air is 0.3 m³ and the pressure is 120 kPa. The piston is held in place and the temperature increased from 15°C to 75°C.
What is the new pressure?
The piston is now pulled to the right until the volume increases to 0.45 m³.
Determine the final pressure.

7 Absolute zero is an important point on the temperature scale.
Explain what is meant by **absolute zero**.

8 Using a kinetic model explain what happens in each of the following cases.
a) When the volume of a fixed mass of gas is reduced without changing the temperature the pressure increases.
b) A sealed flask containing air is transferred from water at room temperature into melting ice. There is a reduction in the pressure of the gas.
c) A syringe containing air is sealed at one end and placed in water.
When the water is heated the gas expands against atmospheric pressure and the plunger rises.

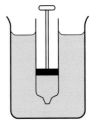

Topic 1.6 Test 2

1   Explain how the air in the atmosphere exerts a pressure on the floor of a room.

2   State the relationship between the pressure and volume of a fixed mass of gas when the temperature is unchanged.

3   Air is enclosed in a metal container and the temperature is raised using an electrical heating coil.
What is the relationship between pressure and temperature?

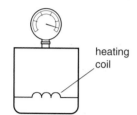

heating coil

4   The apparatus shown is used to investigate the expansion of air when the pressure was kept constant and the temperature varied. The volume is noted when the levels of oil in each limb are the same.

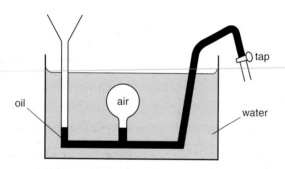

tap

oil

air

water

The following results were obtained:

volume V_1 = 26.5 cm³ T_1 = 21°C
volume V_2 = 33.6 cm³ T_2 = 100°C

What relationship do these illustrate?

5   a)   Average body temperature is 37 degrees Celsius. What is this in kelvin?
   b)   The boiling point of nitrogen is 77 K.
      Express this in degrees Celsius.
   c)   Olive oil is put into a pan at 15°C and brought to the boil at 297°C.
      Express this temperature rise in kelvin.

6   An experiment is carried out on a sample of air.

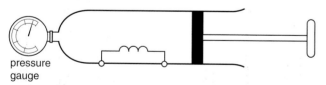

pressure gauge

300 cm³ of air at 15°C has a pressure of 105 kPa.
The piston is pushed in until the volume is reduced to 200 cm³.
The heating coil is switched on and the temperature is increased to 60°C.
Calculate the final pressure of the gas.

7   A statement from a textbook reads as follows:

   'the lowest possible temperature attained when an object has given up all the thermal energy that it can'.

   What is this temperature called?

8   a)   Air is enclosed in a cylinder using a closely fitting piston which is free to move.

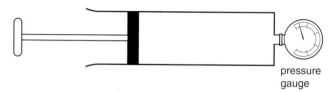

pressure gauge

The piston is pushed to the right so that the volume is reduced. Using a kinetic model, explain why the pressure has increased although the temperature is the same.
   b)   The air is now surrounded by ice. Explain why the pressure of the gas is reduced.
   c)   A column of air is trapped by a bead of mercury in a capillary tube.
      The bead of mercury is open to atmospheric pressure at the top.
      The column of air is moved from room temperature into boiling water.
      Explain what happens to the length of the column of air.

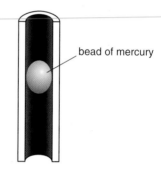

bead of mercury

Topic 1.6 Test 3

1   A kinetic model of gases assumes that a gas contains a large number of molecules which are in a state of continuous motion. What is the number of collisions per second made by the molecules a measure of?

2 A sample of gas is compressed without changing its temperature. Which graph correctly shows the relationship between pressure and volume?

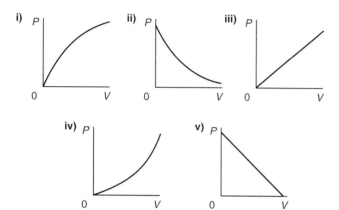

i) P ... V
ii) P ... V
iii) P ... V
iv) P ... V
v) P ... V

3 Air is sealed in a flask to which a pressure gauge has been fitted. This is placed in oil and the temperature of the oil is raised and the pressure noted.
Which graph correctly shows the relationship between pressure and temperature?

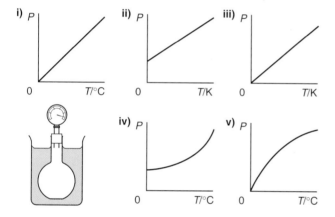

i) P ... T/°C
ii) P ... T/K
iii) P ... T/K
iv) P ... T/°C
v) P ... T/°C

4 A sample of an ideal gas expands from volume V_1 to volume V_2 when the temperature rises from T_1 in degrees Celsius to T_2 in degrees Celsius.
If the pressure of the gas does not change, which of the following relationships is true?

i) $\dfrac{V_1}{T_1} = \dfrac{V_2}{T_2}$

ii) $V_2 - V_1 = T_2 - T_2$

iii) $\dfrac{V_1}{V_2} = \dfrac{T_1 + 273}{T_2 + 273}$

iv) $\dfrac{V_1}{V_2} = \dfrac{T_1}{T_2} + 273$

v) $V_1 = 273\,(V_2 - V_1)$

5 a) Convert 77°C into kelvin.
 b) Methanol melts at 175 K.
 What is this in degrees Celsius?
 c) It requires 273 joules to raise the temperature of a substance by 1 degree Celsius.
 How many joules of energy will be required to raise the temperature by 1 kelvin?

6 A sample of carbon dioxide is trapped in a cylinder with a tightly fitting piston.
The initial volume is 28 cm³, the pressure is 95 kPa and the temperature is 19°C.
The volume is reduced to 21 cm³ and temperature is increased to 57°C.
What is the final pressure of the carbon dioxide?

7 A flask containing air is sealed with a stopper which has a pressure gauge attached.

This is surrounded by melting ice and the pressure is 91 kPa. It is now placed in boiling water and the pressure rises to give a final reading of 124 kPa. Explain how you would use these results to estimate absolute zero of temperature.

8 a) A sample of gas is put into a large syringe which has a sealed end. The plunger is pushed in until the volume is halved. The temperature has not changed so that the molecules are still moving with the same average speed but because the space in which they move has been halved they collide twice as often with the sides of the container. This causes the pressure to be doubled. Which law does this kinetic model describe?
 b) A balloon is fully blown up in a cold room and tied to the wall. Some time later the room becomes very hot and the balloon bursts.
 Explain why this happens.
 c) A flask of air is fitted with a U-shaped tube containing some oil as shown. The top is open to the atmosphere.
 When the flask is at room temperature the oil levels are the same.
 When the temperature of the flask is raised one of the oil levels rises above the other.
 Using a kinetic model explain why this happens.

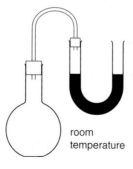
room temperature

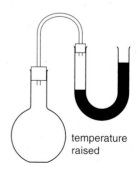
temperature raised

Unit 2
Electricity and Electronics

Topics

Topic 2.1
Electric Fields and Resistors in Circuits

Objectives

When you have completed the work of this topic you should be able to:

1 state that, in an electric field, a charge experiences a force;
2 state that an electric field applied to a conductor causes the free electric charges in it to move;
3 state that when a charge Q is moved in an electric field, work W is done;
4 state that the potential difference (voltage V) between two points is a measure of the work done in moving one coulomb of charge between the two points;
5 state that if one joule of work is done moving one coulomb of charge between two points, the potential difference between the two points is one volt;
6 state the relationship $V = W/Q$;
7 carry out calculations involving the relationship $V = W/Q$;
8 state that the e.m.f. of a source is the electrical potential energy supplied to each coulomb of charge which passes through the source;
9 state that an electrical source is equivalent to a source of e.m.f. with a resistor in series (internal resistance);
10 describe the principles of a method of measuring the e.m.f. and internal resistance of a source;
11 explain why the e.m.f. of a source is equal to the open circuit p.d. across the terminals of the source;
12 explain how the conservation of energy leads to the sum of the e.m.f.s round a closed circuit being equal to the sum of the p.d.s round the circuit;
13 derive the expression for the total resistance of any number of resistors in series, by consideration of the conservation of energy;
14 derive the expression for the total resistance of any number of resistors in parallel, by consideration of the conservation of charge (current);
15 state the relationship among resistors in a balanced Wheatstone bridge;
16 carry out calculations involving the resistances in a balanced Wheatstone bridge;
17 state that for an initially balanced Wheatstone bridge, as the value of one resistor is changed by a small amount, the out-of-balance p.d. is proportional to the change in resistance;
18 use the following terms correctly in context: terminal p.d.; load resistor; bridge circuit; lost volts.

2.1 Electric Fields and Resistors in Circuits

Electric charge

A polythene rod rubbed with a duster becomes negatively charged as a result of friction: the rod gains electrons from the duster. Similarly, a nylon rod can be positively charged by friction because it loses electrons to the duster.

There are only two types of electric charge: positive and negative. A pair of charges gives rise to an **electric force** between them. If two rods that have been oppositely charged are brought near to each other, there is a force of attraction between them. Two rods having the same type of charge repel each other.

The movement of air during a thunderstorm causes thunder clouds to be charged by friction. Very large quantities of positive and negative charge are built up: when these are discharged, a huge spark of lightning results. Figure 1.

A flow of electron current occurs when an electric fire is switched on: electrical energy is converted to heat energy and light energy.

There are two ways of detecting charge, by measuring:
a) the **flow** of charge, e.g. electric current;
b) the **force** between charges, e.g. the charged polythene and nylon rods.

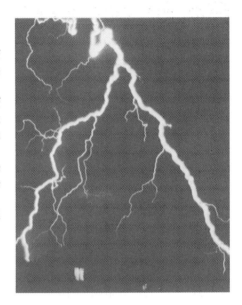

Figure 1 Lightning

Electric field

The gravitational force of attraction of the mass of the Earth for other masses can be described in terms of a gravitational field. The force between charged particles can similarly be described in terms of an **electric field**.

The fundamental unit of charge is the charge on an electron which is equal and opposite to the charge on a proton. However, in describing electric forces, we shall be concerned only with the effects of groups of these charged particles which are spread over the surface of an object: these are simply described as the **charge** on an object.

In Figure 2, the two small objects Q_1 and Q_2 are identical and both are negatively charged. They are placed some distance apart, but there is a force of repulsion between them because they both have a negative charge.

Figure 3 shows a small charged object Q_3 and a large object Q_4 which is also charged. The charge on Q_4 is spread over a larger surface so that the forces of repulsion are more complicated: the forces are in many directions and the electrons are at various distances from each other.

To simplify the problem, we must consider only very small charged objects called **point charges**.

Figure 2

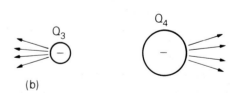

Figure 3

Direction of electric field force

In Figure 2, the force exerted by charge Q_1 on charge Q_2 is directed from Q_1 to Q_2 along the line joining them. There is an equal electric force in the opposite direction from Q_2 to Q_1.

The apparatus shown in Figure 4 is used to investigate the electric field. The glass dish contains oil on which is sprinkled a little grass seed. Two metal 'point' electrodes dip into the oil, and they are connected to a high voltage supply. When the supply is switched on, the electrodes become positively and negatively charged and the seeds form a pattern as shown. The lines in the pattern indicate the direction of the electric force, and the pattern shows the electric field between the two electrodes.

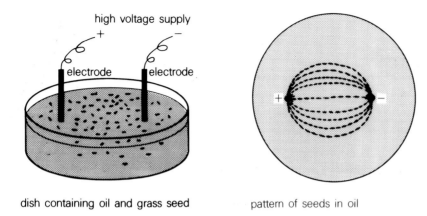

Figure 4

Field patterns and lines of force

The field strength g of the Earth's gravitation has an approximate value of 10 newtons per kilogram. This means that the gravitational force of attraction is proportional to the gravitational field strength *and* the mass which is near the earth.

In a similar way the electric field strength near a charged object has a value, which is measured in newtons per coulomb. It is also the case that the electrical force on a charge is proportional to the electrical field strength *and* the amount of charge at that point in the field.

The two types of field with their lines of force are shown in Figure 5. The arrows on the lines of force indicate the direction in which the mass or positive charge moves. If the object creating the electric field force is positively charged, then the arrows on the lines of force are reversed, Figure 6, so that they still indicate the direction of movement of a positive charge.

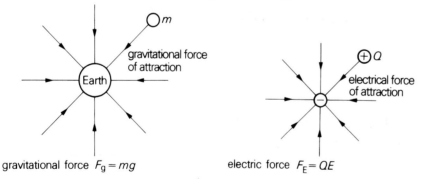

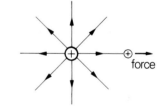

Figure 6

Figure 5   Gravitational and electric field patterns

An electric field pattern may be plotted from the shadows cast on a screen from a lamp, Figure 7. The direction of each line of force is found from the shadow cast by a thin metal foil that is charged and held on an insulating rod between the charged metal plates. Each line of force can be marked on the screen. Figure 8 shows the electric field patterns obtained in this way for various arrangements.

The variation in strength of the electric field is indicated by the spacing of the lines of force; the closer the spacing, the stronger is the field. Notice that the lines

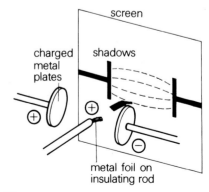

Figure 7

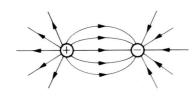
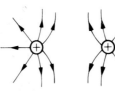
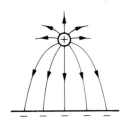

Figure 8 Electric field patterns

of force between a pair of parallel charged metal plates are evenly spaced showing that the electric field is uniform.

In calculations concerning a charge in an electric field, we shall always assume that the field is uniform.

Potential difference and work done

If the lines of force in an electric field are evenly spaced, the field is uniform. This means that a charged particle experiences the same force throughout the electric field.

A positive charge Q is placed in a uniform electric field caused by a potential difference of V volts being applied across the space, Figure 9.

In order to move a positive charge from the right-hand side to the left-hand side a certain amount of work W must be done, due to the opposing force effect of the field.

If W joules of work are needed to move Q coulombs of charge, then $\dfrac{W}{Q}$ joules are needed to move 1 coulomb of charge.

Now the greater the potential difference V, the greater is the field strength and hence the greater the work required to move the charge.

The work done per coulomb is a measure of the potential difference

i.e. V is proportional to $\dfrac{W}{Q}$

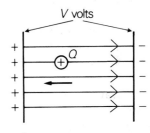

Figure 9

If 1 joule of work is done in moving 1 coulomb of charge, then the potential difference is defined as 1 volt.

Therefore $V = \dfrac{W}{Q}$

Example 1

The charge on an electron is -1.6×10^{-19} C. Calculate the increase in energy if an electron is accelerated from rest through a uniform field caused by a p.d. of 20 V.

$$Q = -1.6 \times 10^{-19} \text{C}; \quad V = 20 \text{ V}$$

$$V = \frac{W}{Q}$$

∴ Work done by field $W = QV$

$$\Rightarrow \quad W = -1.6 \times 10^{-19} \times 20 = -3.2 \times 10^{-18}$$

The electron gains 3.2×10^{-18} joules.

Movement of charged particles in electric fields

The electron beam in the tube of a cathode ray oscilloscope moves parallel to an electric field in the electron gun and at right angles to an electric field between the Y-plates, Figure 10.

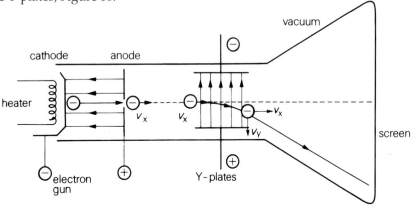

Figure 10

Electrons released from the heated cathode are accelerated by the uniform electric field between the cathode and anode. On reaching the anode they travel at a constant velocity v_x until they reach the region of electric field between the Y-plates. The passage of electrons through this region, where the field is at right angles to their motion, resembles the trajectory of a projectile when projected horizontally through the Earth's gravitational field, and in fact the electrons follow a similar parabolic path. The horizontal velocity v_x of the electrons remains constant as they travel from the electron gun through a vacuum towards the Y-plate region. In this region there is an acceleration towards the lower, positive plate and they gain a vertical component of velocity v_y as well as maintaining their horizontal velocity v_x. The electron beam strikes the screen, having been deflected by the electric field. The electric field between the Y-plates depends on the p.d. applied to them and so the deflection of the beam can be used to compare p.d.s. In a solid the application of an electric field to a conducting material causes the 'free electrons' to drift. In a circuit, the applied potential difference sets up an electric field within the conductors, giving the conduction electrons their drift velocity.

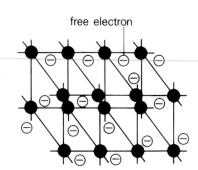

Figure 11 Metal atoms

Electrical conduction in solids

A material through which electric charge can flow is called a **conductor**. A material through which electric charge will *not* flow is called an **insulator**. Conduction may take place through gases, liquids or solids, but here we shall consider solids.

Most solid conductors are metals. It is useful to build up a model of the process of conduction. Figure 11 depicts a piece of metal with one 'free electron' per atom. The black circles represent the nuclei and fixed electrons of the metal atoms. Atoms have nuclei surrounded by electrons, most of which are bound tightly to the nucleus. However in metal atoms, some of the outer electrons are free to move. These are shown in the diagram and are called 'free electrons'. The American scientist Edwin Hall showed experimentally that in most metals one or two 'free electrons' per atom are available for conduction of electricity.

Figure 12 Edwin Hall

These electrons have relatively high speeds (about $10^6\,\mathrm{m\,s^{-1}}$) in random directions. When a conductor is placed in a circuit containing a battery, this general movement becomes directed towards the positive terminal, Figure 13. There is a drift of all the free electrons at a speed of about $10^{-4}\,\mathrm{m\,s^{-1}}$ as soon as the circuit switch S is closed. The electron current is from negative to positive terminal (conventional current is in the reverse direction).

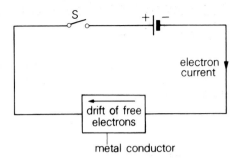

Figure 13 Conduction in a metal

Potential difference and resistance

The energy required to drive the electron current round the circuit is provided by a chemical reaction in the battery or by the mains power supply. The **potential difference** across any component X in a circuit can be measured by placing a voltmeter in parallel with it, Figure 14. The component X is said to have a **resistance** if a potential difference (p.d.) is needed in order to drive a current through it.

The graph in Figure 15 shows the relationship usually obtained between the current I through a resistor (component X) and the potential difference V across it. This shows that the current varies directly as the potential difference.

$$I \propto V \text{ or } V \propto I$$
$$\Rightarrow \quad V = \text{constant} \times I$$
$$\Rightarrow \quad \frac{V}{I} = \text{constant} = R$$

where the constant R is called the resistance. The ratio V/I is the resistance of the component.

The resistance can be thought of as a measure of the potential difference needed to drive a current of 1 ampere through the component. If 1 volt is required to drive a current of 1 ampere through a component, it is said to have a resistance of 1 ohm.

$$R = \frac{V}{I}$$

If $V = 1$ volt, $\quad I = 1$ ampere, $\quad$ then $R = 1$ ohm

1 ohm = 1 volt per ampere

$$1\,\Omega = 1\,\mathrm{V\,A^{-1}}$$

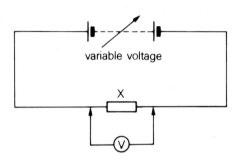

Figure 14 Measuring potential difference

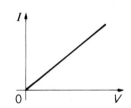

Figure 15 Current–voltage graph for a resistor

Example 2

What potential difference is required to drive a current of 1 A through a resistor **a)** of value $2\,\Omega$ **b)** of value $120\,\Omega$?

A $1\,\Omega$ resistor requires 1 V to drive a current of 1 A.
A $2\,\Omega$ resistor requires ? V to drive a current of 1 A
– twice the resistance: twice as difficult, so twice the voltage needed, i.e. 2 V.

So, the $120\,\Omega$ resistor requires 120 V to drive a current of 1 A.

The electrical energy in a circuit, supplied by the source, is converted to other forms of energy in the components which make up the circuit. The amount of electrical energy converted into other forms of energy when the coulomb of charge passes from one point in the circuit to another is called the **potential difference** between the two points.

If 1 coulomb of charge passes between two points A and B in a circuit and releases 1 joule of energy, then we say that there is a potential difference of 1 volt between A and B, Figure 16.

If the p.d. is 2 volts, then 2 joules of energy is released per coulomb of charge which passes between A and B.

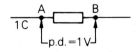

Figure 16 Source connected to a resistor

If the p.d. is V volts then V joules of energy is released per coulomb of charge which passes between A and B.

If Q coulombs of charge pass between A and B when the p.d. is V volts then the energy released, W, is given by $W = QV$.

The rate of flow of charge is the electric current I, where $I = Q/t$. We can express the energy released by the equation

$$W = QV = I t V \text{ joules}$$

Example 3

Calculate the energy converted in a 4 ohm resistor when connected to a 12 volt source for 2 minutes.

$$R = \frac{V}{I} \quad \Rightarrow \quad 4 = \frac{12}{I} \quad \Rightarrow \quad I = 3 \text{ amperes}$$

$$W = I t V \qquad t = 2 \times 60 \text{ seconds}$$

$$\Rightarrow \quad W = 3 \times 2 \times 60 \times 12 = 4320$$

4320 joules of energy are converted in the 4 ohm resistor.

Electromotive force

A source of electrical energy, such as a battery, provides an electromotive force (e.m.f.) to drive an electron current through the circuit. The e.m.f. of the source governs the electrical energy supplied to each unit charge that passes through the source, i.e. the number of joules of energy per coulomb of charge. Alternatively, the e.m.f. of the source is the work done on unit charge when it passes through the source.

The units of e.m.f. are the same as those of p.d.

$$1 \text{ J C}^{-1} \equiv 1 \text{ V}$$

The e.m.f. of a source is the potential difference across the terminals when no current is flowing, i.e. on open circuit. If a current is flowing, the terminal potential difference (t.p.d.) is lower than the e.m.f. as explained on the next page.

When, however, a current is flowing through a series of resistors in a circuit, Figure 17, then the sum of the energies which are produced in each resistor is equal to the total energy provided by the source. This is because energy is conserved.

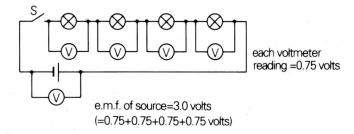

each voltmeter
reading =0.75 volts

e.m.f. of source=3.0 volts
(=0.75+0.75+0.75+0.75 volts)

Figure 17

This means that the e.m.f. of the source equals the sum of the p.d.'s around the circuit.

Internal resistance

Consider the circuit in Figure 18. We might expect the potential difference V across the resistor R to be the same as the e.m.f. of the source. In reality a set of results for various values of R is obtained like those in the table below.

resistor value R (Ω)	100	10	5	2	1
voltmeter reading V (volts)	2.0	1.7	1.4	1.0	0.7

Table 1

We find that the value of the external resistance R affects the terminal potential difference. This is because the cell used as a source has an **internal resistance** which resists the current.

Measurement of internal resistance

The circuit in Figure 19 is used for determining the value of the internal resistance r of a cell of e.m.f. 1.8 V by measuring the current and the t.p.d. for various values of external resistance R. Table 2 shows a typical set of results.

current I (amperes)	0.0	0.1	0.2	0.3	0.4	0.5	0.6	0.7	0.8
t.p.d. V (volts)	1.8	1.6	1.4	1.2	1.0	0.8	0.6	0.4	0.2

Table 2

These results are plotted on a graph of t.p.d. against current, Figure 20. Notice that when switch S is open and no current flows, the t.p.d. has a maximum value which is equal to the e.m.f. of the cell: the cell is on 'open circuit'.

The graph is a straight line of the form

$$y = mx + c$$

where m is the gradient of the line and c is the intercept on the vertical axis.

$$\Rightarrow \quad V = mI + c$$
$$\Rightarrow \quad V = -2.0I + 1.8$$

because the gradient of the line is -2.0 and the intercept on the vertical axis is $+1.8$ V (the e.m.f. E).

$$\Rightarrow \quad V = E - Ir \text{ where } r = -m, \text{ the gradient.}$$

The terminal potential difference V is less than the e.m.f. by some quantity Ir where r is the internal resistance of the cell. The value of Ir is sometimes called the 'lost volts'.

Because $m = -2.0$, the internal resistance r of the cell is 2.0 Ω.

Energy is lost in driving the current through the chemicals which make up the cell, and this causes the cell to have an internal resistance r.

Note also the value 0.9 A of the intercept on the horizontal axis. This shows that the maximum current which the cell is capable of delivering (i.e. when the cell is on short-circuit) is 0.9 A.

Example 4

A circuit contains a battery of e.m.f. 4.0 V and internal resistance 1.5 Ω. If the external resistor has a value of 6.5 Ω, find the value of

a) the current in the circuit **b)** the t.p.d. **c)** the short-circuit current.

In the circuit on the right, the battery is shown as an e.m.f. of 4.0 V and an internal resistance r of 1.5 Ω in series.

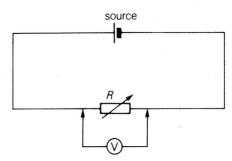

Figure 18 Measuring internal resistance

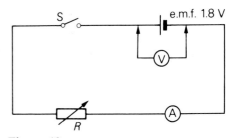

Figure 19

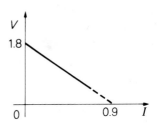

Figure 20

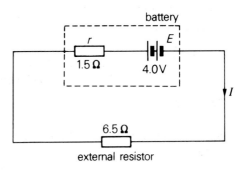

a)   Total circuit resistance = $6.5 + 1.5 = 8.0\,\Omega$
e.m.f. of battery = $4.0\,V$

$$I = \frac{V}{R}$$

$$\Rightarrow \quad I = \frac{4.0}{8.0} = 0.5$$

The current in the circuit is 0.5 A.

b)   The t.p.d. is equal to the p.d. across the external resistor.

$$V = IR$$

$$\Rightarrow \quad V = 0.5 \times 6.5 = 3.25$$

The t.p.d. is 3.25 V.

c)   The short-circuit current is the current when the voltage V is zero.

$$V = E - Ir$$

$$\Rightarrow \quad\quad 0 = 4.0 - I \times 1.5$$

$$\Rightarrow \quad 1.5 \times I = 4.0$$

$$\Rightarrow \quad\quad I = \frac{4.0}{1.5} = 2.7$$

The short-circuit current is 2.7 A.

Example 5

Calculate the internal resistance of each of the following sources of e.m.f. when
inserted in the circuit shown on the right.

a)   a U2 dry cell,   e.m.f. = $1.5\,V$,   t.p.d. = $1.2\,V$
b)   a car battery,   e.m.f. = $12.0\,V$,   t.p.d. = $11.7\,V$
c)   a calculator battery,   e.m.f. = $9.0\,V$,   t.p.d. = $3.6\,V$

$$V = E - Ir \quad \text{where} \quad r \text{ is internal resistance of source.}$$

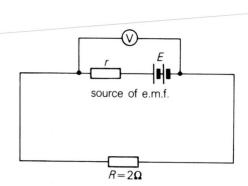

source of e.m.f.

but $$I = \frac{E}{R + r} \quad\quad\quad R \text{ is external resistance}$$

$$\Rightarrow \quad\quad V = E - \left(\frac{E}{R + r}\right)r$$

$$\Rightarrow \quad V(R + r) = E(R + r) - Er$$

$$\Rightarrow \quad VR + Vr = ER$$

$$\Rightarrow \quad\quad r = \frac{R(E - V)}{V}$$

a)   For the U2 dry cell $E = 1.5\,V$, $V = 1.2\,V$, $R = 2\,\Omega$

$$\therefore \quad\quad r = \frac{2(1.5 - 1.2)}{1.2} = 0.5$$

Internal resistance of U2 cell = $0.5\,\Omega$.

b)   For the car battery $E = 12.0\,V$, $V = 11.7\,V$, $R = 2\,\Omega$

$$\therefore \quad\quad r = \frac{2(12.0 - 11.7)}{11.7} = 0.05$$

Internal resistance of car battery = $0.05\,\Omega$.

c)   For the calculator battery $E = 9.0\,V$, $V = 3.6\,V$, $R = 2\,\Omega$

$$\therefore \quad\quad r = \frac{2(9.0 - 3.6)}{3.6} = 3.0$$

Internal resistance of calculator battery = $3.0\,\Omega$.

Potential dividers: resistors in series

We now consider ways of varying the available potential difference. For this purpose we assume that the power supply has zero internal resistance and a fixed e.m.f.

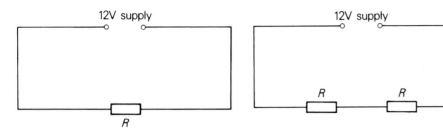

Figure 21   **Figure 22**

In Figure 21 the external resistor R is supplied with energy: 12 joules of energy for every coulomb of charge which passes through it ($12\,\mathrm{J\,C^{-1}} \equiv 12\,\mathrm{V}$).

If two identical external resistors are connected across the supply, Figure 22, the current through each resistor is the same: the rate of transformation of electrical energy to heat is the same for each resistor. The energy passing round the circuit is still $12\,\mathrm{J\,C^{-1}}$, so 6 joules of energy is released for every coulomb of charge passing through each resistor. This means that the potential difference across each resistor is 6 volts, Figure 23.

$$V_1 + V_2 = 12$$

In general, for any number of resistors in series in a circuit, the total energy supplied by the source is the sum of the energies supplied to the resistors, since energy is conserved.

Figure 24 shows four unequal resistors in **series**. The total resistance in a series circuit is the sum of the resistances of the individual resistors.

$$R = R_1 + R_2 + R_3 + R_4$$

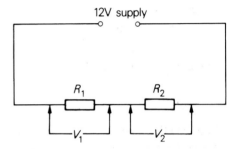

Figure 23

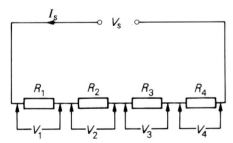

Figure 24

Because the resistors are in series, the current in each is the supply current I_s; multiply both sides of the above equation by I_s:

$$I_s R = I_s R_1 + I_s R_2 + I_s R_3 + I_s R_4$$

Then, because $V = I \times R$,

$$V = V_1 + V_2 + V_3 + V_4$$

The series of resistors in Figure 24 thus provides a range of potential differences.

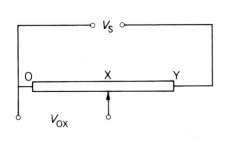

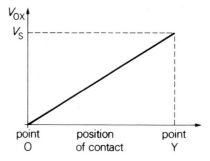

Figure 25 Potential divider   **Figure 26** Variation of potential

The range of possible p.d.s can be increased by using a continuous length of resistance wire. Figure 25 shows a source of e.m.f. of V_s volts and how various p.d.s can be tapped off. The position of the contact point X on the resistance wire controls the p.d. V_{ox} between points O and X. Moving the contact from O to Y changes the p.d. V_{ox} as in the graph in Figure 26.

The maximum value of V_{ox} is V_s when the contact is at point Y.

Halfway between O and Y, the p.d. is half V_s.

One-third of the way from O to Y the p.d. is one-third of V_s.

By tapping off various lengths of the resistance wire, smaller divisions of the total potential can be obtained. This arrangement is called a **potential divider**, the resistor OY being referred to as a **load resistor**.

This arrangement can provide a completely variable range of p.d.s by varying the position of a contact on a variable resistor (rheostat) as shown in Figure 27.

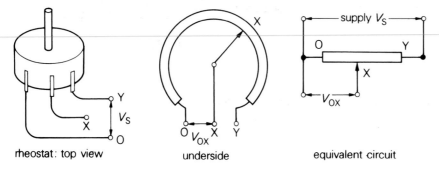

rheostat: top view   underside   equivalent circuit

Figure 27 Variable resistor as a potential divider

Example 6

A potential divider consists of a rheostat of resistance 25 ohms and is connected across a supply. If a constant current of 60 milliamperes passes through the rheostat, what range of p.d.s can it provide?

With the contact at point O, the p.d. is zero,

i.e. $V_{ox} = 0$ because X and O coincide.

With the contact at point Y, the p.d. V_{oy} is V_s,

i.e. $V_{oy} = V_s = I_s R$

The total resistance R of the divider is 25 ohms.

The current I_s through this resistor is 60×10^{-3} amperes.

$\Rightarrow \quad V_{oy} = 60 \times 10^{-3} \times 25 = 1.5$

$\Rightarrow \quad$ maximum voltage obtainable is 1.5 V

The potential divider can provide a range of voltages from 0 V to 1.5 V.

Current dividers: resistors in parallel

In the circuit of Figure 28 the resistors R_1 and R_2 are connected in **parallel** to a supply of V_s volts giving a supply current of I_s amperes.

The system can be represented by an equivalent circuit shown in Figure 29 in which R_p is the equivalent resistance and I_s is the supply current.

A current I_s travels to a pair of parallel resistors and then divides at the junction into two currents I_1 and I_2, Figure 30.

From Figure 30, $I_s = I_1 + I_2$

Also the two resistors are in parallel:

$\Rightarrow$ p.d. across R_1 = p.d. across $R_2 = V_s$

$\Rightarrow$ $I_1 \times R_1 = I_2 \times R_2 = V_s$

$\Rightarrow$ $I_1 = \dfrac{V_s}{R_1}$ and $I_2 = \dfrac{V_s}{R_2}$

From Figure 29, $I_s = \dfrac{V_s}{R_p}$

But $I_s = I_1 + I_2$

$\Rightarrow$ $\dfrac{V_s}{R_p} = \dfrac{V_s}{R_1} + \dfrac{V_s}{R_2}$

Divide both sides of this equation by V_s:

$$\frac{1}{R_p} = \frac{1}{R_1} + \frac{1}{R_2}$$

This important relationship gives the equivalent resistance of two resistors in parallel. In general, for more than two resistors in parallel, the equation becomes

$$\frac{1}{R_p} = \frac{1}{R_1} + \frac{1}{R_2} + \frac{1}{R_3} + \frac{1}{R_4} + \dots$$

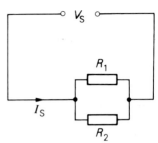

Figure 28

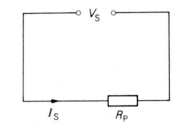

Figure 29

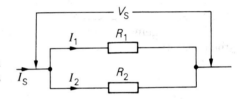

Figure 30

Example 7

Calculate the equivalent resistance of four resistors of 2 ohms, 3 ohms, 4 ohms and 5 ohms connected in parallel.

$$\frac{1}{R_p} = \frac{1}{2} + \frac{1}{3} + \frac{1}{4} + \frac{1}{5}$$

$$= \frac{30 + 20 + 15 + 12}{60} = \frac{77}{60}$$

$\Rightarrow$ $R_p = \dfrac{60}{77}$ (remember to invert the fraction)

$= 0.779$

The equivalent resistance of the four resistors is 0.78 ohms.

Example 8

Calculate the total resistance of the network in Figure 31.

The circuit has a 'parallel' pair of resistors in series with the 2 ohm resistor, and all these are in parallel with a 5 ohm resistor.

a) The equivalent resistance R of the 'parallel' pair of resistors: 3 ohms and 4 ohms:

$$\frac{1}{R} = \frac{1}{3} + \frac{1}{4} = \frac{4 + 3}{12} = \frac{7}{12}$$

$\Rightarrow$ $R = \dfrac{12}{7}$

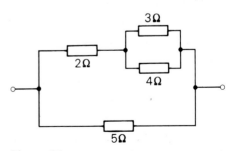

Figure 31

b)   The equivalent resistance R' of the top arm of the circuit:
2 ohms and $\frac{12}{7}$ohms. These are in series, so

$$R' = 2 + \frac{12}{7} = \frac{26}{7}$$

c)   The equivalent resistance R'' of the whole circuit:
$\frac{26}{7}$ ohms and 5 ohms in parallel:

$$\frac{1}{R''} = \frac{1}{\frac{26}{7}} + \frac{1}{5} = \frac{7}{26} + \frac{1}{5}$$

$$\Rightarrow \quad \frac{1}{R''} = \frac{35 + 26}{130} = \frac{61}{130}$$

$$\Rightarrow \quad R'' = \frac{130}{61} \approx 2.1$$

The total resistance of the network is approximately 2 ohms.

Wheatstone bridge circuit

The Wheatstone bridge circuit, a resistor network for determining resistance, was devised by the English physicist Sir Charles Wheatstone. It can provide accurate measurements of resistance and does not depend for its accuracy on the accuracy of a meter. It does however require a **sensitive** meter. The form of circuit most often encountered is shown in Figure 32. G represents a sensitive centre-zero galvanometer.

It is often helpful to consider this circuit re-drawn as in Figure 33. (The galvanometer has been omitted.)

Consider AC as a potential divider made from two resistors R_1 and R_2. Applying Ohm's Law:

p.d. across R_1 $\qquad V_{AB} = I_1R_1$
p.d. across R_2 $\qquad V_{BC} = I_1R_2$
$$V = V_{AB} + V_{BC}$$

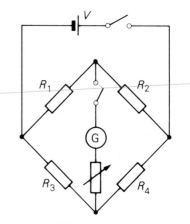

Figure 32 Wheatstone bridge circuit

Consider DF as another potential divider in parallel with the first:

p.d. across R_3 $\qquad V_{DE} = I_2R_3$
p.d. across R_4 $\qquad V_{EF} = I_2R_4$
$$V = V_{DE} + V_{EF}$$

If the resistor values are chosen so that $V_{AB} = V_{DE}$ then it follows also that $V_{BC} = V_{EF}$ since the sum of the individual p.d.s gives the supply p.d. which is V.

$$\Rightarrow \quad I_1R_1 = I_2R_3 \qquad \Rightarrow \quad \frac{R_1}{R_3} = \frac{I_2}{I_1}$$

and $\qquad I_1R_2 = I_2R_4 \qquad \Rightarrow \quad \frac{R_2}{R_4} = \frac{I_2}{I_1}$

so that $\qquad \dfrac{R_1}{R_3} = \dfrac{R_2}{R_4}$ or $\qquad \dfrac{R_1}{R_2} = \dfrac{R_3}{R_4}$

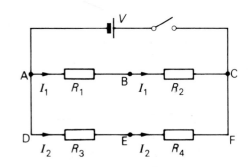

Figure 33

Now when $V_{AB} = V_{DE}$, then a voltmeter connected between points B and E registers zero p.d. (null deflection) since points B and E are **at the same potential**: there is no potential difference between them and so $V_{BE} = 0$.

When the resistor values are selected so that the meter reads zero, the bridge is said to be **balanced**.

In practice three of the resistors in this circuit are accurately known standard resistors while the fourth one is of unknown value to be determined using the bridge. By choosing a suitable ratio for resistors R_1 and R_2 and then gradually adjusting the value of R_3 until the bridge is balanced, it is possible to find R_4 from the ratio

$$\frac{R_1}{R_2} = \frac{R_3}{R_4}$$

The size of potential difference V_{BE} depends on the extent to which the resistor values are not in the correct ratio.

Example 9

The Wheatstone bridge shown in Figure 34 is balanced. If $R_1 = 120\,\Omega$, $R_2 = 400\,\Omega$ and $R_3 = 80\,\Omega$, what is the value of the unknown resistor X?

Since the bridge is balanced $\dfrac{R_1}{R_2} = \dfrac{R_3}{X}$

$$\Rightarrow \qquad X = \frac{R_2 \times R_3}{R_1}$$

$$\Rightarrow \qquad X = \frac{400 \times 80}{120} = 267$$

The value of the unknown resistor X is 267 ohms.

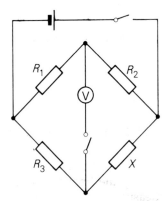

Figure 34

The unbalanced Wheatstone bridge

The circuit in Figure 35 represents a balanced bridge.

If the value of resistor R_1 is increased by a small amount ΔR, then the voltmeter indicates an out-of-balance p.d. The set of results in Table 3 illustrates typical behaviour of this circuit.

increase in resistance $\Delta R(\Omega)$	0	1.0	2.0	3.0	4.0	5.0	6.0	7.0	8.0	9.0	10
out of balance p.d. ΔV (mV)	0	17.5	35	50	65	85	100	115	135	150	170

Table 3

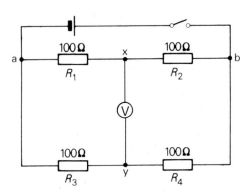

Figure 35

A graph of change in resistance ΔR against p.d. ΔV indicates that, for an initially balanced bridge, as the value of one resistor is changed by a small amount, the p.d. change is proportional to the change in resistance, Figure 36.

Describing this instead in terms of p.d.; when the bridge is balanced $V_{ax} = V_{xb} = V_{ay} = V_{yb}$. Points x and y have the same potential. If however R_1 is increased then $V_{ax} > V_{xb}$, while V_{ay} remains $= V_{yb}$. There is then a difference in the potential of points x and y and an out-of-balance p.d. is developed.

If resistor R_1 is replaced by a heat sensitive resistor called a thermistor then the out-of-balance current indicates temperature change, Figure 37. Alternatively, resistors R_1 and R_2 could be replaced by an identical pair of electrical strain

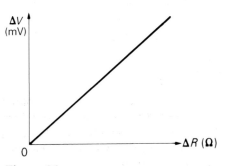

Figure 36

gauges (resistors whose resistance alters with changes in stress) and the out-of-balance p.d. would give information about mechanical strain, Figure 38. Replacing the voltmeter by a differential operational amplifier, with output attached to a voltmeter can provide a better way of monitoring the bridge 'output'.

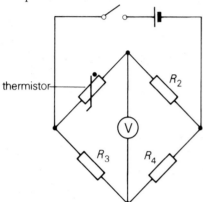

Figure 37 Measuring temperature

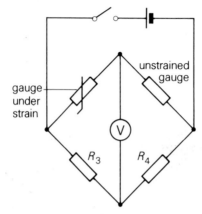

Figure 38 Measuring strain

Metre bridge

An alternative form of Wheatstone bridge circuit which uses only one standard resistor is called the metre bridge, Figure 39. With this arrangement two of the resistors are replaced by a one-metre length of uniform resistance wire with a movable contact P.

The position of the contact point P decides the ratio R_1 to R_2 since, provided the wire is of uniform thickness, the ratio can be expressed as the ratio of the two lengths of wire l_1 to l_2.

i.e. $$\frac{R_1}{R_2} = \frac{l_1}{l_2} = \frac{R_3}{R_4}$$

and since the wire is 1 metre long, $l_2 = 100 - l_1$

$$\Rightarrow \quad \frac{l_1}{100 - l_1} = \frac{R_3}{R_4}$$

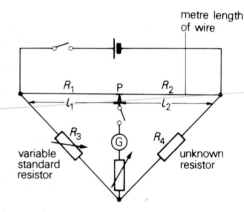

Figure 39 Metre bridge

This method provides an accurate determination of resistance: the error in the measurement of l_1 and l_2 can be less than 1% since these lengths can be measured to the nearest millimetre.

Example 10

A metre bridge is balanced when the movable contact is 64 cm from the end of the wire, Figure 40. What is the value of the unknown resistor?

At balance $\dfrac{l_1}{100 - l_1} = \dfrac{R_3}{R_4}$ $l_1 = 64\,\text{cm} \quad R_3 = 100\,\Omega \quad R_4 = X$

$$\Rightarrow \quad \frac{64}{100 - 64} = \frac{100}{X}$$

$$\Rightarrow \quad \frac{64}{36} = \frac{100}{X}$$

$$\Rightarrow \quad X = \frac{36 \times 100}{64}$$

$$X = 56.25$$

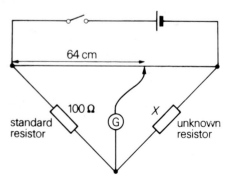

Figure 40

The unknown resistor has a value of 56 ohms.

Summary

The direction of an electric field is given by the direction of the force on a positive charge placed in the field.

The magnitude of an electric field is given by the magnitude of the force on a unit positive charge placed in the field and is measured in newtons per coulomb, $N C^{-1}$.

The work done W in transferring Q coulombs of charge through a p.d. of V volts is given by $W = Q \times V$ joules.

The potential difference between two points is equal to the work done per unit charge in moving charge from one point to another.

$$V = \frac{W}{Q}$$

A component is said to have a resistance of 1 ohm when 1 volt is required to drive a current of 1 ampere through it.

$$R = V/I, \ 1 \text{ ohm} = 1 \text{ volt per ampere}, \ 1\,\Omega = 1\,V\,A^{-1}$$

If Q coulombs of charge pass between two points A and B where the p.d. is V volts, the energy released W is given by

$$W = Q V \text{ joules}$$

If a current I passes for t seconds through a p.d. of V volts, the energy released is

$$W = I t V \text{ joules}$$

The e.m.f. (electromotive force) of a source is the energy converted when a coulomb of charge passes through the source. If 1 joule of energy is supplied by every 1 coulomb of charge, then the e.m.f. is 1 volt.

An electrical source is equivalent to an e.m.f. with a resistor in series, where the resistor corresponds to the internal resistance.

The e.m.f. of a source is equal to the p.d. across the terminals of the source when no current is being delivered: on open circuit.

The terminal potential difference of a source is related to its e.m.f. and internal resistance by the equation:

$$V = E - I \times r \text{ where } V = \text{terminal potential difference}$$
$$E = \text{e.m.f. of source}$$
$$r = \text{internal resistance}$$
$$I = \text{current through the source}$$

Electrical power P is given by

$$P = I \times V$$
$$1 \text{ watt} = 1 \text{ ampere} \times 1 \text{ volt}$$

A potential divider may be used to provide fixed or variable p.d.s from a given source, using fixed or variable resistors.

The total resistance in a series circuit is given by the sum of the individual resistors:

$$R_s = R_1 + R_2 + R_3 + \dots$$

For resistors in parallel the total resistance can be calculated from:

$$1/R_p = 1/R_1 + 1/R_2 + 1/R_3 + \dots$$

An ammeter is connected in series in a circuit. A good ammeter has a low resistance.

A voltmeter is connected in parallel in a circuit. A good voltmeter has a high resistance.

For the balanced Wheatstone bridge shown below:

$$\frac{R_1}{R_2} = \frac{R_3}{R_4}$$

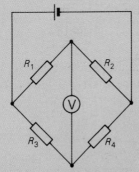

For an initially balanced bridge, as the value of one resistor is changed by a small amount, the voltage change is proportional to the change in resistance.

117

Questions

1 a) A cell of e.m.f. E and internal resistance r is connected in series with an external resistor R.

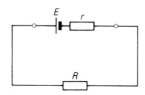

For this circuit, show that $R = \dfrac{E}{I} - r$, where I is the current in the circuit.

b) The e.m.f. and internal resistance of a d.c. supply are to be measured. The d.c. supply is connected in series with an ammeter and an external resistor R of variable resistance.

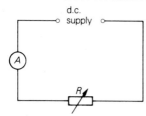

The current I is measured for various values of R. The results are shown in the table.

R (ohms)	5.00	10.0	15.0	20.0	25.0
I (amps)	0.667	0.400	0.286	0.222	0.182

i) It would appear from the relationship in part (a) that a graph of R against $\dfrac{1}{I}$ will be a straight line. (E and r being taken as constant.) Using the data in the table draw a graph to verify this statement. (Use graph paper.)

ii) From this graph calculate values for the e.m.f. and internal resistance of the d.c. supply. Explain your working.

SQA

2 a) A d.c. supply has a constant e.m.f. of 12 V and an internal resistance of 3.0 Ω. A load resistor of resistance 1.0 Ω is connected across the supply terminals.
Calculate **i)** the power delivered to the load resistor;
ii) the voltage across the supply terminals.

b) Calculation of the power delivered to various values of load resistor is repeated giving the following results:

R (ohms)	0.6	1.0	2.5	3.5	5.0	9.0
P (watts)	6.7		11.9	11.9	11.3	9.0

i) Using suitable scales, draw a graph of P against R, including the point obtained in part **a)** i).
ii) From your graph determine the value of load resistor to which maximum power is delivered from this supply.
iii) Another 12 V d.c. supply has an internal resistance of 6.0 Ω. Suggest, with brief justification, the value of load resistor which should be connected to this supply for maximum power to be delivered to this load resistor.

c) On many signal generators there are two sets of output terminals – one set marked 6 Ω and the other marked 600 Ω. Suggest a reason for this provision.

SQA

3 a) A 10 Ω resistor is connected across a battery of e.m.f. 6 V with internal resistance of 2 Ω.
i) What is the current in the circuit?
ii) What is the potential difference between the battery terminals?

b) To investigate the characteristics of a power supply unit a girl uses an ammeter and a resistance box in the following circuit.

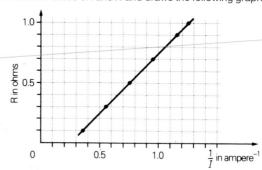

i) For this circuit derive the expression

$$R = \frac{E}{I} - r$$

where E is the e.m.f. of the power supply unit,
r is its internal resistance,
R is the total external resistance,
and I is the current in the circuit.
She collects values of I and R and draws the following graph.

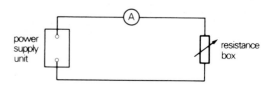

ii) Explain why she chooses to draw a graph of R against $\dfrac{1}{I}$.

iii) Extend the graph and deduce from it:
(A) the maximum current if the power supply unit were short circuited.
(B) the internal resistance of the power supply unit.
(C) the e.m.f. of the power supply unit.

SQA

4 The following circuit is used to provide output voltages of 3.0 V and 6.0 V from a 9.0 V battery of negligible internal resistance.

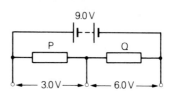

a) If the resistance of Q is 100 Ω, find the resistance of P.
b) When a 6 V, 0.060 A lamp is connected across the resistor Q, it does not operate at its normal brightness.
Give an explanation.

SQA

5 Three resistors are available. Their values are 4 Ω, 6 Ω, and 12 Ω. Describe how two, or all three, of the resistors might be combined to give each of the following resistances.
   a) 10 Ω,   b) 3 Ω,   c) 8 Ω.

   SQA

6 Certain resistors are constructed by depositing a thin film of conducting material on top of an insulating base. Connection to the film is made with gold pads at each end of the film as shown.

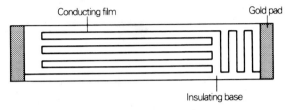

The resistance between the end gold connectors depends on the breadth of the conducting film. The results below show the resistance for various breadths of film of the same length and thickness.

Breadth (µm)	150	87	67	60	55
Resistance (Ω)	80	140	180	200	220

Find the relationship between the resistance and the breadth of the conducting film. You must show how the data were used to arrive at the relationship.

   SQA

7 A platinum-film resistor is to be used to indicate changes in temperature.
To find the resistance at room temperature the resistor is placed in one of the arms of a Wheatstone bridge. A variable resistor and fixed resistors of 6.00 kΩ and 4.00 kΩ are placed in the other arms.

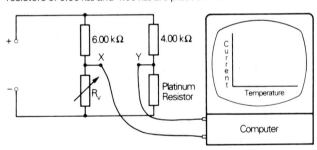

A computer is connected across XY and programmed to read the current between X and Y.
   a) The computer shows that the current between X and Y is zero when the variable resistor is set at 162 Ω. Calculate the resistance of the platinum-film resistor at room temperature.

b) The computer is now programmed to plot a graph of the current in XY against the temperature of the platinum-film resistor. Suggest and explain the shape of graph you would expect as the temperature of the platinum-film resistor is increased.

   SQA

8 In the following circuit, the p.d. across the 16 ohm resistor is 40 volts when switch S is **open**.

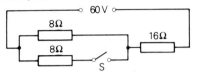

What is the p.d. across the 16 ohm resistor when the switch S is **closed**?

   SQA

9 In the following circuit the current in the milliammeter is zero.

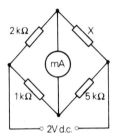

   a) Calculate the resistance X.
   b) Draw a circuit diagram to show how this value of resistance would be measured as accurately as possible using a suitable ammeter-voltmeter method.

   SQA

10 Each cell in the circuit below has an e.m.f. of 2 V and an internal resistance of 1 Ω.

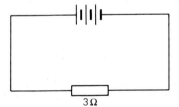

Calculate the current in this circuit.

   SQA

Topic 2.1 Test 1

1   If a charge is placed in an electric field what does it experience?

2   What happens to the free electric charges in a conductor if an electric field is applied?

3   When a charge Q is in an electric field, work W is done. How can this happen?

4   Define the potential difference between two points.

5   What is the potential difference between two points if one joule of work is done moving one coulomb of charge between them?

6   Write an equation which describes the relationship between potential difference, work done and charge.

7   How much work is done if 6 C of charge is moved between two points whose potential difference is 15 volts?

8   What name is given to the electrical potential energy supplied to each coulomb of charge which passes through a source?

9   What does the diagram below illustrate?

10   Draw a circuit diagram to show the experiment you would perform to determine the internal resistance of a battery. Explain what readings you would take and how you would calculate the internal resistance.

11   What is the 'short-circuit' current for a battery of e.m.f. 4.5 V and internal resistance 0.9 Ω?

12   Energy is conserved. Explain how this leads to the sum of the e.m.f.s round a closed circuit being equal to the sum of the p.d.s around the circuit.

13   Derive an expression for the total resistance of any number of resistors in series, by consideration of conservation of energy.

14   Derive an expression for the total resistance of any number of resistors in parallel, by consideration of conservation of charge (current).

15   Draw a Wheatstone bridge circuit, and state the relationship among the resistors if the bridge is 'balanced'.

16   The Wheatstone bridge shown below is balanced. Calculate the value of the unknown resistor X.

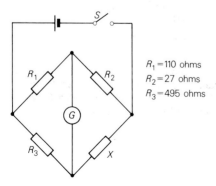

$R_1 = 110$ ohms
$R_2 = 27$ ohms
$R_3 = 495$ ohms

17   For an initially balanced Wheatstone bridge, as the value of one resistor is changed by a small amount, what happens?

Topic 2.1 Test 2

1   What experiences a force in an electric field?

2   What moves when an electric field is applied to a conductor?

3   When a charge is moved in an electric field, what is required to make this happen?

4   What is a measure of the work done in moving one coulomb of charge between two points?

5   If one joule of work is done moving a charge Q between two points with a potential difference of one volt between them, what value does the charge have?

6   State the relationship between work done, charge and potential difference.

7   If 16 joules of work is done moving a charge of 32 coulombs between two points, what is the potential difference between them?

8   Explain what is meant by the electromotive force of a source.

9   The diagram below illustrates an electrical source. Explain the items shown as r and E.

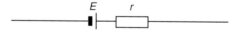

10   Describe the principles of a method of measuring the e.m.f. and internal resistance of a source.

11   The 'short-circuit' current for a battery is 6 A and its internal resistance is 0.8 Ω. What is its e.m.f.?

12   The circuit diagram shows two cells whose e.m.f.s and internal resistances are known, connected to two resistors. If the current is 0.1 A show, by consideration of conservation of energy, that the sum of the e.m.f.s is equal to the sum of the p.d.s around the circuit.

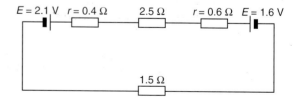

13   Derive the expression $R_s = R_1 + R_2 + R_3 + \ldots$ by considering the conservation of energy.

14 Derive the expression $1/R_p = 1/R_1 + 1/R_2 + 1/R_3 + \ldots$ by considering conservation of charge (current).

15 The Wheatstone bridge circuit shown below is balanced. State the relationship among the resistors.

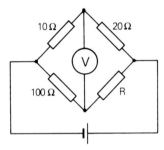

16 On setting up the following bridge circuit, a pupil finds that there is no reading in the voltmeter.

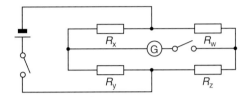

What is the resistance of the unknown resistor R?

17 In an initially balanced Wheatstone bridge circuit, one resistor is changed by $0.002\,\Omega$ and the out-of-balance p.d. changes by 8 mV. What out-of-balance p.d. change would be observed if the same resistor was changed by $0.0015\,\Omega$?

Topic 2.1 Test 3

1 What will experience a force in an electric field?

2 If an electric field is applied to a length of copper wire, what happens to the free electric charges in it?

3 What is required to move a charge in an electric field?

4 'The potential difference V between two points is a measure of the .... done in moving one coulomb of charge between the points.' What is the missing word?

5 If one joule of work is done moving a certain amount of charge Q through a potential difference of one volt, what is the size of the charge?

6 Write an equation which gives the relationship between charge, work done and potential difference.

7 If 8 C of charge is moved through a potential difference of 12 volts, how much work is done?

8 Define the e.m.f. of a source in terms of energy and charge.

9 An electrical source, like a battery, is depicted as composed of two components. What are they?

10 Describe how you would measure the e.m.f. and internal resistance of an electrical source.

11 The 'short-circuit' current for a battery is 6 A and its e.m.f. is 4.5 V, what is its internal resistance?

12 The circuit diagram shows three cells, with e.m.f.s and internal resistances shown, connected to three resistors.

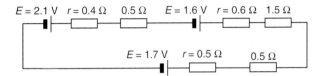

Calculate the current and then show by consideration of conservation of energy that the sum of the e.m.f.s is equal to the sum of the p.d.s around the circuit.

13 Derive the expression for the total resistance of four resistors in series, by considering conservation of energy.

14 Derive the expression for the total resistance of three resistors in parallel by considering conservation of charge (current).

15 State the relationship among the resistors in this balanced Wheatstone bridge circuit.

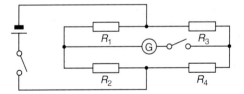

16 Calculate the resistance of the thermistor in this balanced Wheatstone bridge circuit.

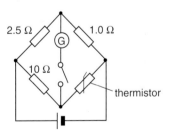

17 A balanced Wheatstone bridge has a thermistor in one arm. When the temperature changes by 0.5°C the thermistor resistance changes and there is a resulting out-of-balance p.d. of 5 mV. What p.d. would you expect if the temperature changed by 1.5°C?

Topic 2.2
Alternating Current
and Voltage

Objectives

When you have completed the work of this topic you should be able to:

1 describe how to measure frequency using an oscilloscope;
2 state the relationship between peak r.m.s. values for a sinusoidally varying voltage and current;
3 carry out calculations involving peak and r.m.s. values of voltage and current;
4 state the relationship between current and frequency in a resistive circuit.

2.2 Alternating Current and Voltage

Alternating current

The electricity supplied to homes is an alternating current at an alternating voltage of 230 V having a frequency of 50 Hz. An a.c. supply is used so that a transformer can step up or step down the voltage: less energy is wasted if the electrical power is transmitted at high voltage.

A supply of alternating current is generated using an a.c. generator. The generation of alternating current in a generator is illustrated in Figure 1.

When a coil is rotated in a magnetic field, an electromotive force E is induced which will drive a current I through the external circuit of resistance R. At any instant the current is given by $I = E/R$.

The slip rings and carbon brushes of this generator ensure that one output terminal is always connected to one side of the coil, whether that side is moving up or down through the magnetic field as it rotates. This means that the direction of the induced electromotive force changes every half revolution of the coil.

We can use an oscilloscope to give a trace which shows how the e.m.f. varies with time. The shape of the trace is the same as for a graph of e.m.f. against time; e.m.f. is on the vertical axis and time on the horizontal axis, Figure 2.

The induced e.m.f. varies between zero and a maximum value E_m known as the peak e.m.f. We can deduce how this variation takes place if we consider the coil as it rotates. Figure 3 shows the cross-section of a coil as it rotates in a magnetic field.

The size of the induced e.m.f. is proportional to the rate at which the coil cuts through the field lines. If the resistance of the external circuit is constant, then the induced current I is proportional to the induced e.m.f. E.

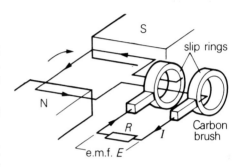

Figure 1 a.c. generator

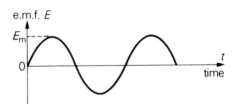

Figure 2 a.c. generator output

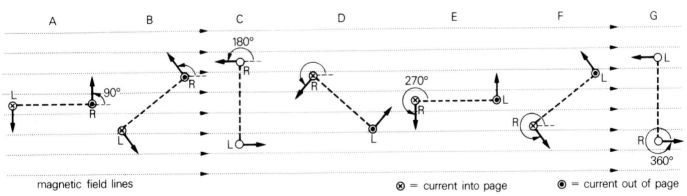

Figure 3 Coil rotating in a magnetic field

The direction of the induced current is shown at each stage. One side of the coil is labelled L and the other side R.

Consider the variation of current in the side of the coil marked R, Figure 3. When the side of the coil is moving at right angles to the magnetic field, the induced e.m.f. is a maximum. This occurs when the coil is in positions A and E. In these two cases the currents are in opposite directions. At positions B, D and F, the induced currents are less than maximum because the loop is moving at an angle to the field. At positions C and G, the sides of the coil are moving parallel to

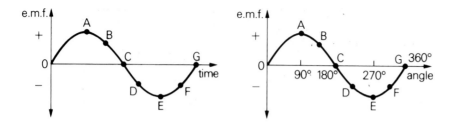

Figure 4 Generated e.m.f.

the magnetic field and are therefore not cutting the field lines, so the induced e.m.f. is zero, Figure 4.

The pattern of e.m.f. variation is repeated at regular intervals if the generator coil rotates at a constant rate. One complete pattern is called a cycle. The time to complete one cycle is the period T which is related to the frequency f:

$$T = \frac{1}{f}$$

Electricity supplied to homes has a frequency of 50 Hz, i.e. 50 cycles per second. So the period T of voltage variation is as follows.

$$T = \frac{1}{50} = 0.02\,\text{s}$$

This is the time taken for the generator coil to rotate through 360°, i.e. 2π radians.

Figure 5 shows the trace obtained on a cathode ray oscilloscope of the change in generator e.m.f. E with angle θ; it is a sine curve in which the e.m.f. varies between 0 V and the peak e.m.f. E_m.

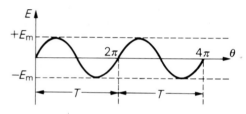

Figure 5

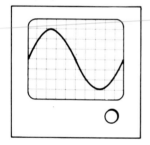

Figure 6

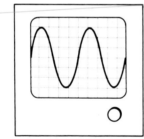

Figure 7

Frequency can be measured using a C.R.O. by comparing a waveform of unknown frequency with one of known frequency. The time-base is first adjusted until one complete wavelength is visible on the screen, Figure 6. Without altering the controls of the C.R.O. the frequency of the unknown is found by comparing the number of complete waves, Figure 7. There are two waves produced in the same time, and therefore the unknown frequency is twice the known one. In this case, if the known frequency is 50 Hz, the unknown frequency is 100 Hz.

The frequency of a wave can also be determined by referring to the time-base setting of the C.R.O.

The time-base is often calibrated in milliseconds per centimetre (ms cm^{-1}). This tells us how long it takes the trace to travel 1 cm to the right of the screen.

Example 1

The time-base of a C.R.O. is calibrated to $2\,\text{ms cm}^{-1}$. If four complete waves occupy 10 cm, what is the frequency of the wave?

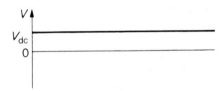

2 ms/cm

The trace moves 1 cm in 2 ms
$\Rightarrow$ The trace moves 10 cm in $10 \times 2 = 20\,\text{ms}$
$\Rightarrow$ The wave travels **one** complete wavelength in $\frac{1}{4}$ of 20 ms
$\Rightarrow$ The wave travels **one** complete wavelength in $5\,\text{ms} = \frac{1}{200}\,\text{s}$
$\Rightarrow$ The frequency of the wave = $200\,\text{s}^{-1} = 200\,\text{Hz}$.

The frequency of the wave is 200 Hz.

Comparison of a.c. and d.c.

The current and the p.d. of an a.c. supply vary continuously and so the effective value of these quantities is less than the maximum value.

The circuit in Figure 8 can be used to compare the heating effect of a d.c. supply with that of an a.c. supply. A light meter is placed to measure the output of lamp B first from a low voltage a.c. supply and then from a d.c. supply. Resistor R is adjusted until the lamp is equally bright from both sources. The peak voltage V_m of the a.c. supply and the equivalent steady voltage V_{dc} of the d.c. supply are measured on the calibrated screen of a C.R.O., Figure 9.

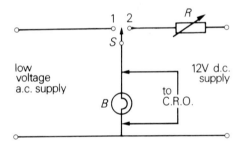

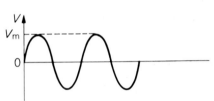

Figure 8 Comparison of a.c. and d.c. supplies   **Figure 9**

Typical results for three different lamps are shown in Table 1 below.

	V_m (volts)	V_{dc} (volts)	V_{dc}/V_m
lamp 1	12.0	8.5	0.7
lamp 2	3.0	2.1	0.7
lamp 3	2.0	1.4	0.7

Table 1

These show that the equivalent d.c. voltage V_{dc} for the same power output is about 70% of the maximum a.c. voltage V_m.

$$V_{dc} = 0.7\,V_m$$

A more mathematical analysis indicates that an alternating voltage of peak value V_m delivers the same power as a d.c. voltage of $V_m/\sqrt{2}$. This is termed the root mean square voltage, V_{rms}.

$$V_{rms} = V_m/\sqrt{2}$$

Similarly the root mean square current I_{rms} is given by $I_{rms} = I_m/\sqrt{2}$

Example 2

Calculate the peak voltage of a 240 V a.c. supply.

$$V_{rms} = V_m/\sqrt{2}$$

where V_{rms} = 240 V and V_m is the peak voltage

$$\Rightarrow \quad V_m = \sqrt{2} \times V_{rms} = \sqrt{2} \times 240 \approx 339$$

The peak voltage of a 240 V a.c. supply is 339 V.

Example 3

The peak value of an alternating current in a 10 Ω resistor is 3.0 A. Calculate the power developed in the resistor.

$$I_{rms} = 0.7\,I_m \qquad\qquad \text{power developed} = I_{rms}^2 \times R$$
$$\text{where} \quad I_m = 3.0\ A \qquad\qquad\qquad = 2.1^2 \times 10$$
$$\Rightarrow I_{rms} = 0.7 \times 3.0 = 2.1 \qquad\qquad\qquad = 44$$

The resistor develops a power of 44 W.

Resistors in a.c. circuits

When some components are connected to a d.c. supply, their p.d.s and currents do not reach their maximum values at the same instant: delays occur. The observation of these delays while we are using a varying a.c. supply is difficult unless we reduce the supply frequency to about 1 Hz. This can be achieved using a slow a.c. generator of the type shown in Figure 10, or by using the very low frequency output from a variable frequency signal generator.

Figure 10 Slow a.c. generator

Phase difference

Using the circuit in Figure 11 it is possible to observe the potential difference and current variation when a **resistor** is supplied with low frequency a.c.

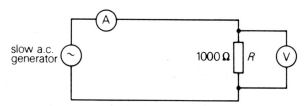

Figure 11 Phase in a resistor circuit

There is **no** difference in phase between the voltmeter readings and the ammeter readings as shown in Figure 12.

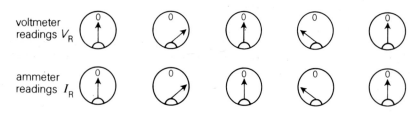

Figure 12

The current and voltage variations match, and we say that the current and voltage are **in phase**. This can be represented graphically as in Figure 13.

The current I_R and voltage V_R reach their maximum values at the same instant.

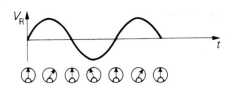
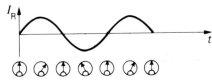

Figure 13

Measuring the opposition

The opposition of a component to alternating current in a circuit is called its **impedance**. Impedance is measured in ohms and is defined as the ratio of the r.m.s. potential difference to the r.m.s. current for the component in question. In fact, it is the potential difference across the component divided by the current in the component. When dealing with a.c. circuits, we use a.c. meters to give r.m.s. values.

The ratio V_R/I_R remains constant whatever their values: this means that the resistance remains constant. The ratio does not depend upon the frequency of the supply.

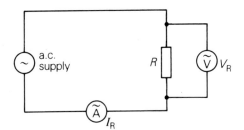

Figure 14

The impedance of a resistor is the same for both a.c. and d.c. and is its resistance R. For the resistor in Figure 14.

$$R = \frac{V_R}{I_R}$$ where V_R = r.m.s. voltage across R
I_R = r.m.s. current in R

Summary

V_{rms} is the root mean square voltage and represents the d.c. equivalent of an a.c. voltage variation

$$V_{rms} = \frac{V_m}{\sqrt{2}} = 0.7\,V_m$$

When a resistor is inserted in an a.c. circuit, the current and p.d. variation are in phase.

In an a.c. circuit

resistance $R = \dfrac{V_R}{I_R}$ where V_R is r.m.s. voltage across R and I_R is r.m.s. current in R

The impedance of a resistor is independent of the frequency.

Questions

1 Describe an experiment to determine the relationship between peak voltage and root mean square voltage.

2 What is the peak voltage of a 12 V r.m.s. supply?

3 The peak value of an alternating current in a 3 Ω lamp filament is 4 A. Calculate the power of the lamp.

4 In the specification of a certain non-electrolytic capacitor, the maximum operating voltage is given as 63 volts d.c. What, therefore, is the greatest r.m.s. voltage allowed when this capacitor is used in an a.c. circuit?

SQA

5 The diagram below represents an alternating voltage. What is the corresponding r.m.s. voltage?

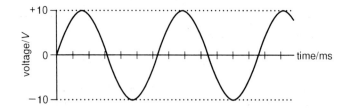

6 An oscilloscope was connected across a lamp in a circuit and the following trace was obtained.

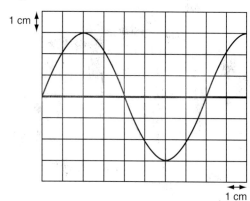

If the peak voltage shown is 12 volts and the time base setting 0.2 ms cm⁻¹, calculate:
  a) the supply frequency;
  b) the r.m.s. voltage across the lamp.

7 Draw the expected pattern of a 20 Hz 6 volts peak a.c. waveform on a 10 cm wide oscilloscope screen if the timebase setting is 0.1 ms cm⁻¹.

8 Draw the expected waveform pattern of a 14 volts r.m.s. supply whose frequency is 50 Hz if the oscilloscope screen is 10 cm by 10 cm and the Y-setting is 5 V cm⁻¹.

9 Which of the following sources will supply the greatest power to a resistor of 100 Ω?
  i) 14 volts peak 100 Hz
  ii) 20 volts r.m.s. 50 Hz
  iii) 30 volts peak 10 Hz

10 A 3 Ω resistor is connected to a 12 volts peak 50 Hz supply. What is the r.m.s current?

Topic 2.2 Test 1

1 Describe how to measure the frequency of an electrical signal using an oscilloscope.

2 What is the relationship between the peak and r.m.s. value of a sinusoidally varying voltage?

3 The peak of an a.c. supply is 20 V, what is the r.m.s. value?

4 The following set of results was obtained as a frequency of a fixed voltage source was varied and the corresponding current through a resistor measured.

f (Hz)	10	100	1000	10 000	20 000
I (mA)	5	5	5	5	5

What does this tell you about the relationship between current and frequency in a resistive circuit?

Topic 2.2 Test 2

1 A student connected a mains frequency low voltage supply to an oscilloscope in order to measure its frequency.

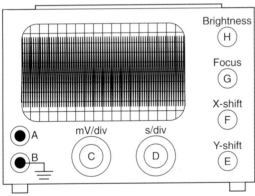

a) Where was the supply connected to the oscilloscope?
b) What controls are adjusted, in what way, and what readings are taken?
c) How is the frequency then worked out?

2 The following readings were obtained from a variable a.c. supply.

V_{rms}	7.0	14.0	21.0	28.0	35.0
V_{peak}	10	20	30	40	50

What is the relationship between V_{peak} and V_{rms}?

3 The peak voltage of a supply is 70 V, what is the r.m.s. value?

4 A fixed voltage source delivers a current of 5 mA of frequency 35 Hz to a resistive circuit. If the fixed voltage source supplies the same resistive circuit with a current at 70 Hz, what is the current?

Topic 2.2 Test 3

1 A student measures a frequency of an a.c. supply and obtains the following trace on the oscilloscope screen.

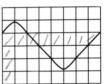

If the screen grid has 1 cm squares and the controls have the following settings:
  y-gain   3mV/cm
  timebase   2ms/cm
What is the frequency of the supply?

2 What is the relationship between the peak and the r.m.s. value of a sinusoidally varying current?

3 The peak current in an a.c. circuit is 25 A, what is the r.m.s. current in the circuit?

4 If the r.m.s current in a resistive circuit is 3 A when the frequency is 21 Hz, what is the value of the r.m.s. current when the frequency of the fixed voltage source is reduced to 7 Hz?

Topic 2.3
Capacitance

Objectives

When you have completed the work of this topic you should be able to:

1 state that the charge Q on two parallel conducting plates and the p.d. V between them are proportional to each other;

2 describe the principles of a method to show that the p.d. across a capacitor is proportional to the charge on the plates;

3 state that capacitance C is the ratio of charge to p.d.;

4 state that the unit of capacitance is the farad and that one farad is one coulomb per volt;

5 carry out calculations using $C = Q/V$;

6 explain why work must be done to charge a capacitor;

7 state that the work done to charge a capacitor is given by the area under the graph of charge against p.d.;

8 state that the energy stored in a capacitor is given by $\frac{1}{2}$(charge × p.d.) (and equivalent expressions);

9 carry out calculations using $\frac{1}{2}QV$ or equivalent expressions;

10 draw qualitative graphs of current against time and of voltage against time for the charge and discharge of a capacitor in a d.c. circuit containing a resistor and capacitor in series;

11 carry out calculations involving voltage and current in CR circuits;

12 state the relationship between current and frequency in a capacitive circuit;

13 describe the principles of a method to show how the current varies with frequency in a capacitive circuit;

14 describe and explain the possible functions of a capacitor – storing energy, storing charge, blocking d.c. while passing a.c.

2.3 Capacitance

Capacitors

Capacitors are used for storing charge. They vary in shape, size and type according to their applications, Figure 1.

The circuit in Figure 2 can be used to illustrate some properties of a capacitor in a d.c. circuit.

When switch S is turned to position 1, the lamp L_1 glows brightly, dims and then goes out. The current is at a maximum immediately after the switch is closed and rapidly falls to zero, Figure 3(a). If the switch S is then turned to position 2, the lamp L_2 glows brightly, dims and then goes out even though the battery is no longer part of the circuit. The current is once again at a maximum immediately after the switch is closed and rapidly falls to zero although in this case the current is in the **opposite direction**, Figure 3(b).

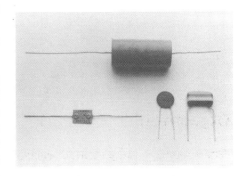

Figure 1 Capacitors

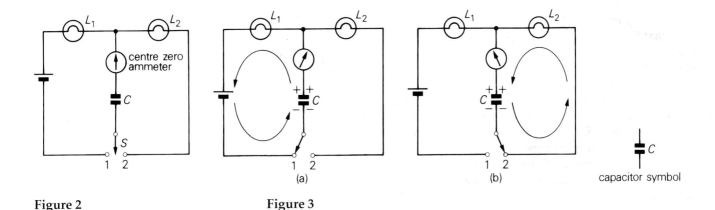

Figure 2   **Figure 3**

When a current passes for a certain time, a quantity of charge is transferred from one part of the circuit to another. Figure 3(a) shows the battery transferring electrons from the top plate to the lower plate of the capacitor. We say that the capacitor has been **charged**. In Figure 3(b) the capacitor releases the stored charge; electrons flow back to the top plate and we say that the capacitor is **discharging**.

A capacitor consists of two metal plates (or foils), separated by an insulating material. Figure 4 shows the construction of a typical capacitor.

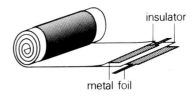

Figure 4 Capacitor construction

Charging the capacitor required a potential difference, so work was done in transferring charge between the plates. The relationship between the quantity of charge Q transferred to the plates and the potential difference V between them is investigated using the apparatus shown in Figure 5. The parallel plate capacitor shown consists of two metal foil plates whose separation and area of overlap can be varied. One form of this apparatus is called the 'Aepinus Capacitor', as shown; other forms have horizontally placed sheets of foil with insulating separators.

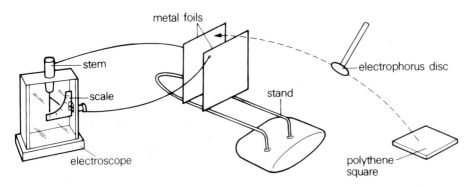

Figure 5

As charge is supplied to the capacitor plate, a potential difference is set up between the plates. Charge can be supplied using an electrophorus. When the electrophorus disc is placed on the negatively charged polythene square and earthed, the disc becomes positively charged by induction. An equal quantity of charge is transferred by the disc to the capacitor plate each time.

As more and more charge is transferred to the capacitor, more and more work is being done by the experimenter as he/she charges the capacitor. As the quantity of charge stored in the capacitor builds up, so too does the electric field between the parallel plates.

If one plate of the capacitor is connected to the case and the other to the stem of the electroscope, the deflection of the gold leaf gives a measure of the potential difference between the plates.

As more charge is transferred to the capacitor, the potential difference increases and is measured by the number of divisions of deflection of the gold leaf. This experiment provides results of the form shown in Table 1.

quantity of charge transferred (number of charge transfers)	Q	1	2	3
potential difference (electroscope divisions)	V	2	4	6

Table 1

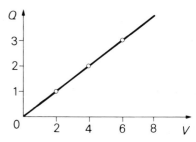

Figure 6

A graph of Q versus V has a constant slope and passes through the origin (Figure 6), so that Q and V are related by the equation, $Q = \text{constant} \times V$.

This can be written

$$\frac{Q}{V} = \text{constant} \quad \Rightarrow \quad \frac{Q}{V} = C$$

The constant C defines the capacitance of the capacitor

$$\text{capacitance } (C) = \frac{\text{charge } (Q)}{\text{potential difference } (V)}$$

When Q is measured in coulombs and V is measured in volts, the capacitance is measured in farads.

If a charge of 1 coulomb (1 C) is transferred to the plate of a capacitor and this results in a potential difference between the plates of 1 volt (1 V), then the capacitance is 1 farad (1 F).

In practice one farad is a very large capacitance and most capacitors have much smaller values which may be expressed in microfarads (µF), nanofarads (nF) or picofarads (pF).

$$1\,\mu F = 1 \times 10^{-6}\,F \qquad 1\,nF = 1 \times 10^{-9}\,F \qquad 1\,pF = 1 \times 10^{-12}\,F$$

Example 1

What quantity of charge is needed to charge a 2.0 microfarad capacitor to a potential difference of 12 volts?

$$C = \frac{Q}{V} \quad \text{where } C = 2.0 \times 10^{-6}\,\text{F} \quad V = 12\,\text{V}$$

$$\Rightarrow \quad 2.0 \times 10^{-6} = \frac{Q}{12}$$

$$\Rightarrow \quad 12 \times 2.0 \times 10^{-6} = Q$$

$$\Rightarrow \quad Q = 24 \times 10^{-6}$$

24 μC of charge is required to charge the capacitor.

Example 2

A charge of $3.0 \times 10^{-12}\,\text{C}$ transferred to the plate of a capacitor produces a potential difference of 2.0 mV. What is the capacitance of the capacitor?

$$C = \frac{Q}{V} \quad \text{where } Q = 3.0 \times 10^{-12}\,\text{C} \quad V = 2.0 \times 10^{-3}\,\text{V}$$

$$\Rightarrow \quad C = \frac{3.0 \times 10^{-12}}{2.0 \times 10^{-3}}$$

$$\Rightarrow \quad C = 1.5 \times 10^{-9}$$

The capacitor has a capacitance 1.5 nF.

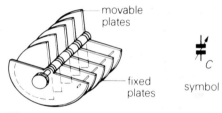

Figure 7

Factors affecting capacitance

Area of plates

The capacitance of a capacitor is directly proportional to the area of overlap of its plates.

The dependence of capacitance on the area of overlap has been used in the variable capacitor used for tuning a radio, Figure 7. Movement of the semicircular metal plates (vanes) relative to each other produces a variation of the capacitance.

Distance between capacitor plates

As the plate separation is increased, the potential difference V increases; since $C = Q/V$, this means that the capacitance decreases. In fact the capacitance increases as the plate separation d decreases.

This dependence of capacitance on plate separation is used in the 'trimmer' capacitor (used to make very fine adjustments to the tuning of a radio), Figure 8. The spacing of the metal plates is adjusted by turning the screw and hence the capacitance varies.

Material between capacitor plates

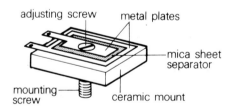

Figure 8 Trimmer capacitor

The dependence of capacitance on the type of material between the plates of the capacitor is expressed by the constant k.

The insulating material between the plates is called a **dielectric** and the constant k is the factor by which the capacitance is increased when that material is inserted between the plates. The k values given in Table 2 show that different materials influence the capacitance by different amounts.

material between plates	k factor
air	1.0
waxed paper	2.7
polyester	3.8
mica	7.0

Table 2

For general purposes, capacitors use waxed paper as the dielectric between the two metal foils as already shown in Figure 4. Other materials are chosen for special applications.

Another type of capacitor, the electrolytic capacitor has plates of aluminium foil, one of which has an oxide coating. There is a layer of chemical-soaked paper (electrolyte) between the foils. This type of capacitor is well sealed to prevent leakage, Figure 9. It is important to connect this type of capacitor with the correct polarity in a d.c. circuit as it can be damaged by incorrect connection. The electrolytic capacitor has its own symbol.

Capacitors have a 'working voltage' printed on them. This is the maximum recommended p.d. which should be applied to them without the risk of the insulation of the dielectric breaking down. This could result in a large current surge between the plates and rapid heating, leading to a dangerous explosion.

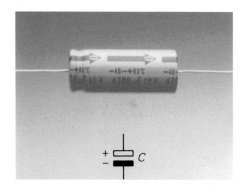

Figure 9 Electrolytic capacitor

Energy stored in a capacitor

It was shown how the p.d. between the plates of a capacitor increased as the quantity of charge stored increased, Figure 10. The quantity of work done (or energy stored) can be found from the area under the Q versus V graph.

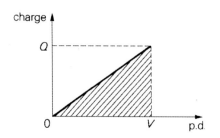

area of shaded triangle
$= \frac{1}{2} \times$ base $\times$ height
$= \frac{1}{2} \times V \times Q$

Figure 10 Energy stored in a capacitor

The energy stored in a capacitor $= \frac{1}{2} Q V$ joules.

Alternatively, since $C = \dfrac{Q}{V}$

$$\text{energy} = \tfrac{1}{2} C V^2 = \tfrac{1}{2} \frac{Q^2}{C}$$

Example 3

A 100 µF capacitor is connected to a 12 V supply. Calculate the charge on the capacitor and the energy stored.

$$C = \frac{Q}{V} \qquad \text{where } C = 100\,\mu\text{F and } V = 12\,\text{V}$$

$$\Rightarrow \quad Q = CV = 100 \times 10^{-6} \times 12$$
$$\Rightarrow \quad Q = 1.2 \times 10^{-3} \text{ coulombs}$$
$$\text{energy} = \tfrac{1}{2}QV$$
$$= \tfrac{1}{2} \times 1.2 \times 10^{-3} \times 12 = 7.2 \times 10^{-3} \text{ joules}$$

The charge on the capacitor is 1.2×10^{-3} C and the energy stored is 7.2 mJ.

Capacitors in d.c. circuits

Charging a capacitor

The circuit in Figure 11 can help us to 'see' more clearly the current variation which takes place when a capacitor is charged from a d.c. supply.

The capacitor C is initially uncharged. When switch S is closed, electrons flow in an anti-clockwise direction: the lower plate becomes negatively charged and the upper plate positively charged. Thus there is a growth of potential difference across the capacitor. This potential difference opposes further flow of charge, thus reducing the charging current, Figure 12.

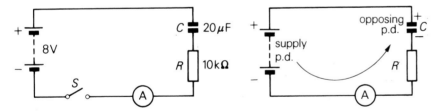

Figure 11

Figure 12 Charging a capacitor

Eventually enough charge has flowed to C so that the potential difference across C is equal to the supply potential difference (8 volts, in this case). At this stage, the potential difference across the capacitor is equal and opposite to that of the supply and so the net charge flow is zero. The variation of charging current with time is shown in Figure 13. The corresponding voltage variation is shown in Figure 14.

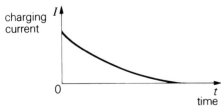

Figure 13 Change of current on charging a capacitor

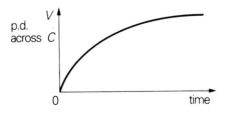

Figure 14 Change of voltage on charging a capacitor

Discharging a capacitor

The discharge of a capacitor can be observed in detail if it is first fully charged to a given potential difference with switch S at position 1 in the circuit in Figure 15.

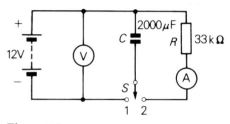

The voltmeter indicates when the capacitor has been charged to the required potential difference. Switch S is then moved to position 2. Since the capacitor has a large potential difference across it, the charge flow from it is a maximum at the start. As charge flows from one capacitor plate to the other through R and the ammeter, Figure 16(a), the potential difference across them reduces and hence the discharge current reduces. The variation of discharge current with time is shown in Figure 16(b), and voltage variation is shown in Figure 16(c).

Figure 15

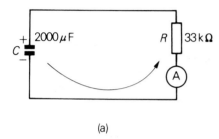

(a)

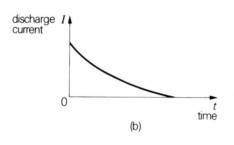

(b)

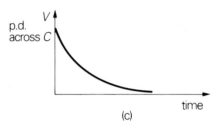

(c)

Figure 16

When a larger resistor R is substituted in the circuit, the current is reduced. Therefore the rate of flow of charge from the capacitor plates is reduced, with the result that it takes longer for the capacitor to discharge. Similarly, if a larger capacitor C is substituted then the total charge Q that it can store is increased; it therefore takes longer for the capacitor to discharge, Figure 17.

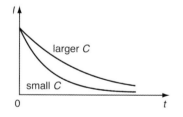

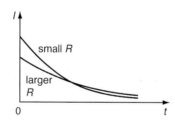

Figure 17 Capacitor discharge

These graphs of discharge show the variation of current in the opposite direction. If we show the charge and discharge currents for a capacitor using the same set of axes, we obtain the curves shown in Figure 18(a). The corresponding voltage variation is shown in Figure 18(b).

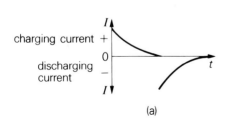

(a)

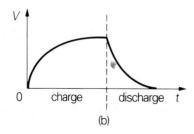

(b)

Figure 18 Charging and discharging a capacitor

Capacitors in a.c. circuits

Figure 19 shows a 200 µF capacitor connected in series with a slow a.c. generator and an ammeter.

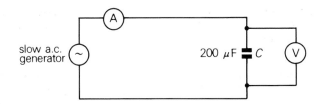

Figure 19 Phase in a capacitor circuit

There is a **difference** in phase between the voltmeter readings and the ammeter readings as shown in Figure 20.

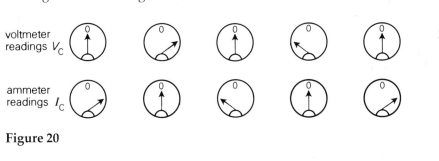

Figure 20

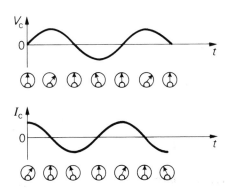

Figure 21

The current and voltage variations do not match and we say that the current and voltage are **out of phase**. This is shown graphically in Figure 21.

The current I_c reaches its maximum value before the voltage V_c reaches its maximum value. **The current leads the voltage**.

Factors affecting capacitor current

a) Frequency

The circuit in Figure 22 is used to investigate how the current I_c depends on the supply frequency. Table 3 shows the results obtained for a constant supply voltage, and these are plotted on the graph in Figure 23.

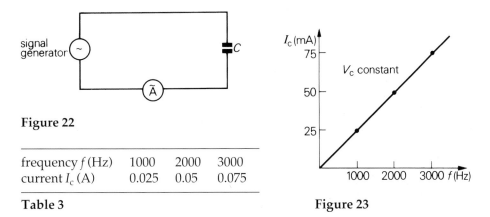

Figure 22

Figure 23

frequency f (Hz)	1000	2000	3000
current I_c (A)	0.025	0.05	0.075

Table 3

A straight line through the origin is obtained showing that the current I_c varies directly as the frequency.

$$I_c \propto f$$

b)   Capacitance

The same circuit can be used to investigate how the current I_c depends on the capacitance C. Table 4 shows the results obtained for a constant supply voltage and signal generator frequency when various capacitors are inserted in the circuit. The results are plotted on the graph in Figure 24.

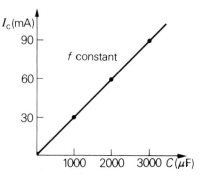

capacitance C (μF)	1000	2000	3000
current I_c (A)	0.03	0.06	0.09

Table 4

The graph shows that the current I_c varies directly as the capacitance.

$$I_c \propto C$$

Figure 24

Some uses of capacitors

A d.c. supply has zero frequency, and so, since I_c is dependent on frequency, the current is zero.

Figure 25(a) shows the graph of an electrical signal that has both an a.c. component V_{ac} and a d.c. component V_{dc}. When this signal is supplied to the circuit shown in Figure 26 the voltage variation V_R across resistor R no longer includes the d.c. component, Figure 25(b). The capacitor has blocked the d.c. signal.

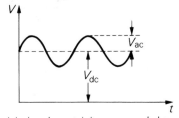

(a) signal containing a.c. and d.c.

(b) d.c. signal blocked

Figure 25

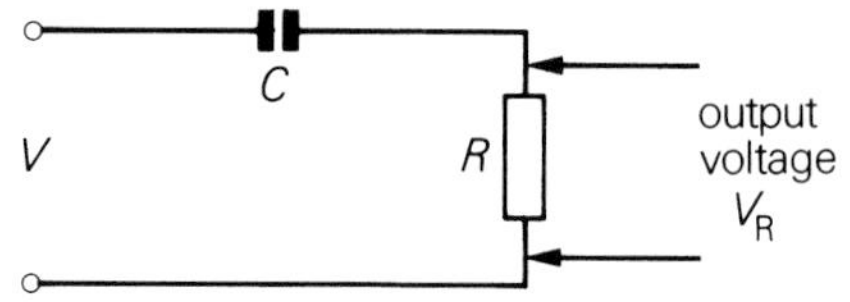

Figure 26

A capacitor can also be used to smooth rectified a.c. to give d.c. The circuit in Figure 27 can be used to demonstrate the smoothing action of a capacitor C. Without C, the variation in output voltage would be as shown in Figure 28(a). When capacitor C is included in the circuit, the output is smoothed to the form shown in Figure 28(b). The smoothing action is due to the charging and discharging of capacitor C. This output is called a ripple voltage.

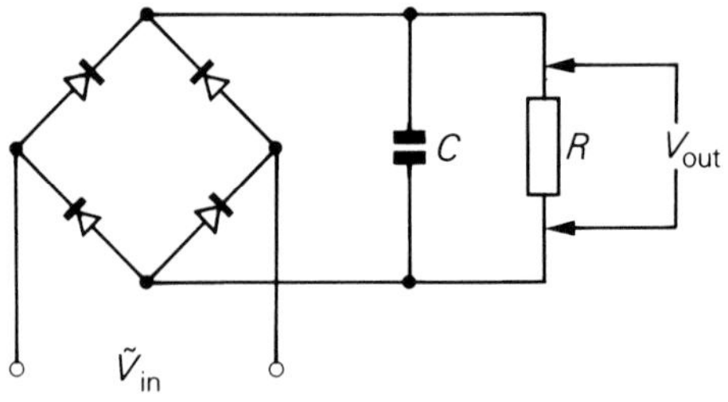

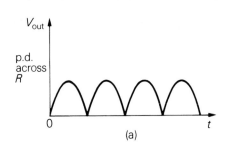

(a)

(b)

Figure 27

Figure 28 Capacitor smoothing

Summary

The potential difference across two parallel conducting plates is directly proportional to the charge on them.

Capacitance is defined by the ratio charge to potential difference.

$$C = \frac{Q}{V}$$

1 farad = 1 coulomb per volt; $1\,F = 1\,C\,V^{-1}$

The energy stored in a capacitor of capacitance C farads, charged to a p.d. of V volts is given by

$$E = \tfrac{1}{2}C V^2 \text{ joules.}$$

When a capacitor is charged from a d.c. supply, the current is at first large and gradually reduces to zero; the p.d. across the capacitor rises from zero to a maximum value during this time.

When a capacitor is inserted in an a.c. circuit, the current and voltage across the capacitor are out of phase. The current reaches its maximum value before the voltage reaches its maximum value. The current leads the voltage.

Questions

1 Draw current–time graphs for the charging of a large and a small value capacitor for a constant voltage d.c. supply.

2 Draw current–time graphs to illustrate the effect of a large and a small resistor on the charging of a capacitor from a constant voltage d.c. supply.

3 Consider the circuit shown.
   a) What is the maximum charging current?
   b) What is the final p.d. across C?
   c) How much charge is transferred to the capacitor?

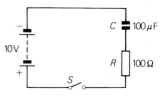

4 The capacitor C is charged with a steady current of 1 mA by carefully adjusting the variable resistor R.

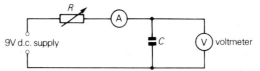

The voltmeter reading is taken every ten seconds as in the table.

time (s)	0	10	20	30	40
voltmeter reading (V)	0	1.9	4.0	6.2	8.1

Plot a graph of charge against voltage for the capacitor and hence find its capacitance.

SQA

5 To study the charging of a capacitor the circuit shown is used.

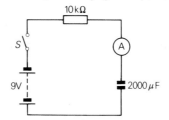

   a) Describe the response of the ammeter after switch S is closed.
   b) How would you know when the potential difference across the capacitor is at its maximum?
   c) Suggest a suitable range for the ammeter.
   d) If the 10 kΩ resistor is replaced by one of larger resistance, what will be the effect on the maximum potential difference across the capacitor?

SQA

6 The charging of a capacitor is studied using the circuit shown. The ammeter *A* is a centre-zero instrument and a constant d.c. supply of 6 volts is used.

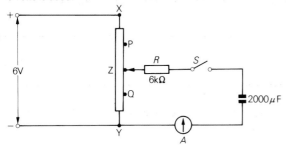

a) The sliding contact *Z* is set at the mid-point of XY and switch *S* is closed.
   i) Calculate the final charge on the capacitor *C*.
   ii) Sketch a graph showing how the charging current varies with time.
b) With the capacitor fully charged as in **a)** describe how the current through the milliameter changes when the sliding contact *Z* is moved, in turn, to a new position
   i) P (nearer to X)
   ii) Q (nearer to Y).
c) At the end of the experiment switch *S* is opened and a short conducting wire is connected directly across the plates of the capacitor.
   Describe what happens to the energy that was stored in the capacitor.

   SQA

7 You are given a capacitor, a battery, a resistor, a switch, a cathode ray oscilloscope and connecting wires.
   You are asked to set up a circuit which would allow you to look at the variation of current as the capacitor is charged up through the resistor.
a) Draw a diagram of your circuit.
b) Draw a sketch to show the variation of current while the capacitor is charging.

   SQA

8 The graph of charge against p.d. for a capacitor is shown below.

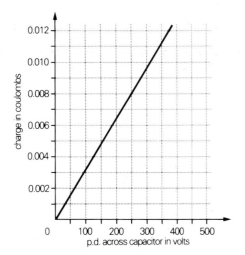

Calculate
   i) the capacitance of the capacitor;
   ii) the energy stored in the capacitor when the p.d. is 300 V.

   SQA

9 The circuit shows an uncharged 470 µF capacitor in series with a 1.2 kΩ resistor. An oscilloscope is connected across the resistor.

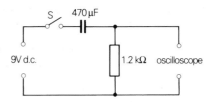

a) Calculate the initial current in the 1.2 kΩ resistor after the switch *S* is closed.
b) Calculate the final charge stored on the capacitor.
c) Sketch the trace shown on a suitably adjusted oscilloscope during the charging period.

   SQA

10 An initially uncharged capacitor is charged using a **constant** current of 90 µA. After 100 seconds the voltage across the capacitor is 12 volts.
   i) How much charge is stored on the capacitor after 100 seconds?
   ii) How much energy is stored in the capacitor after 100 seconds?
   iii) A second capacitor, with a larger capacitance, is charged for the same time using the same current.
      a) How does the voltage across the second capacitor compare with the first?
      b) How does the energy stored in the second capacitor compare with the first?

   SQA

Topic 2.3 Test 1

1 What is the mathematical relationship between the charge, Q, on two parallel conducting plates, and the p.d., V, between them?

2 Describe the principles of a method to show that the p.d. across a capacitor is proportional to the charge on the plates.

3 What does the ratio Q/V represent?

4 What does the symbol 'F' stand for? Express this unit in terms of charge and p.d. units.

5 A capacitor is charged to 10 V when 350 microcoulombs of charge is transferred to its plates. What size is the capacitor?

6 Why must work be done to charge a capacitor?

7 How can you use a plot of charge, Q, versus p.d., V, to determine the work done in charging a capacitor?

8 Which of the following expressions gives the energy stored in a capacitor?
(a) $\frac{1}{2}QV$, (b) $\frac{1}{2}CV^2$, (c) $Q^2/2C$

9 A charge of 6 mC is supplied to a 0.001 μF capacitor. How much energy does this store?

10 A 100 μF capacitor in series with a 100 Ω resistor is connected to a 10 V d.c. supply. Draw the current against time graph as the capacitor is charged.

11 Calculate the maximum charging current in the circuit shown.

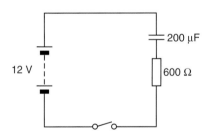

12 Which of the following graphs shows how current and supply frequency are related in a capacitive circuit?

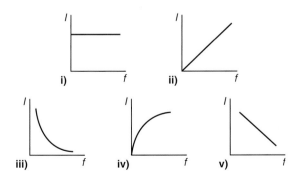

13 Describe how you would demonstrate practically how the current varies with frequency in a capacitive circuit.

14 An amplifier circuit diagram contains the following part.

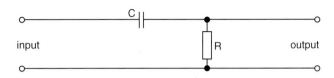

What is the function of capacitor C? (What does this circuit do to the amplifier signals?)

Topic 2.3 Test 2

1 The p.d. between two parallel conducting plates is measured as the charge on them is increased and the following results are obtained:

charge Q (mcoulombs)	2	6	10	14	18	22	26	30	34
p.d. between plates V (volts)	1	3	5	7	9	11	13	15	17

What does this set of results suggest about the mathematical relationship between the charge Q and the p.d. V?

2 Describe how to show experimentally that the p.d. across a capacitor is proportional to the charge on the plates.

3 Write an expression for capacitance in terms of p.d. and charge.

4 What is the unit of capacitance? Express it in terms of two other electrical units.

5 What quantity of charge is needed to charge a 5 μF capacitor to a p.d. of 12 V?

6 Explain where the energy in a charged capacitor comes from.

7 The graph depicts the charging of a capacitor to a p.d. of V volts when a charge Q has been transferred to its plates.

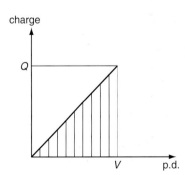

What does the shaded area represent?

8 Which of the following expressions gives the energy stored in a capacitor?

i) $\frac{1}{2}QV^2$,   ii) $Q^2/2C$,   iii) $\frac{1}{2}QV$

9 A charge of 5×10^{-11} C is transferred to the plates of a capacitor and produces a p.d. of 10 mV. What energy is stored in the capacitor?

10 A capacitor, connected in series with a 100 Ω resistor is charged from a d.c. supply. If the maximum charging current is 100 mA, draw a p.d. against time graph to show the charging process.

11 A 2000 μF capacitor in series with a 2 kΩ resistor is charged by connecting it to a d.c. supply as shown.

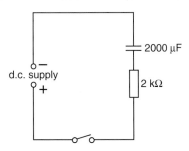

If the maximum p.d. across the capacitor is 2 V, what is the maximum charging current?

12 State the relationship between the current and frequency in a capacitive circuit.

13 Describe the principles of a method to show how the current varies with frequency in a capacitive circuit.

14 What is the function of a large capacitor in a photographic electronic flash unit?

Topic 2.3 Test 3

1 What does the following graph show about the p.d. between two parallel conducting plates as more charge is added?

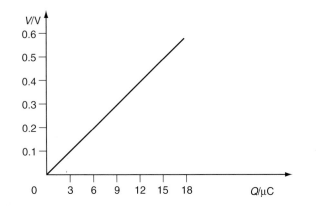

2 Describe how you would use the equipment shown below to show that the p.d. across a capacitor is proportional to the charge on the plates.

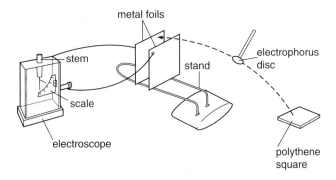

3 Define capacitance in terms of charge and potential difference.

4 What is the unit of capacitance?
Express the unit of capacitance in terms of the units of charge and voltage.

5 If 240 μC is transferred to a 30 μF capacitor, what is the p.d. across it?

6 Explain why work must be done to charge a capacitor.

7 The graph shows how the p.d. across the plates of a capacitor changed as more charge was added.

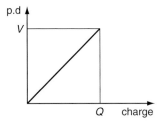

How much work was done?

8 Write three different equivalent expressions for the energy stored in a capacitor.

9 A 2000 μF capacitor is connected to a 15 V d.c. supply. Calculate the energy stored in the capacitor.

10 Draw the current/time and p.d./time graphs for a capacitor being charged from a d.c. supply.

11 Calculate the maximum charging current in the circuit when the switch S is closed.

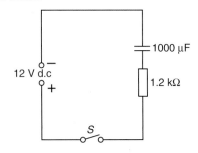

12 Which of the following describes the relationship between current and frequency in a capacitive circuit?

(a) $I \propto f$,   (b) $I \propto 1/f$,   (c) $1/I \propto f$

13 What equipment would you need to use to show how the current varies with frequency in a capacitive circuit? Draw a diagram and show how it would be connected up.

14 A simplified circuit diagram for a high voltage supply unit is shown below.

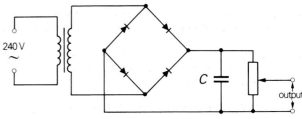

What is the function of 'C'?

Topic 2.4
Analogue Electronics

Objectives

When you have completed the work of this topic you should be able to:

1 state that an op-amp can be used to increase the voltage of a signal;
2 identify circuits where the op-amp is being used in the inverting mode;
3 state that an op-amp connected in the inverting mode will invert the input signal;
4 state that for the ideal op-amp in the inverting mode:
   a) input current is zero, i.e. it has infinite input resistance;
   b) there is no potential difference between the inverting and non-inverting inputs, i.e. both input pins are at the same potential;
5 state the inverting-mode gain expression $V_o/V_1 = R_f/R_1$;
6 carry out calculations using the gain expression $V_o/V_1 = R_f/R_1$;
7 state that an op-amp cannot produce an output voltage greater than the positive supply voltage or less than the negative supply voltage;
8 identify circuits where the op-amp is being used in the differential mode;
9 state that a differential amplifier amplifies the potential difference between its two inputs;
10 state the differential mode gain expression $V_o = (V_2 - V_1) R_f/R_1$;
11 carry out calculations using $V_o(V_2 - V_1) R_f/R_1$;
12 describe how an op-amp can be used to control external devices via a transistor.

2.4 Analogue Electronics

Analogue computers

Analogue electronics is about electrical circuits which have continuously varying signals as opposed to digital ones which deal with pulsed signals. Analogue electronics gets it name from the fact that early computers used the behaviour of electronic components like resistors, capacitors and valves to represent numbers. The physical quantities which the computer dealt with were **analogous to** or representative of the numbers. The size of a voltage could represent the size of a number or physical quantity in an equation.

Analogue computers did mathematics using the properties of various combinations of resistor, capacitor, inductor or diode. They were able to add, subtract, and even do differentiation! Analogue computers were able to simulate experiments which would take too long to carry out without them. They can be used to 'model' how a system will behave under a wide range of conditions and thus save having to do expensive (or disastrous!) experiments. For example, before constructing a bridge a design engineer would use an analogue computer program to predict how the bridge should behave under a wide range of conditions. This procedure can help to avoid such disasters as the Tacoma Narrows bridge which vibrated itself apart under the influence of relatively harmless wind conditions. A computer analysis could have predicted this!

Figure 1 A computer analysis could be used to prevent a disaster like this

One of the most common analogue circuits in use is the amplifier. The amplifiers in early equipment used 'valves', and required a large power consumption when operating. Nowadays we still use amplifiers in analogue electronics applications but we are able to use the 'semi-conductor' variety in a single plastic package called an integrated circuit (I.C.), sometimes also called 'chips', which use much less power. Amplifiers have also found many more modern applications.

Figure 2

Properties of amplifiers

Amplifiers aren't just for stereo systems and pop groups. Amplifiers are designed to increase the size of electrical signals. The signals may be tiny electrical impulses from a beating heart or from within a brain or they could be voltage changes representing the temperature change of a spacecraft's instrumentation.

An **ideal** amplifier should have a very high 'amplification' factor, in other words, no matter how small an input voltage change, we should be able to register an amplified output voltage change. The output voltage should be much greater than the input voltage. The amplifier should not affect the electrical system to which it is connected, for example by drawing large currents from it. It should be capable of making an output device operate. It is also important to know that the amplifier will respond instantaneously in a regular, predictable way as soon as there is either a positive or negative input signal.

This may seem a tall order in terms of specification but an amplifier known as an 'operational amplifier' (or op-amp) was designed to meet these requirements for the early analogue computers. It still has many uses although computers have since become 'digital'. Its designers gave it 'perfect' characteristics for an amplifier. A typical example of an 'op-amp' is the '741' (Figure 3). This is a very common form which is made of a chip containing about 19 transistors, and other components. It was superseded by the TL081, which made use of JFET technology, and it is useful to use it to illustrate the basic principles and operation of operational amplifiers.

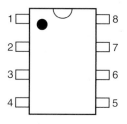

Figure 3

The **symbol** for the op-amp is very simple and doesn't show the actual contents of this chip. Figure 4 shows that it has two 'input' pins and one 'output' pin. The two input pins are shown by a minus sign and a plus sign, and are called the 'inverting' and 'non-inverting' inputs'.

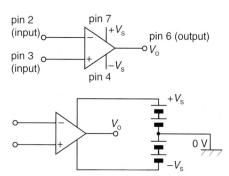

Figure 4 Op-amp symbol and power supply arrangement

The op-amp is operated by two power supplies connected to the $+V_s$ and $-V_s$ pins. This is so that it can respond to both positive and negative signals. This power supply is not usually shown on circuit diagrams but it is of course essential for the working of the amplifier. It is usually in the range ±5V to ±15V.

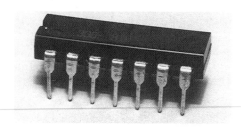

Figure 5 Pin diagram for 741 op-amp

The connection diagram or pin diagram (Figure 5) shows that this is an eight pin chip with four pins on each side. It is described as a 'dual-in-line' package (DIL). Pins 1 and 5 are called the 'offset null' pins, which in certain applications allow adjustments to be made to ensure that when the input is zero the output is also exactly the same. Pin 8 is not used.

Basic characteristics

In theory, if the op-amp is used as shown in Figure 6, and a.c. or d.c. voltage signals are fed to the 'inverting' input and compared with the resulting output signals we would expect the results shown in the table in Figure 7.

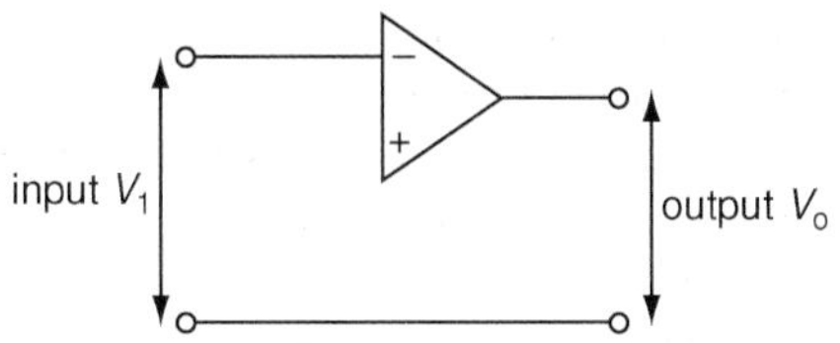

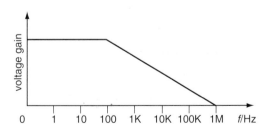

Figure 6 An op-amp in 'inverting' mode'

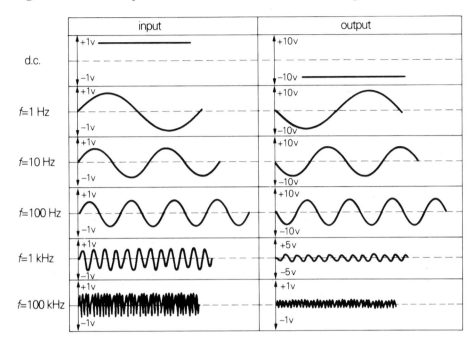

Figure 7 'Inverting mode' features

Studying these results reveals a few general properties.

1. The 'sense' of the output voltage is the opposite of the input so that a positive input voltage results in a negative output voltage. The signal is '**inverted**' – hence the reason why we call this the inverting pin.
2. The amplitude of the output voltages does not change very much for different frequencies of the same input voltage until the frequency becomes greater than 100 Hz. The amplification does not depend on frequency over a given range (in this case 0–100 Hz).
3. As the frequency of input signal increases beyond 100 Hz, the output voltage tends to reduce; there is less amplification. The amplification is frequency-dependent beyond a certain range.

The graph shows that the gain of this op-amp is high for a limited range of input signal frequencies, Figure 8.

Figure 8

This amplifier arrangement has an **extremely large gain.** In fact it can amplify an input voltage by about 100,000 times! Typically, an input voltage change of 10 μV, with this amplification, would result in an output of 10 V. But what if the input voltage change is greater than this? Will the output voltage be greater? Is there any limiting factor? If this amplifier **could only** give an output voltage which was 100,000 times the input voltage it would have limited use because the output can be no greater than the circuit's supply voltage (say 10 V of the power supply). That would mean that any change of input voltage greater than 10 μV would **always** give an output voltage change of 10 V!

Controlling the gain using negative feedback

Fortunately the problem outlined above is dealt with by connecting a resistor R_f from the output terminal back to the negative input terminal as in Figure 9. Now when a voltage is applied between the inputs of an op-amp, the potential of the output changes so that the feedback can ensure that the two inputs are at the same potential.

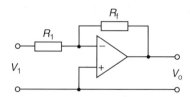

Figure 9 Negative feedback to the inverting input

This feedback resistor allows a proportion of the output voltage to be applied (fed back) to the negative input pin to meet this requirement and the process is called 'negative feedback'. The resulting gain is reduced but it enables us to control the voltage gain of the amplifier to a suitable level to allow us to deal with a wider range of input voltage variations and to operate over a wider range of frequencies (Figure 10).

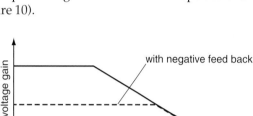

Figure 10 Effect of negative feedback on gain

When a circuit like the one in Figure 9 is set up and input voltage changes are varied then by measuring and plotting the input voltage V_1 against the output voltage V_o we obtain a graph called the **transfer characteristic** of the circuit (Figure 11). These voltages need to be measured using a digital voltmeter or oscilloscope, so that the measuring instrument does not affect the correct working of the circuit.

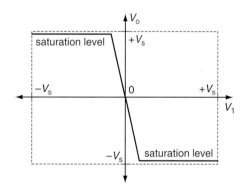

Figure 11 Transfer characteristic for an op-amp with negative feedback

If you look at this graph carefully you will note that:
1. When the input voltage has a small negative value the output voltage has a larger positive value;
2. When the input voltage reaches a certain value there is no further increase in the output voltage, it has reached **saturation** level;
3. If the **gain** is given by the ratio $\Delta V_o / \Delta V_1$ the ratio is **negative** because the input has been inverted.

A formula for the amplifier gain

When considering the inverting mode op-amp circuit it is important to realise that the basic principle behind this (differential) amplifier is that it amplifies the **difference** between the voltages applied to the two inputs (Figure 12). This can be written quite simply as $V_o = A(V_2 - V_1)$, where V_o represents the output voltage and V_1 and V_2 are the input voltages, which are amplified by a factor A.

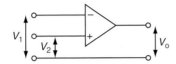

Figure 12

In the case of the amplifier operating in the 'inverting mode', the voltage applied to the non-inverting input terminal, V_2, is zero and so the expression becomes:

$$V_o = A(0 - V_1)$$
$$= A(-V_1)$$
$$\Rightarrow \quad V_o = -AV_1$$

Notice too that the output voltage V_o must be in the opposite sense (inverted) because the equation has a negative sign.

Table 1 shows typical output voltages V_o obtained from the circuit in Figure 13, when various sets of resistors are inserted in the R_1 and R_2 slots.

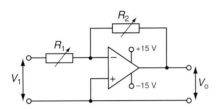

Figure 13

V_1 (V)	R_2 (kΩ)	R_1 (kΩ)	R_2/R_1	V_o (V)
− 1	100	100	1	+ 1
− 1	10	2	5	+ 5
+ 1	100	10	10	− 10
+ 1.5	2	10	0.2	− 0.3
+ 1.5	2	1	2	− 3

Table 1 Table of results

Inspection of these results indicates the relationship

$$V_o = -\frac{R_2}{R_1}V_1$$

Comparing this with $\quad V_o = -AV_1$ as derived above,

it follows that $\quad A = \dfrac{R_2}{R_1}$

The **gain** of the amplifier depends **only** on the values of R_1 and R_2 the external resistors!

Example 1

An op-amp in inverting mode has a + 5 μV signal applied to its input. If the feedback resistor, R_f, is 10 kΩ and the input resistor, R_1, is 1 kΩ, what is the output voltage, V_o.

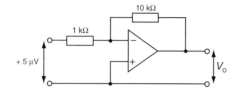

$$V_o = (R_f/R_1) \times V_1$$
$$\Rightarrow \quad V_o = (10/1) \times (+5)$$
$$\Rightarrow \quad V_o = -50 \, \mu V$$

Making use of the inverting mode

If two voltages are applied via input resistors R_1 and R_2 to an op-amp, Figure 14, the circuit can perform addition.

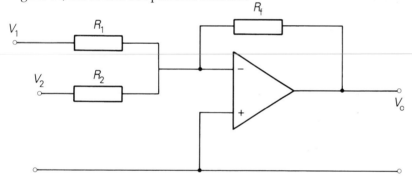

Figure 14

Using the usual notation, if V_1 and V_2 are the input voltages and V_o is the output voltage, the equation is:

$$V_o = \left(\frac{-R_f}{R_1}\right) \times V_1 + \left(\frac{-R_f}{R_2}\right) \times V_2$$

If $R_1 = R_2 = R_f$

this simplifies to $V_o = - (V_1 + V_2)$

The output voltage is equal to the **sum** of the input voltages.

This circuit could form the basis of a simple 'mixer' to combine the output of an electric guitar with that from a microphone. It also has the obvious mathematical ability of being able to add two (voltage) numbers.

This type of circuit arrangement can also be used in the conversion of digital voltages to analogue voltages. Computers are increasingly being used to control analogue systems, but computers deal with 'digital' signals. Sometimes the signals have to be converted from analogue to digital, and at other times from digital to analogue. For example, the digital signals from the autopilot computer on board an aircraft are converted to analogue form in order to operate the rudder or flaps, Figure 15.

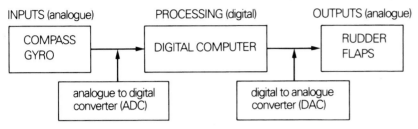

INPUTS (analogue) PROCESSING (digital) OUTPUTS (analogue)

COMPASS GYRO → DIGITAL COMPUTER → RUDDER FLAPS

analogue to digital converter (ADC)

digital to analogue converter (DAC)

Figure 15

The information which it senses is analogue and the tasks it needs to perform are analogue. The computer output needs to be converted to analogue using a digital-to-analogue convertor. Another example is the **compact disc** player; it deals with digital information which must be converted to analogue form for the loudspeakers.

The conversion can be demonstrated using an op-amp as a summing amplifier with four input resistors, Figure 16. The values of the resistors are chosen so that they are in the ratio $1:2:4:8$
(in binary notation, $2^0 = 1$, $2^1 = 2$, $2^2 = 4$ and $2^3 = 8$). The set of input resistors is thus called a binary 'weighted' resistor network.

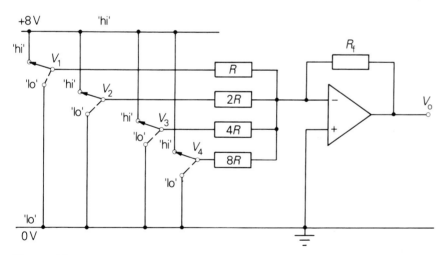

Figure 16

The output voltage V_0 is given by:

$$V_0 = -\left[\left(\frac{R_f}{R}\right) \times V_1 + \left(\frac{R_f}{2R}\right) \times V_2 + \left(\frac{R_f}{4R}\right) \times V_3 + \left(\frac{R_f}{8R}\right) \times V_4\right]$$

and if $R = R_f$

$$V_0 = -(V_1 + \tfrac{1}{2}V_2 + \tfrac{1}{4}V_3 + \tfrac{1}{8}V_4)$$

Now if V_1, V_2, V_3 and V_4 are digital, they can only be 'lo' or 'hi', say values 0 volts or 8 volts, and this can result in a large number of output voltages V_o as shown in Table 2.

V_1	V_2	V_3	V_4
lo	lo	lo	lo
lo	lo	lo	hi
lo	lo	hi	lo
lo	lo	hi	hi
lo	hi	lo	lo
lo	hi	lo	hi
and so on until ...			
hi	hi	hi	hi

$\rightarrow$

V_1	V_2	V_3	V_4	V_o
0	0	0	0	0
0	0	0	$\frac{8}{8}$	1
0	0	$\frac{8}{4}$	0	2
0	0	$\frac{8}{4}$	$\frac{8}{8}$	3
0	$\frac{8}{2}$	0	0	4
0	$\frac{8}{2}$	0	$\frac{8}{8}$	5
$\frac{8}{1}$	$\frac{8}{2}$	$\frac{8}{4}$	$\frac{8}{8}$	15

Table 2

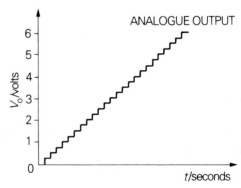

Figure 17

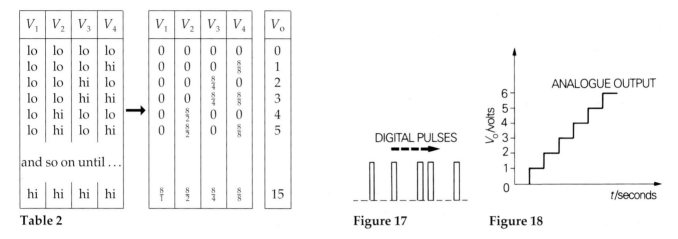

Figure 18

If the voltage values for V_1, V_2, V_3 and V_4 follow the sequence shown above, the output voltage will show a steadily increasing (but stepped) value.

The graph in Figure 18 does not appear to be a particularly continuous or 'analogue' form of output variation.

The same voltage change could be described by 8- or 16-bit binary pulses, Figures 19 and 20, instead of four-bit pulses. This results in a much more 'analogue' output. The 'steps' are much smaller and the variation of voltage looks more 'continuous'.

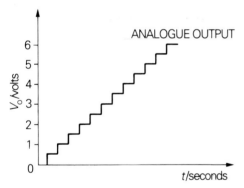

Figure 19 8-bit sampling

Figure 20 16-bit sampling

Saturation

Varying the gain ratio

The inverting mode amplifier has its limitations. From earlier discussion, it would seem that by inserting any pair of resistors R_1 and R_2 in the circuit, it should be possible to provide any gain and thus a very wide range of output voltages from very low to extremely high.

The circuit shown in Figure 21 can illustrate the behaviour of an inverting-mode amplifier as the gain is increased.

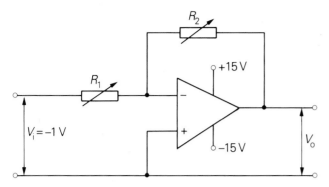

Figure 21

R_1 and R_2 are resistance boxes which can be changed to different values quite conveniently. As they are altered, the following set of data results, showing the typical behaviour of such a system, Table 3.

Figure 22 shows the graph of output voltage V_o against gain A. It becomes clear that, no matter what value of gain the amplifier is given, the output voltage can go no greater than the positive supply voltage (+15 volts in this case). A similar pattern is observed with a positive input voltage; the output goes no greater than the negative supply voltage (–15 volts).

Input voltage V_i (V)	R_1 (kΩ)	R_2 (kΩ)	A	Output voltage V_o (V)
–1	100	100	1	+ 1
–1	50	100	2	+ 2
–1	10	100	10	+ 10
–1	10	150	15	+ 15
–1	10	200	20	+ 15
–1	10	250	25	+ 15

Table 3

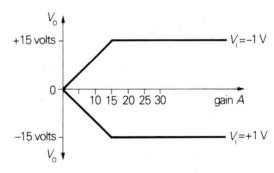

Figure 22

Varying the input voltage

An investigation into how the output voltage is affected by the input voltage for a given gain factor A can be carried out using the circuit shown in Figure 23. The input voltage V_i is varied using a variable voltage power supply, and the corresponding output voltage V_o is measured.

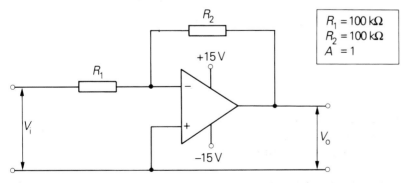

$R_1 = 100 \text{ k}\Omega$
$R_2 = 100 \text{ k}\Omega$
$A = 1$

Figure 23

Typical results from an experiment of this kind are shown in Table 4.

Input voltage V_i (V)	Output voltage V_o (V)	Input voltage V_i (V)	Output voltage V_o (V)
− 1	+ 1	+ 1	− 1
− 2	+ 2	+ 2	− 2
− 3	+ 3	+ 3	− 3
− 5	+ 5	+ 5	− 5
− 10	+ 10	+ 10	− 10
− 15	+ 15	+ 15	− 15
− 20	+ 15	+ 20	− 15
− 25	+ 15	+ 25	− 15

Table 4

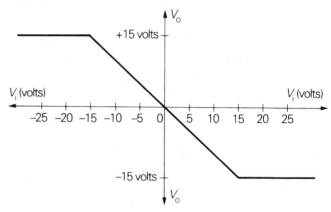

Figure 24

A graph of output voltage V_o versus input voltage V_i is illustrated in Figure 24. Once again the conclusion is similar. The greater the value of the input, the greater the output voltage also becomes; but the output voltage cannot increase beyond the positive or negative supply voltage value.

For this particular amplifier, in order to obtain an output voltage of magnitude 15 volts, positive or negative, all that is required is an input of value 15 volts or above – any value above 15 will do.

This behaviour of the op-amp is known as **saturation**, and it merely illustrates the inability of the device to output any higher voltage than its supply voltage. This property can be used to advantage in many of its applications – it is not a problem!

Saturation and a.c. inputs

The effect which saturation has on a.c. signals applied to the input of an op-amp in the inverting mode can be investigated as follows. The circuit is shown in Figure 25.

Since 'saturation' means that the output voltage can be no greater than the supply voltage, a stage is reached when the amplified output voltage *should* be greater, but is *unable* to be. This stage can be reached as the 'gain' of the amplifier is gradually increased.

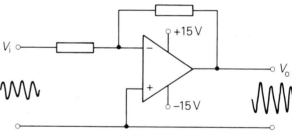

Figure 25

When 'gain' multiplied by 'input voltage' is greater than the supply voltage value, the output voltage waveform is **clipped**. The output looks as if it has had the top chopped off. Figure 26 illustrates this effect.

When the supply voltage is much smaller than the output voltage, the output waveform becomes approximately a 'square' wave. This is a simple way of generating square waves, with their on-off-on-off voltage variation.

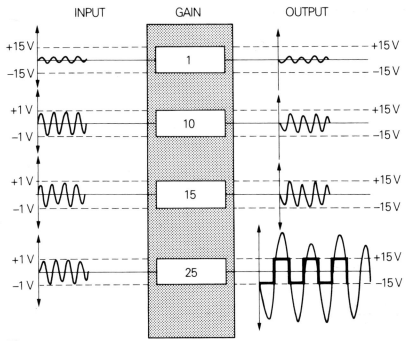

Figure 26

Differential mode

An op-amp connected as shown in Figure 27 is arranged in the differential mode. In this arrangement the amplifier provides an output which depends on the difference between the two inputs V_1 and V_2.

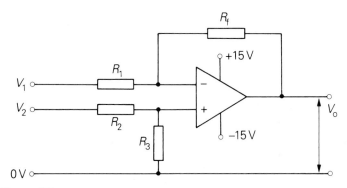

Figure 27

The equation governing the behaviour of the amplifier in this mode takes the form:

$$V_0 = (V_2 - V_1) \times \frac{R_f}{R_1} \qquad \text{provided that } \frac{R_f}{R_1} = \frac{R_3}{R_2}$$

This equation may look a little familiar – it reverts to the 'inverting mode' form (where $V_2 = 0$):

i.e. $V_0 = -V_1 \times \dfrac{R_f}{R_1}$

Now if the resistors R_f and R_1 are equal, implying that R_2 and R_3 are also equal, then the differential mode equation is:

$$V_0 = (V_2 - V_1)$$

This is straightforward subtraction.

R_1 (kΩ)	R_2 (kΩ)	R_3 (kΩ)	R_f (kΩ)
100	100	100	100
(values of resistors chosen)			

Results follow the predicted pattern, shown in Table 5.

The differential amplifier circuit can be usefully employed even when both inputs are identical. If the same signals are applied at the same time to both inputs, there is no output voltage. The differential amplifier only amplifies the **difference** between the two inputs. If there is a signal which is common to both inputs it effectively 'ignores' it. This is called 'common-mode rejection'. A very important example of this application is when the input leads pick up, for example, mains signals. Since the signals are in both leads they are not amplified along with the signal of interest. This voltage might, for example, be the tiny electrical signal which the ECG machine is amplifying from the patient's heart.

V_2 (V)	V_1 (V)	V_0 (V)
+ 1.5	+ 0.5	+ 1.0
+ 0.5	+ 1.5	−1.0
− 1.5	+ 1.5	− 3.0
+ 0.5	− 1.5	+ 2.0

Table 5

This circuit can cope with very small differences between two voltages by careful choice of resistors. Remember that the original equation was:

$$V_o = (V_2 - V_1) \times \frac{R_f}{R_1}$$

and in the above case, $\dfrac{R_f}{R_1} = \dfrac{100}{100} = 1$

Supposing that the following voltages were applied:

$V_2 = + 1.52$ volts; $V_1 = + 1.50$ volts

The output voltage **should** read + 0.02 volts. The measuring instrument used to monitor the voltage difference might not be sensitive enough to register such a small reading.

The solution is to choose resistors R_f and R_1 so that $\dfrac{R_f}{R_1} = 100$, say.

The resulting voltage output will be + 2.0 volts. By choosing this resistor ratio carefully, it is possible to **scale up** the voltage difference to a measurable size, so that the subtraction can be carried out. This could be called **scaled subtraction**.

Another problem might be that the subtraction **should** provide an answer which is greater than the supply voltage, but of course we know that the output voltage may not exceed the supply voltage! A solution similar to the last one seems right: use a ratio $\left(\dfrac{R_f}{R_1}\right)$ which **scales down** the output voltage.

Supposing that the following voltages were applied

$V_2 = + 1.59$ kilovolts; $V_1 = + 590$ volts

$V_2 - V_1 = [(+ 1590) - (+ 590)] = 1000$

The output voltage **should** read + 1000 volts!

If the resistors are chosen such that $R_f = 10\,\mathrm{k\Omega}$ and $R_1 = 10\,\mathrm{M\Omega}$,

then $\dfrac{R_f}{R_1} = \dfrac{10\,000}{10\,000\,000} = \dfrac{1}{1000}$

and the output voltage for the scaled subtraction would be 1.0 volt.

This **scaling** of the output is useful when the output device being driven by the amplifier is operating within a restricted range of voltages.

The behaviour described above applies to continuously varying (a.c.) input voltages and not just d.c. voltages.

Example 2

Two identical low voltage a.c. power supplies provide the input voltages V_1 and V_2 to an op-amp in the differential mode. The resistors R_f, R_1, R_2 and R_3 and are identical, and equal to $110\,\mathrm{k\Omega}$. Two pupils attempt to show that the output voltage $V_o = (V_2 - V_1)$ but they obtain the results shown on the right.

Can you explain the different results?
In one case it seems that the voltages are subtracted but in the other it seems that they are added. This can be explained quite simply with reference to the phase of these a.c. supplies.

Student A has subtracted a voltage of the opposite sense (out of phase), which results in an addition.

Student B has used the supplies so that their voltage inputs are in phase and, being identical, subtract to give zero.

Student A		Student B	
V_1	2.25 volts	V_1	2.25 volts
V_2	2.25 volts	V_2	2.25 volts
V_o	4.50 volts	V_o	0.00 volts

Example 3

Which of the following circuits shows an op-amp as a differential amplifier?

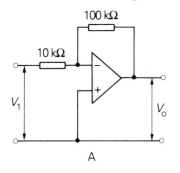

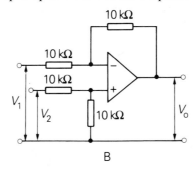

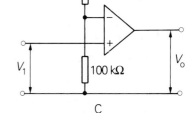

Circuit A has only one input voltage and so it is not a differential circuit.
Circuit B has two inputs, so the ratio $R_f/R_1 = R_3/R_2$.
Circuit C has two inputs but no R_f.
Therefore Circuit B shows an op-amp as a differential amplifier.

Monitoring

The differential amplifier can be used to amplify the output produced by a range of resistive sensors connected in a Wheatstone Bridge arrangement. This allows it to be used in monitoring applications. The circuit shown below in Figure 28 can be used to monitor the strain in or on an object.

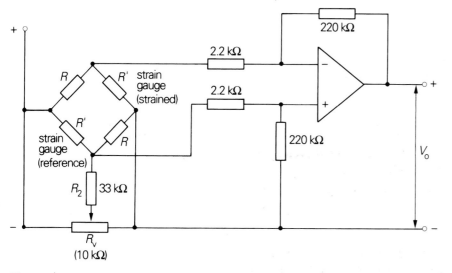

Figure 28

Resistors R_2 and R_v are used to adjust the bridge for zero output voltage. An unstrained gauge which acts as a reference is included in the arm opposite the strained one. This allows for any temperature variations in the surroundings which can cause resistance variations and mask the changes in resistance of the strain gauge resulting from the object to which it is attached.

Example 4

The circuit on the right has a number of 1.3 V cells connected as shown.

a) What output voltage would you expect if R_f, R_1, R_2 and R_3 are chosen such that $\dfrac{R_f}{R_1} = \dfrac{R_3}{R_2} = 1$?

b) What value would be obtained if this ratio is 20?

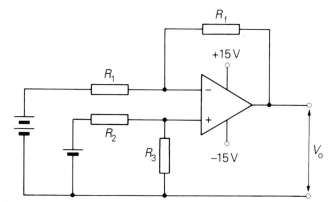

a) The output is given by
$$V_o = (V_2 - V_1) \times R_f / R_1$$
$$V_o = (1.3 - (2 \times 1.3)) \times 1$$
$$V_o = -1.3 \text{ volts}$$

b) If $R_f / R_1 = 20$, then
$$V_o = (1.3 - (2 \times 1.3)) \times 20$$
$$V_o = -26.0 \text{ volts}$$

but the output cannot exceed the supply voltage

so
$$V_o = -15.0 \text{ volts}$$

Driving output devices

If a differential amplifier is to control situations, then it must be able to make something happen at the output of the system of which it forms a part. An output action generally requires a higher current than most op-amps can provide. However, there are some op-amps which do not have this drawback.

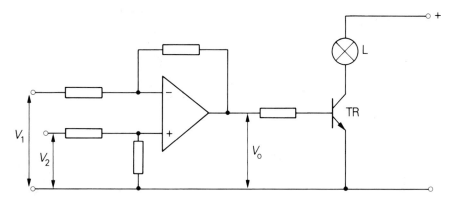

Figure 29

If an op-amp is not powerful enough to give the required current, it can use its output voltage to switch on a transistor with a higher current handling capacity, Figure 29.

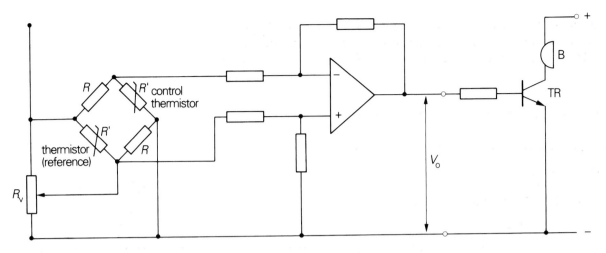

Figure 30

In the circuit shown in Figure 30, two thermistors R' are placed in a Wheatstone bridge circuit; R_v can be adjusted so that there is zero output voltage while both thermistors are at the same temperature. When the temperature difference between the control thermistor and the reference thermistor reaches a pre-determined value, the op-amp output V_o will be great enough to 'switch on' a transistor. The transistor can then operate a warning buzzer, B. This circuit thus warns of an unacceptable temperature rise.

Figure 31 shows a circuit containing a light-dependent resistor (LDR). This will operate a motor (M) when the light level becomes lower than a particular level. The resistor R_v and R_1 adjust zero and switching light level. This system might pull the curtains when it gets dark!

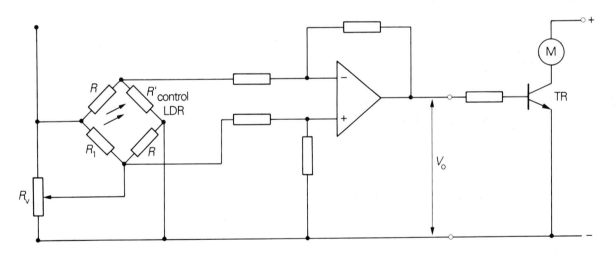

Figure 31

There are many physical situations where the op-amp can be used to monitor and control equipment or conditions.

Summary

An op-amp can be used to increase the voltage of a signal.

An op-amp connected in the inverting mode will invert the input signal.

For the ideal op-amp, the input current is zero, i.e. it has infinite input resistance. There is no potential difference between the inverting and non-inverting inputs, i.e. both inputs are at the same potential.

The gain expression for an op-amp in the inverting mode is $\dfrac{V_o}{V_i} = -\dfrac{R_f}{R_1}$

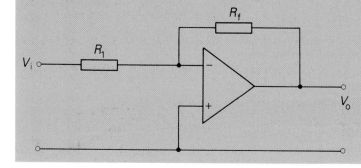

An op-amp cannot produce an output voltage greater than the positive supply voltage or less than the negative supply voltage. The output voltage 'saturates'.

The inverting mode gain equation can be used to 'add'.
$$V_o = -(V_1 + V_2) \text{ when } R_1 = R_2 = R_f$$

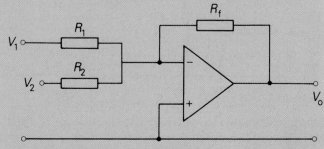

A differential amplifier amplifies the potential difference between its two inputs.

The differential mode gain equation is $V_o = (V_2 - V_1) \times \dfrac{R_f}{R_1}$

Op-amps can be used in monitoring and in control applications.

Questions

1 The diagram shows an operational amplifier connected in the inverting mode.

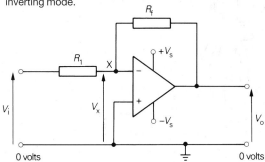

a) R_f and R_1 are the values of the feedback and input resistors. Derive the gain expression for this amplifier.

b) Describe how this circuit could be modified to carry out the following mathematical functions:
(i) multiply by 15   (ii) divide by 20

2 How could this circuit be used to generate square waves from a 20.0 volt sine wave input voltage?

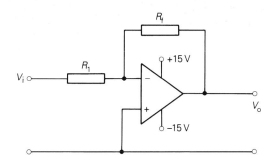

Give suitable values for R_1 and R_f.
What amplitude will the square waves have?

3 Look at the circuit diagram given below and answer the questions which follow.

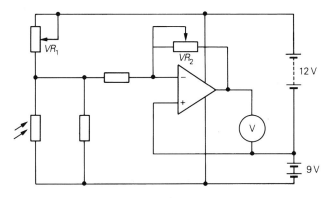

a) What use would the circuit have?
b) What would VR_1 and VR_2 be used for?
c) What will the output voltage V_o be when $V_i = 0$?

4 A physicist designed the circuit shown, to give a voltmeter reading which was dependent on the load applied to the beam on which the strain gauge was attached.

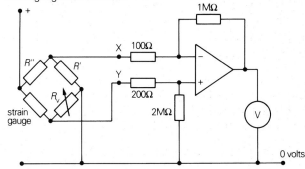

a) In what mode is the op-amp working?
b) Explain the purpose of the variable resistor R_v.
c) For a particular load on the beam the voltage between points X and Y is 0.3 mV. What is the reading on the voltmeter?

5 a) Derive an expression for the gain of an op-amp in the inverting mode.

b) The circuit in Figure 1 represents an operational amplifier used to combine V_1 and V_2.

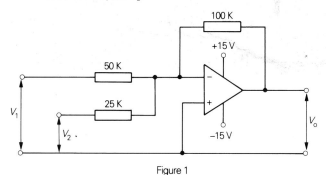

Figure 1

V_1 is maintained at + 1.0 V d.c. The voltage V_2 has the form as shown in Figure 2 with a frequency of 1 kHz.

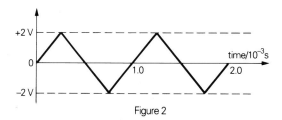

Figure 2

i) Draw to scale the output voltage V_o for the same two cycles shown in Figure 2. Label the axes clearly and show numerical values.
ii) Indicate what modification in V_o occurs if the supply voltages to the operational amplifier are reduced to ± 9 V.
c) i) Describe, with the aid of a suitable circuit diagram, how an operational amplifier can perform the process of subtraction.
ii) Explain how this arrangement can be used in the control of the speed of a motor.

SQA

6 a) Draw the circuit diagram for an operational amplifier connected in the inverting mode.
b) You are asked to design an amplifier using an op-amp connected in the inverting mode.

Unit 2 Electricity and electronics

The following two design points should be taken into account: the input impedance of the op-amp in this mode is approximately, the same as the value of the input resistor; the input impedance of the amplifier should be at least 100 times the output impedance of the device feeding into it. Give suitable values for the input and feedback resistors of a single-stage inverting amplifier taking its input from a microphone of impedance 600 Ω and having a gain of 1000.

SQA

7 The diagrams below, Figures 1 and 2, show the construction and circuit for a sun-tracker.

The shadow cast by the card divider falls on the LDR changing its resistance. The motor then turns the tracker until both LDRs are equally illuminated.

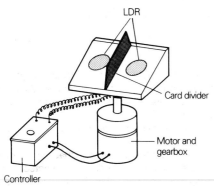

Figure 1

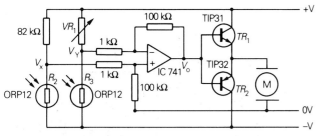

Figure 2

i) Describe what happens when the LDR R_2 is shaded by the card.
ii) What is the function of the variable resistor VR_1?
iii) Why are transistors TR_1 and TR_2 needed?
iv) Derive the relationship between the output potential V_o and the two input potentials V_X and V_Y.

SQA

8 a) Circuit 1 shows an operational amplifier used in the differential mode.

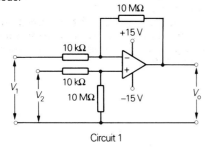

Circuit 1

i) Explain what is meant by the term 'differential mode'.
ii) Calculate the output voltage V_o when $V_1 = 500\,\text{mV}$ and $V_2 = 510\,\text{mV}$.

b) Electrical signals from the heart produce pulses of potential difference of the order of 1 mV between the hands. The body also picks up 50 Hz signals from the mains supply. This mains signal is of the order of 20 mV with respect to earth at both hands and makes the small 1 mV heart signal undetectable. A biological amplifier may be used to reject the mains signal and amplify the heart signal only.

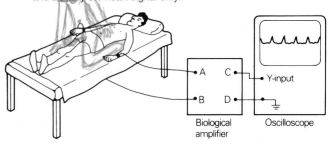

Diagram 2

i) Show how the differential amplifier in Circuit 1 could be connected to A, B, C and D to amplify the heart signals only.
ii) Explain how your circuit works.

SQA

9 a) An ideal operational amplifier has
i) infinite input impedance,
ii) zero output impedance.
Explain why each of these properties is desirable.

b) Figure 1 shows an operational amplifier circuit which uses a ± 15 V supply (not shown).

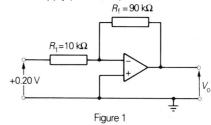

Figure 1

i) What is the purpose of R_f?
ii) Calculate the output voltage V_o for an input voltage of + 0.20 V.
iii) Draw a circuit, using the same components, to illustrate how an input of + 0.20 V can produce an output of + 2.0 V. Show by calculation that the required voltage is obtained.

c) Figure 2 shows the operational amplifier connected in another circuit.

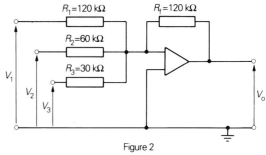

Figure 2

i) Calculate the output voltage V_o when $V_1 = 1\,\text{V}$, $V_2 = 0\,\text{V}$, and $V_3 = 1\,\text{V}$.
ii) The inputs V_1, V_2 and V_3 can be set to either zero or one volt. For appropriate inputs, give the magnitudes of the maximum and minimum output voltages.

SQA

10 **a)** An operational amplifier is used in the circuit as shown. In each case, the amplifier is connected to a power supply with outputs of + 15 V and – 15 V. An a.c. signal of peak voltage 1.0 V is applied to the input.

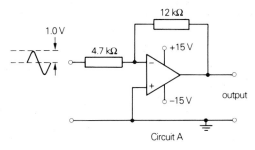

Circuit A

i) How does the phase of the output compare with that of the input?

ii) Calculate the peak output voltage.

iii) Sketch the waveform of the voltage obtained at the output if the input signal remains the same but the gain is changed to 20. Indicate the amplitude of this waveform.

b) An operational amplifier is used in the differential mode, as shown in Circuit B.

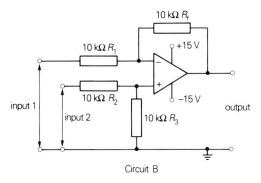

Circuit B

i) What arithmetic operation does this circuit perform?

ii) Calculate the output voltage of Circuit B if the voltage at input 1 is – 0.7 V and the voltage at input 2 is + 3.4 V.

c) The diagram shows the signals received at input 1 (Signal 1) and input 2 (Signal 2) of Circuit B when a microphone is connected to these inputs by means of a long pair of wires.

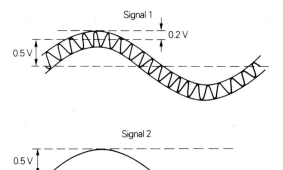

Signal 1 is a sine wave of frequency 1 kHz and amplitude 0.2 V combined with another sine wave of frequency 50 Hz and amplitude 0.5 V. Signal 2 is a sine wave of frequency 50 Hz and amplitude 0.5 V.
Sketch the waveform at the output of Circuit B. Indicate clearly its amplitude and frequency.

d) A temperature sensor has a resistance that varies between 1.0 kΩ at 0°C and 1.6 kΩ at 100° C. It is connected in the bridge circuit shown. The resistance of each of the three fixed resistors in the circuit is 1.0 kΩ.

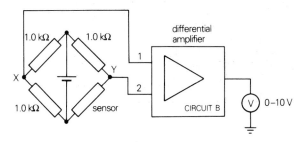

The outputs X and Y of the bridge circuit are connected to inputs 1 and 2 respectively of Circuit B.

i) What is the temperature of the sensor when the potential difference across XY is zero?
In order to change the gain of Circuit B, the values of R_f and R_3 are altered together, so that they remain equal. R_1 and R_2 are unchanged.
When the sensor is placed in boiling water, the potential difference across XY is 0.61 V.

ii) Calculate the values required for R_f and R_3 in Circuit B so that the voltmeter at the output of Circuit B will read 10.0 V. Assume that the values of R_1 and R_2 in Circuit B are unchanged at 10 kΩ.

SQA

Topic 2.4 Test 1

1   How can an op-amp affect a signal?

2   Which of the following circuits shows an op-amp being used in the inverting mode?

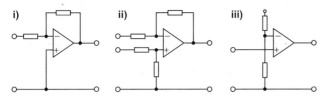

i)   ii)   iii)

3   The diagram below shows the inputs and outputs for an op-amp connected in the inverting mode.

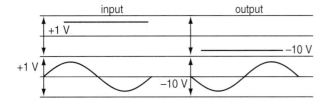

input   output

+1 V

                                    −10 V

+1 V

        −10 V

Describe what has happened to the input signal.

4   For the ideal op-amp in the inverting mode:
   a)   What is the input current?
   b)   What is the p.d. between the inverting and non-inverting inputs?

5   State the inverting mode gain expression for an op-amp.

6   Calculate the gain of this op-amp.

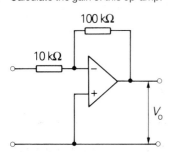

100 kΩ

10 kΩ

V_o

7   A student presents some results 'obtained from this circuit'.

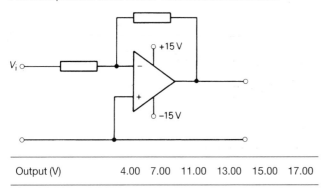

V_i +15 V

                    −15 V

| Output (V) | 4.00 | 7.00 | 11.00 | 13.00 | 15.00 | 17.00 |

Identify any 'suspect' results and explain why they are suspect.

8   Identify the circuit where the op-amp is being used in the differential mode.

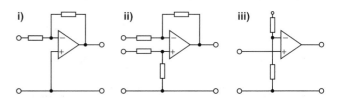

i)   ii)   iii)

9   What potential difference does a differential amplifier amplify?

10   State the differential mode gain expression.

11   Calculate the output voltage for this circuit if each cell provides 1.5 V and $R_2 / R_1 = R_4 / R_3 = 1$.

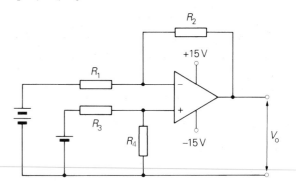

R_2

+15 V

R_1

R_3

R_4 −15 V V_o

12   Describe how this circuit might be used to control an external device.

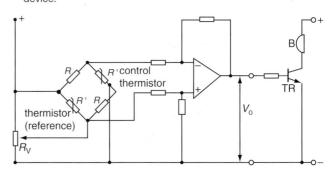

R R'control thermistor

R' R

thermistor (reference)

R_V V_o TR

B

Topic 2.4 Test 2

1 In what way is the voltage of a signal affected by an op-amp?

2 Which of the following circuits shows an op-amp being used in the inverting mode?

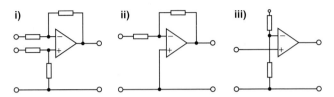

i)   ii)   iii)

3 The diagram below shows the inputs and outputs for an op-amp connected in the inverting mode.

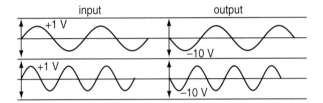

input   output

Describe what has happened to the input signal.

4 For the ideal op-amp in the inverting mode:
  a) How large is the input resistance?
  b) How does the potential of the inverting pin compare with the potential of the non-inverting pin?

5 Which op-amp gain expression is given below?
$$V_o / V_1 = R_f / R_1$$

6 Calculate the gain of this op-amp.

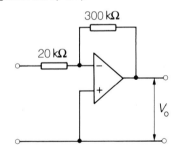

300 kΩ

20 kΩ

V_o

7 A student presents some results 'obtained from this circuit'.

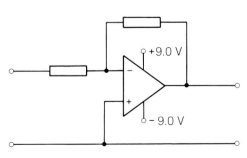

+9.0 V

−9.0 V

Output (V)	4.00	7.00	8.00	9.00	10.00	11.00

Identify any 'suspect' results and explain why they are suspect.

8 Identify the circuit where the op-amp is being used in the differential mode.

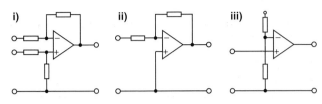

i)   ii)   iii)

9 What potential difference is amplified?

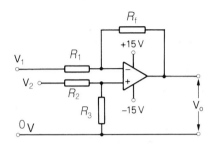

R_f

+15 V

V_1 R_1

V_2 R_2

R_3 −15 V V_o

0 V

10 State the gain expression for the amplifier in the previous question.

11 Calculate the output voltage for this circuit if each cell provides 1.4 V and $R_2 / R_1 = R_4 / R_3 = 2$.

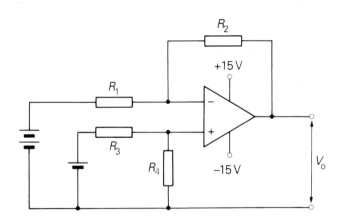

R_2

+15 V

R_1

R_3

R_4 −15 V V_o

12 Describe how this circuit might be used to control an external device.

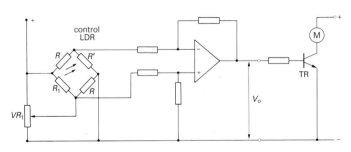

control LDR

R R'

R_1 R

VR_1

M

TR

V_o

Topic 2.4 Test 3

1 Copy and complete the following statement.
'An op-amp can be used to increase the .... of a signal.'

2 Which of the following circuits shows an op-amp being used in the inverting mode?

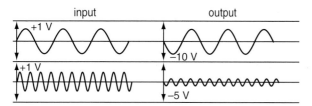

3 The diagram below shows the inputs and outputs for an op-amp connected in the inverting mode.

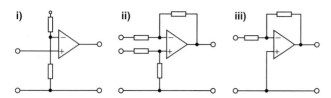

Describe what has happened to the input signal.

4 For the ideal op-amp in the inverting mode:
a) What has infinite resistance?
b) Between which pins is the potential difference zero?

5 Which expression is given below?
$V_o / V_1 = R_f / R_1$

6 Calculate the gain of this op-amp.

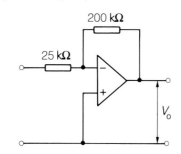

7 A student presents some results 'obtained from this circuit'.

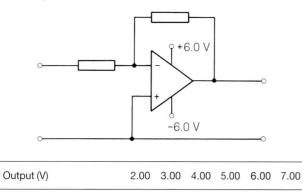

Output (V)	2.00	3.00	4.00	5.00	6.00	7.00

Identify any 'suspect' results and explain why they are suspect.

8 Identify the circuit where the op-amp is being used in the differential mode.

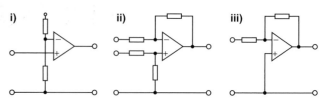

9 What potential difference is amplified?

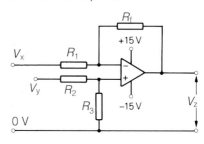

10 State the gain expression for the amplifier in the previous question.

11 Calculate the output voltage for this circuit if each cell provides 1.6 V and $R_2 / R_1 = R_4 / R_3 = 0.5$.

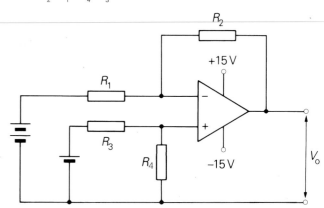

12 Describe how this circuit might be used to control an external device.

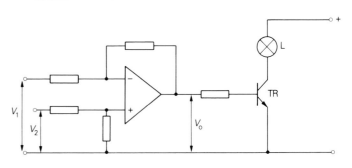

Unit 3
Radiation and Matter

Topics

Topic 3.1
Waves

Objectives

When you have completed the work of this topic you should be able to:

1 state that the frequency of a wave is the same as the frequency of the source producing it;
2 state that the period equals 1/frequency;
3 state that the energy of a wave depends on its amplitude;
4 use correctly, in context, the terms 'in phase', 'out of phase' and 'coherent' when applied to waves;
5 explain the meaning of: 'constructive interference' and 'destructive interference' in terms of the superposition of waves;
6 state that interference is the test for a wave;
7 state that reflection, refraction, diffraction and interference are characteristic behaviours of all types of waves;
8 state the conditions for maxima and minima in an interference pattern formed by two coherent sources in the form:
   path difference = $n \lambda$ for maxima and
   path difference = $(n + \frac{1}{2}) \lambda$ for minima where n is an integer;
9 carry out calculations using the above relationships;
10 describe the effect of a grating on a monochromatic light beam;
11 carry out calculations using the grating equation $d \sin \theta = n \lambda$;
12 describe the principles of a method for measuring the wavelength of a monochromatic light source, using a grating;
13 state approximate values for the wavelengths of red, green and blue light;
14 describe and compare the white light spectra produced by a grating and a prism.

3.1 Waves

Waves and energy

There are many different kinds of waves. One that we all recognize is the **water wave**. When a stone is thrown into a calm pond, waves spread out over the surface, Figure 1.

What is travelling out from the centre of the disturbance? After the waves have passed, the water settles back to its original level, so it is not the water that is travelling out. To answer the question, let us imagine a small piece of wood floating on the pond surface. The piece of wood is seen to vibrate as the wave passes. Since the wave causes the wood to move, it must be supplying energy.

This appears to be the answer to the question. It is **energy** that is travelling out from the centre. It is even more obvious that waves carry energy if we watch waves on the sea, Figure 2.

During stormy weather, the energy carried by the waves has often resulted in great damage, Figure 3.

This energy comes from winds moving over the surface of the sea. Figure 4 is a photograph of a device which can convert wave energy to useful electrical energy.

When we considered the effect of the water wave on the floating piece of wood, we saw that the actual vibrations of the water were in a **vertical** direction, while the energy was transmitted in a **horizontal** direction along the water surface.

A wave in which the vibrations are at right angles to the direction in which the wave is moving is called a **transverse** wave.

Figure 2 Waves smashing against a breakwater

Figure 3 A damaged pier

Figure 1 A circular wave on a pond

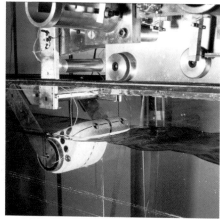

Figure 4 A device for converting wave energy to electricity

Transverse waves and pulses

Transverse waves can be investigated using a long 'slinky' spring stretched out on a bench. One end is held in a fixed position and the other end is moved with your hand, Figure 5.

By moving your hand once from side to side, you would generate what is called a **wave pulse** which would travel down the spring. It can be seen that the actual disturbance is **at right angles** to the direction of the wave pulse.

Another method of showing transverse waves is to use a transverse wave machine, Figure 6.

The beads can be made to move up and down and give the impression that a wave is travelling at right angles to that direction.

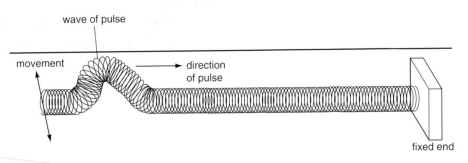

Figure 5   Wave on a 'slinky'

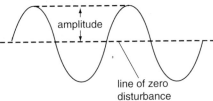

Figure 6   Wave machine

Quantities to describe waves

Various quantities are required to describe waves: they can be investigated using length of rubber tubing on a bench. A travelling wave (often called a **continuous** wave) can be made by holding the tubing and continuously moving your hand from side to side, Figure 7.

Amplitude

The greater the movement of your hand, the more energy is given to the wave and the greater the size of the disturbance which travels down the tubing.
The **amplitude** of a wave is the size of maximum disturbance measured from the zero position, Figure 8. Increasing the amplitude of a wave increases the energy carried by the wave.

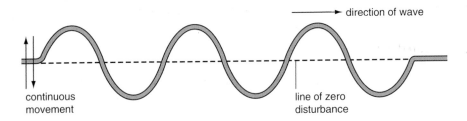

Figure 7   Wave travelling along rubber tubing

Figure 8   Amplitude

Wavelength (symbol λ)

The wave can be seen to repeat itself after a certain distance.

The **wavelength** of a wave is the minimum distance in which a wave repeats itself.

The SI unit for measuring wavelength is the metre (m). Another unit often used is the centimetre (cm). The wavelength may be measured between any two points at which the wave repeats itself, Figure 9.

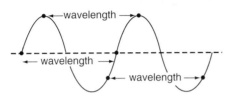

Figure 9 Wavelength

Frequency (symbol *f*)

The faster the movement of your hand, the greater is the number of waves produced in a given time.

The **frequency** of a wave is the number of complete wavelengths produced in one second.

The SI unit for measuring frequency is the hertz (Hz). The word hertz can be thought of as meaning 'per second'. For example if a wave has a frequency of 2 Hz, then two complete wavelengths are produced per second. Hertz was a German physicist who discovered radio waves in 1888. Our unit of frequency is named after him, Figure 10.

Figure 10 Heinrich Hertz

Wave speed (symbol *v*)

The wave travelled along the tubing at a constant speed. The **wave speed** is the distance travelled by the wave in one second.

The SI unit for measuring wave speed is the metre per second (m s^{-1}). Another unit often used is the centimetre per second (cm s^{-1}).

Period (symbol *T*)

If a wave has a frequency of 10 Hz, ten waves are produced every second, the time taken to produce 1 wave is 1/10 second, This time is the 'period' of the wave.

In general terms the period of the wave is given by the equation:

$T = 1/f$

where T is measured in seconds and f is measured in hertz (Hz)

Phase

Let us think about the way the particles of water move in the water wave. First we need two new words, Figure 11. A **crest** is the part of the wave above the line of zero disturbance. A **trough** is the part of the wave below the line of zero disturbance.

Figure 12 represents a wave that has travelled from the position shown by the dotted line to the position shown by the continuous line. The vertical arrows show how the particles at A, B, C, etc. have moved.

Particle A has moved down. Particle F, exactly one wavelength along, has also moved down by exactly the same amount. Particles A and F are said to be **in phase**. Particles B and G are one wavelength apart and have moved up by exactly the same amount so they are also in phase with each other.

Points in a wave separated by a whole wavelength are said to be in phase.

Particle C moved up , while particle E (exactly one half wavelength along) has moved down, but by exactly the same amount. Particles C and E are said to be exactly out of phase. Particles A and D are half a wavelength apart and are also exactly out of phase since particle A has moved down while particle D has moved up by the same amount. Points in a wave separated by half a wavelength are said to be exactly out of phase.

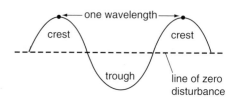

Figure 11 Crests and troughs

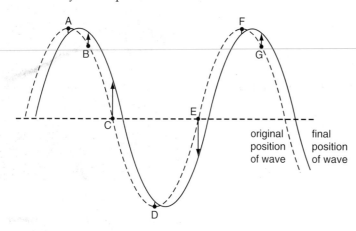

Figure 12 Phase

The term phase is also applied to two overlapping waves. Where the waves are 'in step', the crests of one all coincide with crests of the other and the troughs coincide, the waves are said to be **in phase**, Figure 13. For this to happen the two waves must have exactly the same wavelength and frequency and they are said to be **coherent**. Waves which are 'out of step', so that the crests of one coincide with the troughs of the other, are said to be **out of phase**, Figure 14.

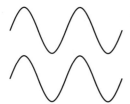

Figure 13 Waves in phase

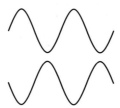

Figure 14 Waves out of phase

Water waves

The properties of waves can be studied by considering the behaviour of water waves because they are easily observed and their wavelengths and frequencies are easily measured. We can use this knowledge to study other forms of wave motion and to explain their behaviour.

The properties of water waves are most easily studied in a ripple tank, Figure 15.

An image of the water wave is produced on the screen underneath the ripple tank. This image is formed by the light shining through the water on to the screen, and consists of a series of bright lines (corresponding to crests), with darker spaces in between (corresponding to troughs).

We can understand how this comes about if we consider how a magnifying glass is used to concentrate the Sun's rays, Figure 16. The curved lens of the magnifying glass bends the rays and brings them to a point. This process is called **focusing**.

Similarly in the ripple tank when the light from the lamp passes throught the water, the curve of the water surface through which a wave is moving acts like a series of lenses and focuses the light to give a series of bright lines, Figure 17.

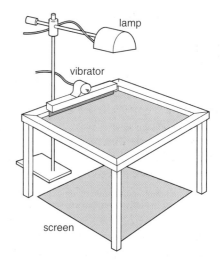

Figure 15 A ripple tank

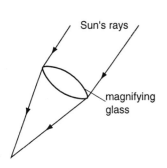

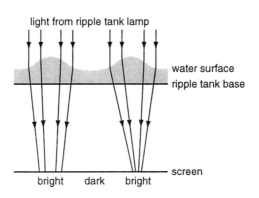

Figure 17

Figure 16 Magnifying glass

Generation of pulses

If a disturbance is created at a point on the surface of the water, a circular pulse travels out from that point. One way of creating such a disturbance is to allow a drop of water to fall on to the surface of the water, Figure 18. As the pulse travels out, it retains its circular shape; the boundary of this shape is called the **wavefront**.

The direction of travel of a pulse is always at right angles to the wavefront. Figure 19 shows a circular wavefront travelling out from O, and the arrows show the direction in which the different parts of the wavefront are travelling.

As a circular pulse spreads out, the circumference of the circle increases, and the amplitude of the wave decreases.

Figure 18 Circular pulse

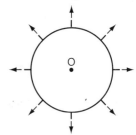

Figure 19 Circular wavefront

If a disturbance is created along a straight line on the surface of the water, a straight pulse is generated. This can be done by dipping a straight object into the water. The straight pulse that is generated continues to move across the surface of the water as a straight line. Again, the direction of travel is at right angles to the wave front, Figure 20.

Reflection of pulses

When a barrier is placed in the path of a pulse, the pulse is reflected. Before it strikes the barrier the pulse is called the **incident pulse**; after it has been reflected the pulse is called the **reflected pulse**.

Figure 21 shows a circular pulse being reflected at a straight barrier. The reflected pulse is also circular in shape, with the centre of the circle at a point behind the barrier. The distance from this point to the barrier equals the distance from the centre of the generated wave to the barrier.

When a straight pulse is reflected from a straight barrier, the reflected pulse is also straight. Such a reflection is illustrated in Figure 22.

The **normal** is the line at right angles to the reflecting surface.

The angle between the path of the incident pulse and the the normal is called the **angle of incidence** ($\angle i$).

The angle between the path of the reflected pulse and the normal is called the **angle of reflection** ($\angle r$).

Whenever a pulse is reflected, it is observed that the angle of incidence is always equal to the angle of reflection. This is called the **Law of Reflection** $\angle i = \angle r$.

Figure 23 shows two examples of straight pulses being reflected by curved barriers.

Figure 20 Straight pulses

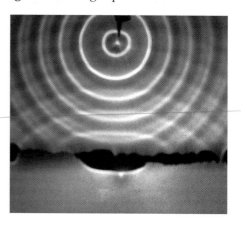

Figure 21 Circular pulses

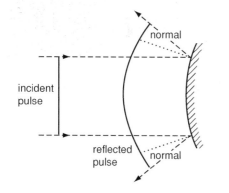

Figure 23

a) Reflection at a convex barrier   **b)** Reflection at a concave barrier

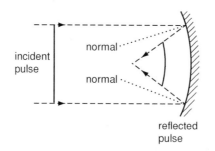

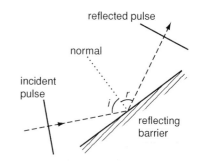

Figure 22

Generation of continuous waves

Figure 24 shows an apparatus that can be used to generate continuous circular waves. As the electric motor rotates, it causes the bar to vibrate; these vibrations cause the dipper to move up and down in the water. The vibrations at a single point on the surface of the water generate a series of pulses which make up a continuous circular wave.

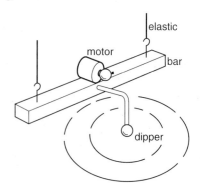

Figure 24

If the whole length of the bar is dipping in the water (Figure 25), the energy from the rotation of the motor is transmitted to the water along the length of the bar. This generates a series of straight pulses that make up a continuous straight wave.

'Stopping' the wave pattern

It is difficult to observe and measure waves that are continuously on the move. One way of 'stopping' or 'freezing' the wave, when we wish to make observations, is to take a photograph and study it. In the laboratory we use a hand stroboscope to 'stop' the wave pattern. The hand stroboscope (Figure 26) consists of a disc with slits in it at regularly spaced intervals. If the disc is rotated in front of your eye, the scene appears whenever a slit is passing the eye but it is blocked for the rest of the time. If the stroboscope is rotated at a steady rate, you see the scene as a series of pictures separated by fixed time intervals.

Figure 27 shows how the stroboscope can 'stop' the wave pattern. Of course the wave does not actually stop, but to the observer it does appear to be stationary.

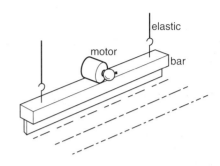

Figure 25

Figure 26 Hand stroboscope

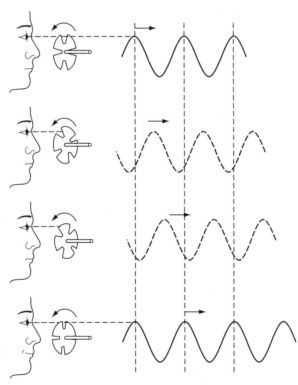

You can see the wave as a slit passes your eye

You can't see anything. Your view is blocked

You still can't see

The next slit arrives and you can see again. It looks the same as it did before. There was a crest there last time.

Figure 27

If the frequency of the series of pictures seen by the observer is such that, whenever he sees the wave, there is a crest in the same position, the observer will see the wave standing still.

Using the ripple tank and the wave generator, we can now generate continuous waves and investigate their behaviour. In some cases it will be easier to make observations if we 'stop' the wave pattern by viewing it through a hand stroboscope. The word 'stroboscope' is often abbreviated to 'strobe'.

Properties of continuous wave

Reflection

A continuous wave consists of a series of pulses. Whenever a pulse is reflected, it obeys the Law of Reflection (Figure 22):

the angle of incidence = the angle of reflection

$$\angle i = \angle r$$

It can be observed that the wavelength does not change when the waves are reflected, Figure 28. Any stroboscope frequency which will 'stop' the incident waves will also stop the reflected waves. This indicates that both the incident waves and the reflected waves have the same frequency.

The wave speed v is also unchanged by reflection. This must be true if both the frequency f and the wavelength λ are unchanged, since the wave equation tells us that $v = f \times \lambda$

Figure 29 shows a straight pulse being reflected by a curved barrier. Again, v, f and λ are unchanged on reflection.

Diffraction

When water waves pass the edge of an obstacle, they bend around the edge. This bending around corners is called **diffraction**, Figure 30.

When a water wave passes an obstacle of **less** than one wavelength in width, the wavefronts are not affected by the obstacle, Figure 31(a). When the width of the obstacle is **greater** than one **wavelength**, the wavefronts do bend around each edge, but do not immediately join up to form the original wavefronts, Figure 31(b).

A gap has two edges, and we have just noted that a wave will bend around an edge. As you can see from Figure 32, waves spread out after passing through a gap. The narrower the gap, the greater is the spreading out of the wave. The narrowest gap results in a circular wave pattern. In fact, whenever the width of the gap is less than one wavelength, the diffracted wavefronts are circular, Figure 32(c).

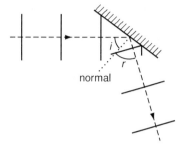

Figure 28

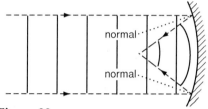

Figure 29

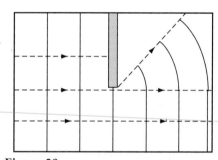

Figure 30

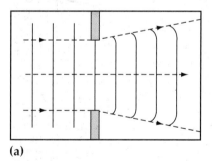

(a)

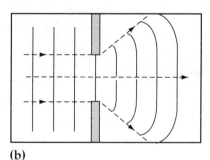

(b)

Figure 32

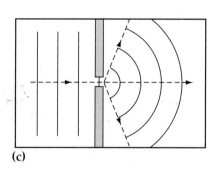

(c)

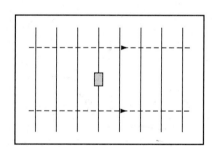

Figure 31(a)

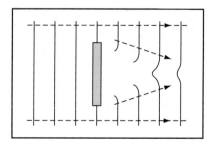

Figure 31(b)

A low frequency wave (longer wavelength) is bent more than a high frequency wave (shorter wavelength) at the edge of an obstacle. This is shown in Figure 33 in which the low frequency wave (a) is diffracted more than the high frequency wave (b).

We may also note that diffraction causes:

a) no change in wavelength (an observed fact);

b) no change in frequency (a strobe frequency that 'stops' the incident wave also 'stops' the diffracted wave);

c) no change in wave speed (because $v \times f\lambda$ and neither wavelength nor frequency change).

Figure 33
(a) Low frequency wave

(b) High frequency wave

Interference

Interference of waves can be demonstrated with water waves in a ripple tank. An interference pattern is produced by two overlapping circular wave patterns from coherent sources, Figure 34. Coherent sources generate waves of identical frequencies.

Two coherent sources of circular wave patterns can be produced by passing a plane wave through two narrow slits. If the width of each slit is less than the wavelength of the wave, two circular wave patterns are produced by diffraction of the wave by the slits.

Figure 34 shows the interference pattern with lines drawn along areas of uniform illumination. This uniform illumination means that, along these lines, the water is calm.

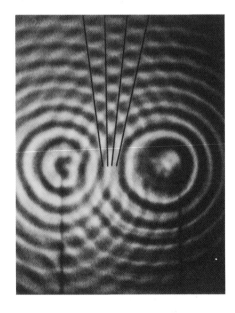

Figure 35 Lines of calm in an interference pattern

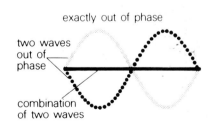

Figure 36 Destructive interference

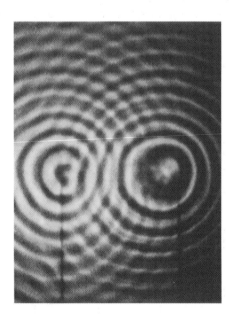

Figure 34 Interference of water waves

These are lines along which destructive interference occurs. This results from the waves being half a wavelength out of phase and cancelling each other out, Figure 36.

Figure 37 shows the interference pattern with lines drawn along areas where the illumination is alternately bright and dark, showing that the water surface has a series of crests and troughs.

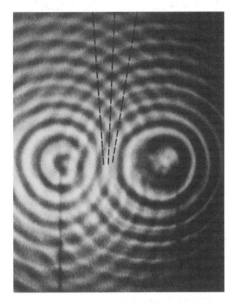

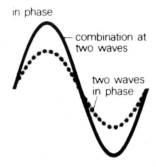

Figure 37 Lines of crests and troughs in an interference pattern

Figure 38 Constructive interference

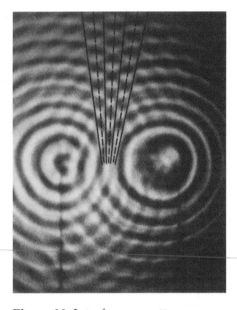

Figure 39 Interference pattern

These are lines along which constructive interference occurs. This results from the waves being in phase and combining to give a wave of greater amplitude, Figure 38.

Thus the interference pattern consists of a series of lines of constructive interference and destructive interference which means that these lines are lines of maximum and minimum wave amplitude, Figure 39.

Young's slits experiment

Young demonstrated the interference of light by splitting a narrow beam of sunlight into two beams. He allowed sunlight to pass through a small hole made by piercing a card with a needle. Across the small hole he placed a very thin card, edge on, to divide the beam of light into two narrow beams. When he did this, Young observed a series of bright and dark lines on the wall opposite. These lines are known as interference fringes, the bright lines being produced by constructive interference and the dark lines resulting from destructive interference.

A similar experiment may be repeated in the laboratory to demonstrate the interference of light. Two narrow slits, very close together, are prepared by using a pin point to scratch two fine lines across a glass slide which has been painted black, Figure 40. Light is passed through these slits and is viewed on a screen, Figure 41.

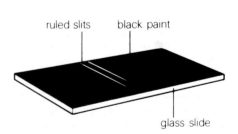

Figure 40 Preparation of glass slide for Young's slits experiment

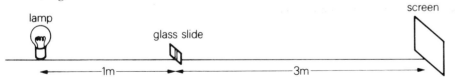

Figure 41 Apparatus to demonstrate the Young's slits experiment

A series of fringes is observed on the screen. With a white light source, the central fringe is white but the other fringes have coloured edges. Interference patterns for different colours of light are produced by inserting different filters between the lamp and the glass slide. When this is done, it is observed that the spacing of the fringes varies with the colour of light. The fringes for light nearer the red end of the spectrum are further apart than fringes for light nearer the blue end of the spectrum. Red light has a longer wavelength than blue light and longer wavelengths produce maxima which are more widely spaced, Figure 42.

When glass slides with slits of different separation are used, the spacing of the fringes is found to depend on the separation of the slits. The fringes are more widely spaced when the slits are closer together, Figure 43.

Another factor which affects the fringe separation is the distance from the slits to the screen. If the screen is moved further from the slits, the fringe separation increases.

The factors found experimentally to affect the fringe separation are listed below.
a) Red light produces fringes of greater separation than those produced by blue light.
b) Smaller slit separation produces greater fringe separation.
c) Greater distance between the screen and the slits produces greater fringe separation.

The way in which fringes are produced can be explained by considering two rays from the slits S_1 and S_2 to the point X on the screen as shown in Figure 44.

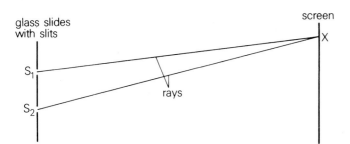

Figure 44 Two rays from the slits to a point on the screen

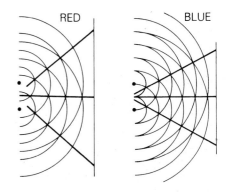

Figure 42 Interference patterns for waves of different wavelengths

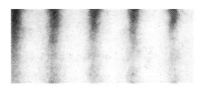

(a) Slits close together

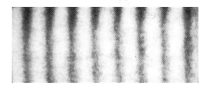

(b) Slits further apart

Figure 43 Effect of slit separation on fringe spacing

The ray from S_1 has travelled a shorter distance S_1X to the screen than the distance S_2X travelled by the ray from slit S_2.

The difference between these two distances is called the **path difference.**

If the path difference is equal to zero or a whole number of wavelengths, the waves will arrive **in phase**, and constructive interference will occur producing a bright fringe, Figure 45. Here the solid lines in the waves indicate wave fronts which left the slits at the same time.

For a path difference of a whole number of wavelengths a bright fringe (maximum brightness) is formed,

path difference = $n\lambda$ for maxima   where n is zero or an integer.

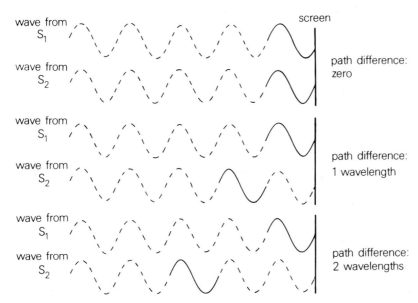

Figure 45 Waves from the two slits arriving in phase

Thus, for a path difference $(S_2X - S_1X)$ of zero or a whole number of wavelengths, a **bright** fringe is formed when

$$S_2X - S_1X = n\lambda \qquad \text{where } n = 0,1,2,3\ldots$$

$$\Rightarrow \qquad \frac{xd}{D} = n\lambda$$

$$\Rightarrow \qquad x = \frac{n\lambda D}{d} \qquad \ldots [1]$$

The centre of the interference pattern is where $x = 0$ and $n = 0$.

The first bright fringe away from the centre is that for which $n = 1$

$$x = \frac{\lambda D}{d}$$

For the next fringe, $n = 2$ $x = \frac{2\lambda D}{d}$

The locations of fringes are summarized in Table 1.

From the table it can be seen that, for successive fringes, the distance from the centre of the pattern increases by $\lambda D/d$. Thus the distance Δx between the fringes in the interference pattern produced by Young's slits is given by

$$\Delta x = \frac{\lambda D}{d} \qquad \text{where } \lambda = \text{wavelength of the light}$$

$$D = \text{distance from slits to screen}$$

$$d = \text{distance between slits}$$

fringe	n	path difference	distance x from the centre of the pattern
central	0	0	0
1st	1	λ	$\dfrac{\lambda D}{d}$
2nd	2	2λ	$\dfrac{2\lambda D}{d}$
3rd	3	3λ	$\dfrac{3\lambda D}{d}$
nth	n	$n\lambda$	$\dfrac{n\lambda D}{d}$

Table 1 Location of bright fringes

White light consists of a mixture of light of different wavelengths or colours. From Table 1 it can be seen that the only fringe position that does not depend on wavelength is that for the central fringe. It is for this reason that, when using a white light source, the central fringe does not have coloured edges. For the other fringes the location depends on the wavelength, longer wavelengths producing fringes that are more widely spaced. This is why, for fringes other than the central fringe, the colours separate out and the fringes have coloured edges.

Dark bands in an interference pattern are formed by destructive interference between the light from the two different slits S_1 and S_2. Destructive interference occurs when two waves are **out of phase** and this occurs when the path difference between the two rays from the slits is equal to an odd number of half wavelengths, Figure 46.

For a path difference of an odd number of half wavelengths a dark band (minimum brightness) is formed,

$$\text{path difference} = (n + \tfrac{1}{2})\lambda \qquad \text{for minima} \qquad \text{where } n \text{ is zero or an integer.}$$

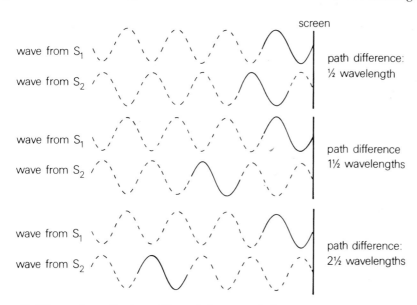

Figure 46 Waves from the two slits arriving out of phase

Example 1

In a Young's slits experiment, the distance from the slits to the screen is 4.0 m and the distance between the centres of the slits is 0.50 mm.

a) Find the fringe spacing for (i) violet light of wavelength 4.0×10^{-7} m; (ii) red light of wavelength 7.0×10^{-7} m.

b) Find the distance from the centre of the interference pattern to the fifth red fringe.

a) The fringe spacing is given by the equation

$$\Delta x = \frac{\lambda D}{d}$$

i) $\lambda = 4.0 \times 10^{-7}$ m for violet
   $D = 4.0$ m
   $d = 0.50 \times 10^{-3}$ m

$$\Rightarrow \Delta x = \frac{4 \times 10^{-7} \times 4}{0.5 \times 10^{-3}} \Rightarrow \Delta x = 3.2 \times 10^{-3}$$

For violet light the fringe spacing is 3.2 mm.

ii) $\lambda = 7.0 \times 10^{-7}$ m for red light
   $D = 4.0$ m
   $d = 0.50 \times 10^{-3}$ m

$$\Rightarrow \Delta x = \frac{7 \times 10^{-7} \times 4}{0.5 \times 10^{-3}} \Rightarrow \Delta x = 5.6 \times 10^{-3}$$

For red light the fringe spacing is 5.6 mm.

b) The distance of the nth slit from the centre of the interference pattern is given by

$$x = \frac{n\lambda D}{d} \qquad \text{and} \qquad \Delta x = \frac{\lambda D}{d}$$

$$\Rightarrow x = n\Delta x$$

for red light $\Delta x = 5.6 \times 10^{-3}$ m   for the fifth fringe $n = 5$

Distance of the fifth fringe from the centre of the interference pattern is given by

$$\Rightarrow x = 5 \times 5.6 \times 10^{-3} \Rightarrow x = 28.0 \times 10^{-3} \text{ m}$$

Distance from centre of interference pattern to 5th fringe is 28.0 mm.

Coloured fringes

White light contains the range of colours in light from violet with a wavelength of 4×10^{-7} m to red light with a wavelength of 7×10^{-7} m. When Young's slits experiment is carried out with white light, multicoloured fringes are formed. How this comes about can be illustrated by producing fringes with light of two different colours. Figure 47 is drawn to scale and shows the relative fringe positions for two different colours. The conditions for maxima and minima depend on the number of wavelengths in the path difference for the two rays. Because the wavelengths of red and blue light are different, the separation for the maxima and minima of each colour will be different.

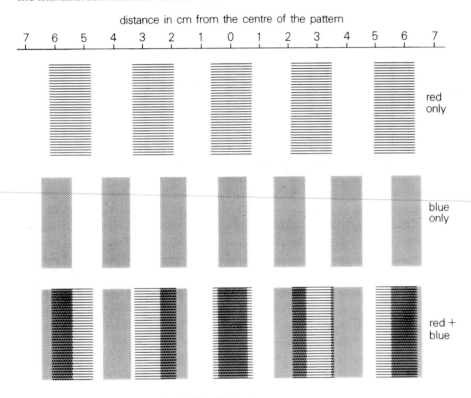

Figure 47 Fringes for red and blue light

Multiple slit interference

When light was passed through two very narrow slits, the amount of light energy passing through was small and the interference fringes were not very bright. A brighter pattern can be obtained by using a greater number of slits.

In Young's experiment we consider rays from the two slits and how they interfere when they meet at the screen. Since the distance d between the slits (less than 10^{-3} m) is very small compared with the distance D from the slits to the screen (usually several metres), two rays to any point on the screen will be effectively parallel, Figure 48.

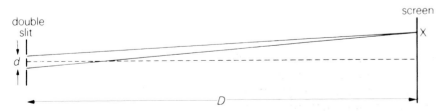

Figure 48 Two rays from the slits to a point on the screen

The condition for constructive interference is that the path difference between these rays is a whole number of wavelengths. For the first fringe away from the centre of the pattern, the path difference between the rays is one wavelength, Figure 49.

When this is the case, the waves in the two rays arrive in phase at the screen, Figure 50, and they produce a bright fringe by constructive interference.

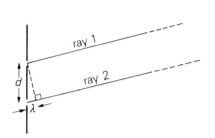

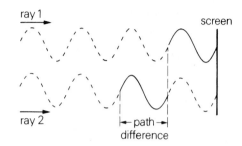

Figure 49 Path difference for first fringe away from the centre of the pattern

Figure 50 Two waves with a path difference of one wavelength

Consider now what happens when a third slit is introduced at a distance d from one of the other slits. Again, because D is very large compared with d, the rays from the slits to a point on the screen will be effectively parallel. If the path difference between ray 1 and ray 2 is 1λ, the path difference between ray 2 and ray 3 will also be 1λ, Figure 51.

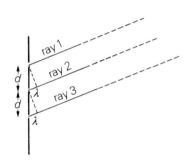

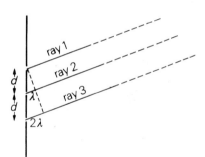

Figure 51 Rays from three slits to a point on the screen

Figure 52 Path differences between rays 2 and 3 and ray 1

Figure 53 Three waves arriving in phase

This means that the path difference between ray 1 and ray 3 is 2λ, Figure 52, and the wave in ray 3 will also arrive in phase with ray 1, Figure 53.

Thus the addition of a third slit has the effect of adding further to the constructive interference producing the bright fringe. The location of the fringe is the same as it was for two slits but it will now be brighter.

The argument can be extended for any number of slits providing they are all equally spaced.

Diffraction grating

The **diffraction grating** is the best and most useful example of a multiple slit used for producing an interference pattern. The diffraction grating is made by a machine cutting very fine, equally spaced grooves on the surface of a glass plate. The light is diffracted by this series of grooves. Normal diffraction gratings may have between 10 000 and 20 000 lines per inch (about 400 to 800 lines per mm).

Diffraction grating and the spectrometer

The spectrometer is an instrument which uses either a prism or a diffraction grating to separate light into its different colours. Figure 54 shows a photograph of a spectrometer and Figure 55 shows a diagram of how it is set up using a diffraction grating.

Figure 54 Spectrometer

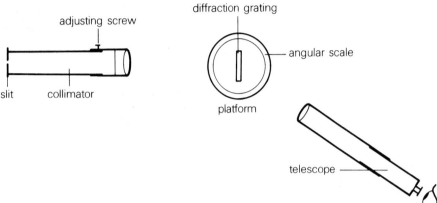

Figure 55 Spectrometer with diffraction grating

The **collimator** is used to form a narrow beam of parallel light. A lamp is placed near the slit in the collimator. The length of the collimator is adjusted so that the slit falls in the focal plane of the collimator lens and this results in the light from the slit emerging as parallel rays from the collimator lens. In practice the telescope is first focused on a distant object so as to receive parallel rays. The telescope is then lined up on the collimator and the collimator length is adjusted until a clear sharp image of the slit is observed through the telescope. Since the telescope is adjusted to focus on parallel rays, the fact that the slit is sharply focused shows that the light emerging from the collimator consists of parallel rays.

Once the collimator and telescope have been adjusted in this way, the diffraction grating or prism is placed on the platform. The angular scale on the platform is used for two purposes: first in setting the platform position so that the grating is at right angles to the beam of light from the collimator, and secondly to measure the angle between the telescope and this beam of light from the collimator.

With the interference pattern produced on a screen, the measurements made on the pattern were on fringe positions and spacings. With the spectrometer, the measurements made are the angles between the beams of light forming the fringes. A simple illustration of this is given in Figure 56.

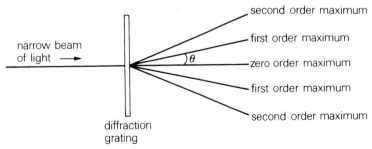

Figure 56 Measurements of angles between maxima

An equation can be derived to relate the path difference S_2N between rays from two slits to the distance d between the two slits and the angle θ through which the rays are being diffracted, Figure 57.

In the triangle, $\quad S_1\hat{N}S_2 = 90°$

$$S_1\hat{S}_2N + S_2\hat{S}_1N = 90°$$

$$S_1\hat{S}_2N + \theta = 90° \text{ (angle between the grating and the normal)}$$

$$S_2\hat{S}_1N = \theta$$

In Figure 58 the distance S_2N is the path difference between the two rays. The triangle S_1S_2N is shown in Figure 58 with the path difference S_2N, the distance d between the two slits, and the angle θ.

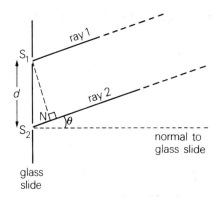

Figure 57 Path difference and angle of diffraction

From Figure 58

$$\sin\theta = \frac{\text{path difference}}{d}$$

$\Rightarrow$ path difference $= d\sin\theta$

The condition for constructive interference is:

$\qquad$ path difference $= n\lambda \qquad$ where $n = 0,1,2,3,\ldots$

$\Rightarrow \qquad\qquad d\sin\theta = n\lambda$

$\Rightarrow \qquad\qquad \sin\theta = \dfrac{n\lambda}{d}$

For constructive interference:

$$\sin\theta = \frac{n\lambda}{d}$$

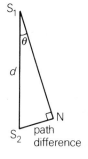

θ = angle of diffraction
n = order of the maximum
λ = wavelength of the light
d = distance between the centres of the slits

Figure 58 Path difference between two rays

While this equation has been derived for two slits, it has already been shown that the same conditions apply for any number of slits providing they are equally spaced.

A spectrometer is usually used to measure the wavelength of light; d is known for the grating and the angle θ is measured: θ is the angle through which the telescope is rotated in going from the central maximum ($n = 0$) to the first order maximum ($n = 1$). This angle is greater for light of longer wavelengths, Figure 59.

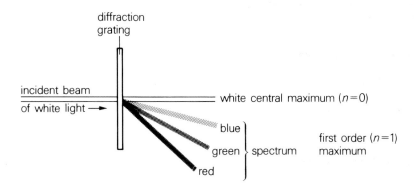

Figure 59 First order maxima for different colours

For the central maximum, $n = 0$

$$\Rightarrow \quad \sin \theta = 0$$
$$\Rightarrow \quad \quad \theta = 0$$

This is independent of wavelength, and is therefore the same for light of all wavelengths. Thus, if the incident beam is white light, the central maximum will be white.

For the first order maximum

$$\sin \theta = \frac{n\lambda}{d} \text{ where } n = 1$$

The wavelength, λ_b of blue light is less than the wavelength λ_r of red light.

For blue light the first order maximum will be at an angle θ_b such that

$$\sin \theta_b = \frac{\lambda_b}{d}$$

For red light the first order maximum will be at an angle θ_r such that

$$\sin \theta_r = \frac{\lambda_r}{d}$$

$$\lambda_b < \lambda_r$$
$$\Rightarrow \sin \theta_b < \sin \theta_r$$
$$\Rightarrow \quad \theta_b < \theta_r$$

Example 2

A parallel beam of white light consisting of light of wavelengths from 4×10^{-7} m (violet) to 7×10^{-7} m (red), is passed through a diffraction grating of 10,000 lines per inch (1 inch = 2.54 cm).

Describe the first order maximum and calculate the angle between the extremes of that maximum.

The first order maximum will be a spectrum of colours ranging from violet nearer the central fringe to red at the outer limit.

diffraction grating has 10000 lines per 2.54 cm

distance between the lines $= \dfrac{2.54}{10000}$ cm

$$d = 2.54 \times 10^{-4} \text{ cm}$$
$$d = 2.54 \times 10^{-6} \text{ m}$$

For the first order maximum $\quad \sin \theta = \dfrac{\lambda}{d}$

For violet $\quad \quad \lambda_v = 4 \times 10^{-7}$

$$\Rightarrow \quad \sin \theta_v = \frac{4 \times 10^{-7}}{2.54 \times 10^{-6}}$$
$$\Rightarrow \quad \sin \theta_v = 0.157$$
$$\Rightarrow \quad \quad \theta_v = 9.1°$$

For red $\quad \quad \lambda_r = 7 \times 10^{-7}$

$$\Rightarrow \quad \sin \theta_r = \frac{7 \times 10^{-7}}{2.54 \times 10^{-6}}$$
$$\Rightarrow \quad \sin \theta_r = 0.276$$
$$\Rightarrow \quad \quad \theta_r = 16.0°$$

$$\Rightarrow \quad \theta_r - \theta_v = 16.0 - 9.1$$
$$\Rightarrow \quad \theta_r - \theta_v = 6.9°$$

The angle between the extremes of the first order maximum is 6.9°.

Units for wavelength

As for any length of distance, the SI unit for wavelength is the metre. However, the wavelength of light is very small, ranging through visible spectrum from about 4×10^{-7} m for blue light to 7×10^{-7} m for red light. Other smaller units are often used to express wavelengths of light and other electromagnetic radiations with small wavelengths. Three commonly used units are the micron (μ), the ångström (Å) and the nanometre (nm).

$$1 \mu = 10^{-6}\,m \qquad 1\,Å = 10^{-10}\,m \qquad 1\,nm = 10^{-9}\,m$$

Example 3

A lamp gives off an intense monochromatic green light. When passed through a diffraction grating with 18 000 lines per inch, this light gives a first order maximum at an angle of 23°.

a) What is the wavelength of the light?
b) Express this wavelength in nanometres, ångströms and microns.

a) For the first order maximum, $\qquad \sin\theta = \dfrac{\lambda}{d}$

The grating has 18 000 lines per 2.54 cm

$$d = \frac{2.54 \times 10^{-2}}{18\,000} = 1.4 \times 10^{-6}$$

$$\Rightarrow \quad \sin 23° = \frac{\lambda}{1.4 \times 10^{-6}}$$

$$\Rightarrow \quad \lambda = 1.4 \times 10^{-6}\sin 23° = 1.4 \times 10^{-6} \times 0.39 = 5.46 \times 10^{-7}$$

Wavelength of the light = 5.46×10^{-7}m.

b)
$$\lambda = 5.46 \times 10^{-7}\,m$$
$$\Rightarrow \quad \lambda = 546 \times 10^{-9}\,m$$
$$\Rightarrow \quad \lambda = 546\,nm$$
$$\Rightarrow \quad \lambda = 5460 \times 10^{-10}\,m \qquad \Rightarrow \quad \lambda = 5460\,Å$$
$$\Rightarrow \quad \lambda = 0.546 \times 10^{-6}\,m \qquad \Rightarrow \quad \lambda = 0.546\,\mu$$

Formation of spectra

A diffraction grating can be used to split light into separate colours and this is the result of an interference pattern being formed. A prism may also be used to split light into separate colours. The prism refracts different colours by different amounts. A prism can be used in place of the diffraction grating on a spectrometer.

With a diffraction grating, it is light of longer wavelength that is seen to make a greater angle with the path of the incident ray. This is because the fringe spacing of the interference pattern is greater for longer wavelengths. With a prism, it is the light with the shorter wavelength that makes the greater angle because light of shorter wavelength is refracted more.

X-ray diffraction

Light produces an interference pattern when it passes through a diffraction grating. The spacing between the lines of the grating is of the same order of magnitude as the wavelength of light. The spacing between atoms in a solid is of the same order of magnitude as the wavelength of X-rays. X-rays, like light, are part of the electromagnetic spectrum, but they have a shorter wavelength than light. When X-rays are passed through a crystalline solid, a diffraction pattern is formed, Figure 60, and this pattern can be analysed to give information about the arrangement and spacing of the atoms in the solid.

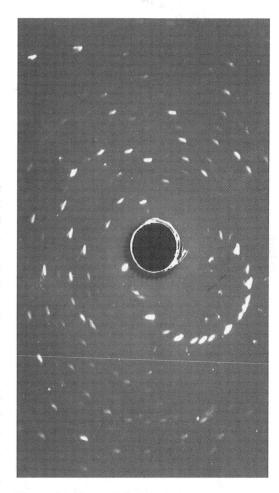

Figure 60 X-ray diffraction pattern

Summary

The frequency of a wave is the same as the frequency of the source producing it.

The period of a wave equals 1/frequency.

The amplitude of a wave is the size of the maximum disturbance, measured from the line of zero displacement.

The energy of a wave depends on its amplitude.

Points in a wave separated by a whole wavelength are in phase.

Points in a wave separated by half a wavelength are exactly out of phase.

Two sources are coherent if they have the same frequency and are in phase with each other or have a constant phase difference.

When light is passed through two very narrow slits very close together (Young's slits), it forms an interference pattern.

When two coherent waves overlap constructive interference occurs where the waves are in phase and destructive interference occurs where the waves are exactly out of phase.

In an interference pattern:
   path difference = $n\lambda$ for a maximum
   path difference = $(n + \frac{1}{2})\lambda$ for a minimum
where $n = 0$ or an integer.

The property of interference is the test for a wave.

A diffraction grating consists of a large number of fine, equally spaced, parallel grooves on the surface of a glass plate and produces an interference pattern similar to that of two slits, but of greater brightness.

For a diffraction grating the angle θ through which the rays are diffracted is given by the equation
   $\sin\theta = n\lambda/d$ where n = order of the maximum
                                     λ = wavelength of the light
                                     d = distance between the centre of the slits.

Common units for the wavelengths of light are:
   1 micron (μ) $=10^{-6}$ m
   1 ångstrom (Å) $=10^{-10}$ m
   1 nanometre (nm) $=10^{-9}$ m

The approximate wavelengths for different colours of visible light are:
   red: 7×10^{-7} m;   green: 5×10^{-7} m;   blue: 4×10^{-7} m

Both prisms and diffraction gratings can produce spectra from white light. With a prism, the blue end of the spectrum is bent most. With a diffraction grating, the red end of the spectrum is further from the centre.

Questions

1   The diagram gives a full-scale representation of the water waves in a ripple tank one second after the vibrator was started. The dark lines represent crests.

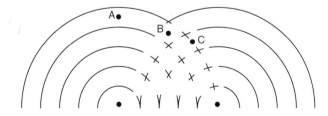

a)   What is represented at A at this instant?
b)   Estimate:
   i) the wavelength;
   ii) the speed of the waves;
   iii) the frequency of the vibrator.
c)   Sketch a suitable attachment which could have been vibrated up and down to produce this wave pattern.
d)   Explain how the waves combine:
   i) at B;
   ii) at C.

2   Which are diffracted least: waves of shorter wavelength or waves of longer wavelength? How does this account for the fact that it was some time before people would accept Huygens' wave theory of light?

3   At the start of the eighteenth century there were two main theories of the nature of light: the Wave Theory and the Corpuscular Theory. What was the experimental evidence, demonstrated by Thomas Young, which strongly supported the Wave Theory?
Explain, with the aid of a diagram, how you would set up apparatus to demonstrate this experimental evidence in the laboratory.

4   A spectrometer has a collimator, a telescope and a platform on which a prism or a diffraction grating is mounted.
State briefly what is the function of:
   a)   the collimator;
   b)   the telescope;
   c)   the prism or diffraction grating.

5   In an experiment to demonstrate the interference of light, red light was passed through two narrow slits ruled in black paint on a glass slide. A pattern of red interference fringes was produced on a screen.

SQA

State what effect each of the following changes would have on the spacing between the interference fringes:

a) Replacing the red light source by a blue light source.

b) Replacing the glass slide by another on which the two narrow slits are closer together.

c) Increasing the distance between the screen and the glass slide.

6 White light can be separated to form a continuous spectrum by passing it through a spectrometer using either a prism or a diffraction grating on the platform. What is the main difference between the angles at which the different colours are observed when using a prism or a diffraction grating?

7 Express the following lengths in metres:
   a) 0.7μ;   **b)** 25.0μ;   **c)** 7000 Å;   **d)** 400 nm.

8 What is 6.6×10^{-7} m when expressed in:
   a) microns;   **b)** nanometres;   **c)** ångstroms?

9 Why are X-rays rather than light used to produce a diffraction pattern of a crystalline solid?

10 A laser is a device which produces a narrow beam of monochromatic light. One type of laser produces red light. Light from this laser is allowed to strike a blackened glass plate on which there are two narrow parallel slits. The light emerging from the slits is viewed on a screen placed a distance from the slits as shown in Figure 1.

On viewing the screen a series of equally spaced fringes is observed, Figure 2.

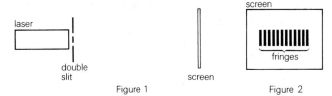

Figure 1

Figure 2

a) Explain how the fringe pattern is produced.

b) Suggest how the pattern observed on the screen would be affected if:

   i) blue light from a second laser replaced the beam of red light;

   ii) the beam of red light was allowed to shine on a pair of slits tapering as shown in Figure 3, the beam being gradually moved from X to Y.

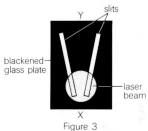

Figure 3

SQA

Topic 3.1 Test 1

1   A student sends waves down a rope by moving the end of the rope from side to side two times per second.
What is the frequency of the wave produced in the rope?

2   Write an equation which relates *f*, the frequency of a wave, to *T*, its period.

3   A wave is produced by a dipper vibrating in water. If the energy of the vibrations is increased, without changing the frequency, what change will be observed in the wave?

4   If two waves are produced from coherent sources, what will the waves have in common?

5   In each of the following cases, state whether the waves are 'in phase' or 'out of phase'.
   a) Two waves of equal frequency overlap so that the troughs of one coincide with the troughs of the other.
   b) Two waves of equal wavelength overlap so that the crests of one overlap with the crests of the other.
   c) Two waves of equal frequency overlap so that the crests of one overlap with the troughs of the other.

6 a) When two overlapping waves are in phase, they combine. How does each of the following quantities of the resulting wave compare with the original waves:
      i) wavelength;
      ii) frequency;
      iii) amplitude?
   b) When two overlapping waves are out of phase, they combine. How does each of the following quantities of the resulting wave compare with the original waves:
      i) wavelength;
      ii) frequency;
      iii) amplitude?
   c) Which of the above cases describes 'constructive interference' and which describes 'destructive interference'?

7 a) Which of the following are characteristic behaviours of waves: reflection; transition; interference; refraction; diffraction; deletion; deference?
   b) Which of these is the test for a wave?

8   When two coherent sources of waves produce an interference pattern, what is the relationship between the wavelength and the path difference to a
   a) maximum in the interference pattern;
   b) minimum in the interference pattern?

9   P is a point in an interference pattern produced by waves from two coherent sources X and Y.

The wavelength of the wave is 2 cm and the distance YP is 20 cm. In each of the following cases, state whether P will be the position of a maximum or a minimum when the distance XP is:
   a) 26 cm   d) 21 cm
   b) 23 cm   e) 22 cm
   c) 29 cm

10

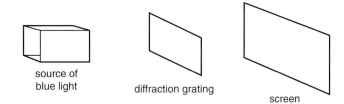

source of blue light   diffraction grating   screen

When a beam of blue light is projected through a diffraction grating on to a screen, describe what would be seen on the screen.

11   Using a spectrometer, light of wavelength 7.0×10^{-7} m is passed through a diffraction grating with 500 lines per mm. What is the angle between the first order maximum and the second order maximum?

12   Describe how you would use a grating to measure the wavelength of light from a monochromatic light source. Your description should state what measurements would be made and what equation would be used.

13   What are the approximate values for the wavelengths of red, green and blue light?

14

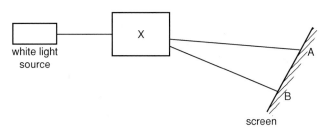

white light source   X   A   B   screen

The apparatus is used to produce a spectrum on the screen, first with a prism in 'X' and then with a grating in 'X'. In each case, describe what would be seen on the screen as you move from A to B.

Topic 3.1 Test 2

1 A dipper dips in and out of water five times every second and sends waves across the surface. What is the frequency of the waves?

2 If a wave has a frequency of 10 Hz, what is its period?

3 Which of the following will increase when the energy of a wave increases:
a) wavelength;
b) period;
c) amplitude?

4 What is the name given to two waves that are generated with exactly the same frequency and wavelength?

5 Draw sketches to show:
a) two waves that are in phase;
b) two waves that are out of phase.

6 Complete the following table with one of the following words in each box: 'increased', 'decreased', 'unchanged':

	frequency	wavelength	amplitude
constructive interference			
destructive interference			

7 a) Which wave behaviour is the test for a wave?
b) Name two other types of behaviour that are shown by all types of waves.

8 If an interference pattern is produced by waves of wavelength λ from two coherent sources, state what will be found at points in the pattern where the path difference to the two sources is:
a) $n\lambda$
b) $(n + \frac{1}{2})\lambda$.

9 P is a point in an interference pattern produced by waves from two coherent sources X and Y.

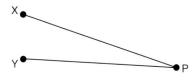

The wavelength of the wave is 4 cm and the distance YP is 40 cm. In each of the following cases, state whether P will be the position of a maximum or a minimum when the distance XP is:
a) 42 cm   **d)** 50 cm
b) 44 cm   **e)** 52 cm
c) 48 cm

10 What piece of equipment could be used to give a pattern of lines, as shown in the diagram, from a single beam of green light?

11 Using a spectrometer, light of wavelength 6.0×10^{-7} m is passed through a diffraction grating with 600 lines per mm. What is the angle between the first order maximum and the second order maximum?

12 a) If a narrow beam of blue light is passed through a diffraction grating on to a screen, what would be observed on the screen?
b) What measurements would have to be made if the above arrangement is to be used to find the wavelength of the blue light?
c) How would you calculate the wavelength from these measurements?

13 From the following wavelengths, select those that are the wavelengths for visible light and list them in the order of red, green and blue:
4×10^{-7} m; 4×10^{-4} m; 5.5×10^{-7} m; 5.5×10^{-4} m; 7×10^{-7} m; 7×10^{-4} m.

14 a) When a beam of white light is passed through a prism to produce a spectrum, which colour at the end of the spectrum is bent most?
b) What other piece of equipment can be used to produce a spectrum from a beam of white light with the colours in reversed order?

Topic 3.1 Test 3

1 Which of the following determines the frequency of a wave:
i) the medium through which it travels;
ii) the wavelength;
iii) the amplitude;
iv) the frequency of the source?

2 What is the relationship between the frequency and the period of a wave?

3 If the amplitude of a wave is increased, which of the following must have increased:
i) wavelength;
ii) period;
iii) energy?

4 a) What word describes two sources that produce waves of exactly the same frequency and wavelength?
b) Which of the following illustrates two waves in phase and which represents two waves out of phase?

i)    ii)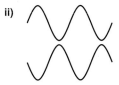

5 a) Which of the following describes 'constructive interference' and which describes 'destructive interference'?

   i) Two coherent waves meet and combine to produce a wave of greater amplitude.

   ii) Two coherent waves meet and cancel each other out.

   b) In each case, explain in terms of crests and troughs, which parts of the waves are meeting.

6 Which property is the best test for a wave?

7 Name three types of behaviour that are characteristic of all waves.

8 a) In an interference pattern, what is located at a point represented by the equation

$$d = n\lambda$$

   b) What do the symbols d, n and λ represent?

9 P is a point in an interference pattern produced by waves from two coherent sources X and Y.

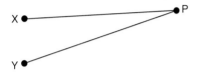

The wavelength of the wave is 2 cm and the distance YP is 25 cm. In each of the following cases, state whether P will be the position of a maximum or a minimum when the distance XP is:

   a) 24 cm   **d)** 21 cm
   b) 23 cm   **e)** 20 cm
   c) 22 cm

10 a) What wave property is demonstrated by passing a beam of monochromatic light through a diffraction grating?

   b) What would be observed?

11 A beam of monochromatic light is passed through a diffraction grating of 4000 lines per cm. If the first order maximum is detected at an angle of 12° to the incident beam, what is the wavelength of the light?

12 What wave quantity can be measured using a diffraction grating. Describe in detail how the experiment would be carried out and how the quantity would be calculated.

13 a) What is the range of wavelengths of the visible spectrum?

   b) Which end of this range is the red end of the spectrum?

14 a) Name two pieces of equipment that can be used to produce a spectrum from a beam of white light.

   b) What would be the main difference in the spectra produced by them?

Topic 3.2
Refraction of Light

Objectives

When you have completed the work of this topic you should be able to:

1 state that the ratio $\sin \theta_1 / \sin \theta_2$ is a constant when light passes obliquely from medium 1 to medium 2;

2 state that the absolute refractive index, n, of a medium is the ratio $\sin \theta_1 / \sin \theta_2$ where θ_1 is in a vacuum (or air as an approximation) and θ_2 is in the medium;

3 describe the principles of a method for measuring the absolute refractive index of glass for monochromatic light;

4 carry out calculations using the relationship for refractive index;

5 state that the refractive index depends on the frequency of the incident light;

6 state that the frequency of light is unaltered by a change in medium;

7 state the relationships $\dfrac{\sin \theta_1}{\sin \theta_2} = \dfrac{\lambda_1}{\lambda_2} = \dfrac{v_1}{v_2}$

for refraction of a wave from medium 1 to medium 2;

8 carry out calculations using the above relationships;

9 explain what is meant by total internal reflection;

10 explain what is meant by critical angle θ_c;

11 describe the principles of a method for measuring critical angle;

12 derive the relationship $\sin \theta_c = 1/n$ where θ_c is the critical angle for a medium of absolute refractive index n;

13 carry out calculations involving the above relationship.

3.2 Refraction of Light

Refractive index

When a ray of light passes from air to glass, it is bent towards the normal so that the angle θ_a between the normal and the ray in air is greater than the angle θ_g between the normal and the ray in glass, Figure 1.

The apparatus shown in Figure 2 is used to investigate the relationship between θ_a and θ_g. Since the glass block is semicircular, any beam of light through the centre of the straight face of the block travels along a radius in the glass and will therefore be normal to the curved face. The lens is used to produce a parallel beam of light and the slit is used to produce a narrow beam. By varying the angle between the ray and the glass block, a series of measurements of θ_a and θ_g is made. Table 1 shows a typical set of such measurements. If these results are plotted on a graph, the graph shown in Figure 3 is obtained.

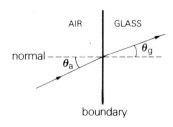

Figure 1 Refraction of light

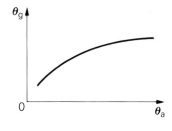

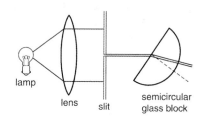

Figure 2 Investigation of relationship between θ_a and θ_g

θ_a	θ_g
10°	6°
22°	12°
29°	16°
40°	21°
55°	27°
63°	30°

Table 1

Figure 3

Neither the table of results nor the graph shows any obvious mathematical relationship between θ_a and θ_g. However, if we take the sines of the angles (Table 2) and plot a graph of $\sin \theta_a$ against $\sin \theta_g$, we obtain the graph shown in Figure 4.

θ_a	θ_g	$\sin \theta_a$	$\sin \theta_g$
10°	6°	0.17	0.10
22°	12°	0.37	0.21
29°	16°	0.48	0.28
40°	21°	0.64	0.36
55°	27°	0.82	0.45
63°	30°	0.89	0.50

Table 2

Since the graph in Figure 4 is a straight line passing through the origin,

$$\sin \theta_a \propto \sin \theta_g$$

$$\Rightarrow \quad \sin \theta_a = \text{constant} \times \sin \theta_g$$

$$\Rightarrow \quad \frac{\sin \theta_a}{\sin \theta_g} = \text{constant}$$

This constant is a property of the glass and is called the **refractive index** of the glass. The symbol for refractive index is n (sometimes the Greek letter μ, pronounced 'mu' is used).

The expression below defines the refractive index n for light passing from a vacuum into a substance.

$$n = \frac{\sin \theta_v}{\sin \theta_s}$$

where θ_v = angle between the ray and the normal in a vacuum
θ_s = angle between the ray and the normal in the substance

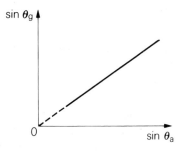

Figure 4

For practical purposes, the difference between the path change for rays passing from air and those passing from a vacuum is so small that we can ignore it: the values given for the refractive index by the two equations are effectively the same.

The refractive indices for some different substances are given in Table 3. The refractive index of a substance can be regarded as a measure of the ability of that substance to bend light: substances having a higher refractive index are those which bend the light more.

substance	refractive index
ice	1.31
water	1.33
crown glass	1.51–1.65
flint glass	1.53–1.93
perspex	1.50
diamond	2.42

Table 3

Refraction and colour

If we allow narrow beams of light of different colours to pass through a prism, we observe that red light is bent less than blue light. This shows that the refractive index n_R for red light is less than the refractive index n_B for blue light. If a beam of white light is passed through a prism, the white light is split up into a spectrum, Figure 5. The white light contains the range of colours red, orange, yellow, green, blue, indigo and violet.

Different colours have different wavelengths. Those colours with longer wavelengths (the red end of the spectrum) are refracted less than those with shorter wavelengths. This indicates that the refractive indices are smaller for light of longer wavelengths.

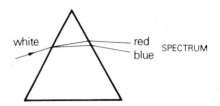

Figure 5 Spectrum from white light

Angles of incidence and refraction

For any ray passing from air into a substance, θ_a is the angle of incidence i, and θ_s is the angle of refraction r, Figure 6.

Thus, $n = \dfrac{\sin i}{\sin r}$ where i = angle of incidence
r = angle of refraction for a ray entering the substance from air
(or more accurately from a vacuum)
n = refractive index of the substance.

For a ray passing from air
into another substance

$$i > r$$
$$\Rightarrow \quad \sin i > \sin r$$
$$\Rightarrow \quad \frac{\sin i}{\sin r} > 1$$

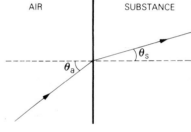

Figure 6

Thus the refractive index of any substance must be greater than one.

Changes in wavelength and speed on refraction

We cannot observe light waves, but interference patterns can be produced by light and this is evidence of the wave nature of light. While the wavelength of light is far too small to be observed directly, we can consider what the change in direction of the waves on refraction means in terms of wavelength. Light consists of wavefronts and the wavefronts are at right angles to the wave direction, Figure 7.

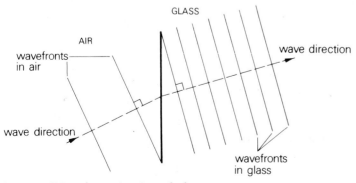

Figure 7 Wavefronts in air and glass

Figure 8 shows one wavefront AC on the air side of the boundary AB and one wavefront BD on the glass side of the boundary.

In triangle ABC, the wavefront AC is at right angles to BC and BC is one wavelength λ_a in air

$$\Rightarrow \quad \sin B\hat{A}C = \frac{\lambda_a}{AB} \quad \dots [1]$$

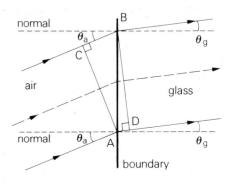

The normal at B is at right angles to the boundary AB

$$\Rightarrow \qquad \theta_a = 90° - A\hat{B}C$$

But in the right-angled triangle ABC,

$$B\hat{A}C = 90° - A\hat{B}C \qquad \text{(sum of internal angles = 180°)}$$

$$\Rightarrow \qquad \theta_a = B\hat{A}C$$

Figure 8

So, from equation [1]

$$\sin \theta_a = \frac{\lambda_a}{AB} \quad \dots [2]$$

Similarly, from the right-angled triangle ABD in which $AD = \lambda_g$

$$\sin \theta_g = \frac{\lambda_g}{AB} \quad \dots [3]$$

Dividing equation [2] by equation [3] gives the refractive index n.

$$\frac{\sin \theta_a}{\sin \theta_g} = \frac{\lambda_a}{\lambda_g} = n$$

The wavefronts in the glass are generated by wavefronts in the air, and so the number of wavefronts generated per second is the same in both the glass and the air, and the frequency f is unchanged.

$$\Rightarrow \qquad \frac{\sin \theta_a}{\sin \theta_g} = \frac{f\lambda_a}{f\lambda_g} = n$$

From the wave equation $v = f\lambda$

$$v_a = f\lambda_a \qquad \text{where } v_a = \text{speed of light in air}$$
$$v_g = f\lambda_g \qquad \qquad v_g = \text{speed of light in glass}$$

$$\Rightarrow \qquad \frac{\sin \theta_a}{\sin \theta_g} = \frac{v_a}{v_g} = n$$

For glass:

$$n = \frac{\text{wavelength in air (or a vacuum)}}{\text{wavelength in glass}}$$

$$= \frac{\text{speed in air (or a vacuum)}}{\text{speed in glass}}$$

This is true for any medium of refractive index n:

$$n = \frac{\text{wavelength in a vacuum}}{\text{wavelength in the medium}}$$

$$= \frac{\text{speed in a vacuum}}{\text{speed in the medium}}$$

Total internal reflection

If a ray of light will travel in one direction, it could travel along the same path in the opposite direction. The semicircular glass block can be used to investigate the bending of a ray of light at one surface only, and we can consider what happens to a ray passing from glass to air, Figure 9.

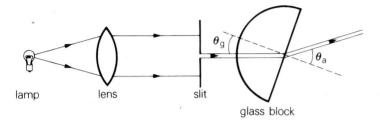

θ_g	θ_a
10°	17°
16°	28°
23°	42°
31°	61°
35°	77°

Figure 9 Ray passing from glass to air

Table 4

If θ_g is varied and pairs of values of θ_g and θ_a are measured, a set of values such as those shown in Table 4 might be obtained.

When θ_g is increased above 36°, the ray of light does not emerge from the glass block, but is reflected at the straight face, Figure 10. The ray is said to be totally internally reflected.

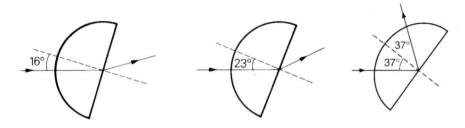

Figure 10 Total internal reflection

For the ray to emerge from the glass, θ_a must be less than 90°. Thus the maximum angle of incidence θ_g for the ray passing from glass to air can be calculated using the following equation.

$$n = \frac{\sin \theta_a}{\sin \theta_g}$$

For maximum value, $\theta_a = 90°$

$$\Rightarrow \qquad \sin \theta_a = 1$$

$$\Rightarrow \qquad n = \frac{1}{\sin \theta_g}$$

$$\text{or } \sin \theta_g = \frac{1}{n}$$

The maximum value of θ_g for which refraction occurs is called the critical angle θ_c.

$$\sin \theta_c = \frac{1}{n}$$

For θ_g greater than θ_c, the ray undergoes total internal reflection.

Summary

For a ray of light crossing the boundary between air (or vacuum) and a substance, the refractive index n of the substance is given by

$$n = \frac{\sin \theta_a}{\sin \theta_b}$$ where θ_a = angle between the ray in air and the normal to the boundary,

θ_b = angle between the ray in the substance and the normal to the boundary.

The refractive index of a substance is greater for light of higher frequency. For a ray of light passing the boundary between air (or vacuum) and a substance of refractive index n

$$n = \frac{\text{wavelength in air (or vacuum)}}{\text{wavelength in the substance}}$$

$$n = \frac{\text{speed in air (or vacuum)}}{\text{speed in the substance}}$$

Within a transparent substance, a ray undergoes total internal reflection if the angle between the ray and the normal is greater than the critical angle θ_c given by:

$$\sin \theta_c = \frac{1}{n}$$

Questions

1 A beam of monochromatic light of frequency 4.85×10^{14} Hz passes from air into liquid paraffin. In liquid paraffin the light has a speed of 2.10×10^8 ms^{-1}.
   a) Calculate the refractive index of the liquid paraffin.
   b) What is the frequency of the light when it is in the liquid paraffin?

SQA

2 The diagram shows a parallel beam of monochromatic light emerging from an underwater spotlight in an ornamental pond.

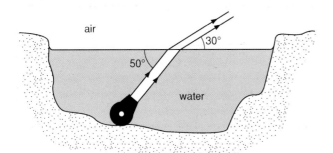

Which of the following is the absolute refractive index of the water in the pond?
   i) 0.65   iv) 1.53
   ii) 0.74   v) 1.66
   iii) 1.35

SQA

3 Light of frequency 6×10^{14} Hz passes from air into glass. The refractive index of the glass is 1.5 and the speed of the light in air is 3×10^8 m s^{-1}.
   Which of the following is the wavelength of this light in the glass?
   i) 5.0×10^{-9} m   iv) 7.5×10^{-7} m
   ii) 3.3×10^{-7} m   v) 1.8×10^{23} m
   iii) 5.0×10^{-7} m

SQA

4 A ray of monochromatic light is directed at right angles into a rectangular glass block as shown below. The centre of the block has a hollow air-filled prism shape.

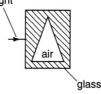

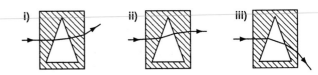

Which diagram (from i) to v) above) correctly shows the path followed by the ray of light as it passes through the block?

SQA

5 A ray of light from a tungsten filament lamp is incident on a glass prism as shown in the diagram.

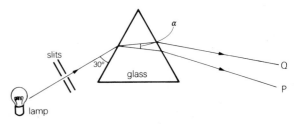

The refractive index of glass is 1.53 for blue light and 1.51 for red light.

a) If P and Q represent the ends of the visible spectrum, which is the blue end?

b) Calculate the angle α.

c) From the refractive indices above, deduce whether red or blue light travels faster through the glass. Show your reasoning.

SQA

6 The diagram shows the path of a ray of red light passing through a glass prism.

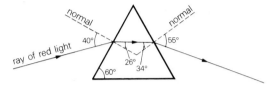

a) Use the information in the diagram to find the refractive index of the glass for the red light.

b) The refractive index of the glass for blue light is 1.58. Draw a diagram similar to the one above to show the path of a ray of blue light through the glass prism. Make the initial angle of incidence 40° as above.

SQA

7 The diagram shows the ray AOB traced by a pupil investigating the refraction of red light using a semicircular glass block.

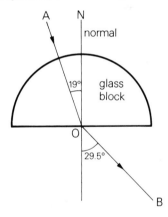

a) Use the information given in the diagram to calculate the refractive index of glass, $_{air}n_{glass}$, for red light.

b) Draw an accurate diagram to show the path of the ray if angle AON is increased to 30°.

c) The speed of red light in air is $3 \times 10^8 \, \mathrm{m \, s^{-1}}$. Calculate the speed of red light in glass.

SQA

8 A swimming pool is illuminated by a lamp built into the bottom of the pool.

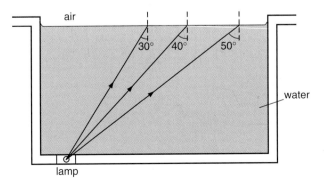

Three rays of light from the same point in the lamp are incident on the water–air boundary with angles of incidence of 30°, 40° and 50°, as shown above.

The reflective index of the water in the pool is 1.33.

a) Draw a diagram to show clearly what happens to each ray at the boundary. Indicate on your diagram the sizes of the appropriate angles.

All necessary calculations must be shown.

b) An observer stands at the side of the pool and looks into the water.

Explain, with the aid of a diagram, why the image of the lamp appears to be at a shallower depth than the bottom of the pool.

SQA

9 a) The diagram below shows the refraction of a ray of red light as it passes through a plastic prism.

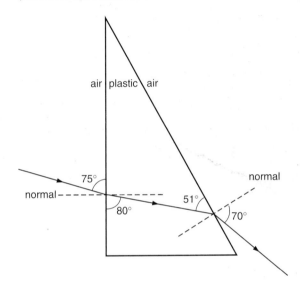

Calculate the refractive index of the plastic for this red light.

b) The refractive index of a glass block is found to be 1.44 when red light is used.

i) What is the value of the critical angle for this red light in the glass?

ii) The diagram shows the path of two rays of this red light, PO and QO, in the glass block.

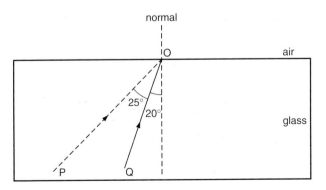

When rays PO and PQ strike the glass–air boundary, **three** further rays of light are observed.
Copy and complete the diagram to show **all five** rays.
Clearly indicate which of the three rays came from P and which came from Q.
The values of all angles should be shown on the diagram.

10 A pupil finds a glass prism of the shape below when she dismantles an old optical instrument.

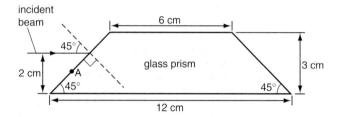

To investigate the optical properties of the prism, she directs a narrow beam of red light towards the prism as shown.
The glass prism has a refractive index of 1.52 for this red light.

a) **i)** Calculate the value of the critical angle for this light in the glass prism.

ii) On square-ruled paper, draw the prism with the dimensions stated in the diagram.
On your diagram, show the passage of the light beam until after it emerges from the prism.
Mark on your diagram the values of all relevant angles.

iii) A second beam of light, parallel to the first and of the same wavelength, is now directed on to the prism at A.
Add to your diagram the complete path of this beam through the prism.

b) How would a distant object appear when viewed through the prism when it is held as shown below?

SQA

Topic 3.2 Test 1

1 The diagram shows a ray of light passing from medium 1 into medium 2.

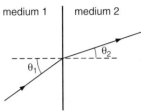

As the angle θ_1 is varied, what can be said about the ratio of $\sin \theta_1$ to $\sin \theta_2$?

2 The diagram shows a ray of light passing from air into medium 1.

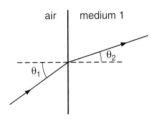

What is the relationship between n, the refractive index of the medium, and θ_1 and θ_2?

3 Describe how you would measure the refractive index of glass, for blue light. Your description should include:
  i) the equipment that you would require;
  ii) how you would set up the equipment;
  iii) what measurements you would make;
  iv) how you would calculate the refractive index from these measurements.

4 The diagram shows a ray of light passing from air into glass of refractive index 1.3.

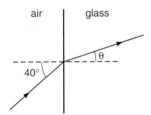

Calculate the angle θ.

5 Is the refractive index of a substance the same for light of different frequencies?

6 When light passes from air into glass, does its frequency decrease, increase or stay the same?

7 The diagram shows a ray of light passing from medium 1 into medium 2.

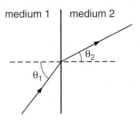

a) What is the equation relating angles θ_1 and θ_2 to λ_1 and λ_2, the wavelengths of the light in medium 1 and medium 2?
b) What is the equation relating angles θ_1 and θ_2 to v_1 and v_2, the speeds of the light in medium 1 and medium 2?

8 The angle of incidence for a ray of light passing from water into glass is 40°. If the refractive index of the water is 1.33 and that of the glass is 1.93, what is the angle of refraction for the ray in the glass?

9 This diagram shows a ray of light passing from glass to air.

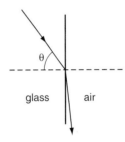

a) Show, by means of a sketch, what happens if the angle θ is increased.
b) What property does this illustrate?

10 For a ray of light incident on the boundary between a medium and air, what is the name given to the maximum angle of incidence for which the ray crosses that boundary?

11 Describe how you would measure the critical angle for perspex in a semicircular block. Your description should detail what other apparatus you would require, what measurements you would make and how you would calculate the critical angle.

12 The diagram shows a ray of light passing through a semicircular glass block.

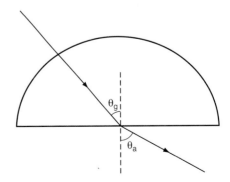

a) What is the relationship between θ_a, θ_g and n, the refractive index of the glass?

b) As θ_a is increased, what is the maximum value of θ_g for the light to emerge from the glass?

c) Use this information to derive an equation relating the critical angle θ_c to the refractive index n.

13 Copy and complete the following table, where the critical angle is that for a ray of light striking the boundary with air.

substance	refractive index	critical angle
diamond		24°
glass	1.5	
ice		50°
water	1.33	

Topic 3.2 Test 2

1 For a ray of light passing from medium 1 to medium 2, which one of the following statements is correct?

i) $\sin \theta_1 \times \sin \theta_2 = $ constant
ii) $\sin \theta_1 / \sin \theta_2 = $ constant
iii) $\theta_1 \times \theta_2 = $ constant
iv) $\theta_1 / \theta_2 = $ constant.

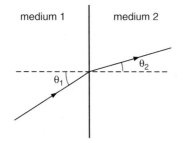

2 Define the refractive index of a substance, in terms of the angles of incidence and refraction, for a ray of light passing from air into the substance.

3 If you are given a block of perspex how would you measure the refractive index of the perspex? State what other apparatus you would require, and how you would carry out the experiment and calculate the value.

4 The diagram shows a ray of light passing from air into water.

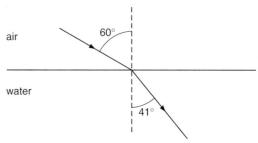

Calculate the refractive index of the water.

5 If three rays of light entering a glass block with equal angles of incidence have different angles of refraction in the glass, what must be different about the rays of light?

6 When light moves from one medium to another which of the following quantities is/are unchanged: frequency; wavelength; velocity?

7 The diagram shows a ray of light passing from water to glass.
a) What equation relates the angles θ_w and θ_g to the wavelengths of the light in water and glass?
b) What equation relates the speeds to the wavelengths of light in water and glass?

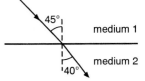

8 The diagram shows a ray of light passing from medium 1 into medium 2.
a) If the speed of light in medium 1 is 2.8×10^8 m s^{-1} what is the speed of the light in medium 2?
b) If the wavelength of the light in medium 1 is 6×10^{-7} m, what is the wavelength in medium 2?

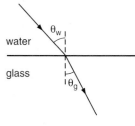

9 The diagram shows a ray of light in medium 2. If the light undergoes total internal reflection:
a) Copy and complete the diagram to show thepath of the ray after it strikes the boundary.
b) Which medium has the greater refractive index?
c) What name is given to the minimum angle θ_1 for which total internal reflection occurs?

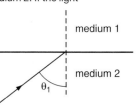

10 The diagram shows two rays of light striking the surface of water. The critical angle for water to air is 49°. Copy and complete the diagram to show the paths of the rays after they strike the boundary. (It is not necessary to calculate the exact angles.)

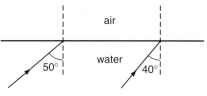

11 Given a semicircular perspex block and a ray box producing a narrow, parallel beam of light, describe how you would measure the critical angle for perspex.

12 For a ray of light passing from water to air the refractive index of the water is given by

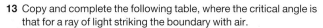

$$n = \sin \theta_a / \sin \theta_w$$

If θ_w is increased until it equals the critical angle, what will be the value of θ_a?
From this, derive an equation that relates the refractive index, n, to the critical angle θ_c.

13 Copy and complete the following table, where the critical angle is that for a ray of light striking the boundary with air.

substance	refractive index	critical angle
diamond	24	
flint glass		37°
glycerol	1.5	
perspex		42°

Topic 3.2 Test 3

1 For a ray of light passing from water to glass

$$\sin \theta_w / \sin \theta_g = 1.2$$

If the ray of light is rotated so that the angle of incidence is doubled, which of the following will be the relationship between the new values of the angles in water and glass?

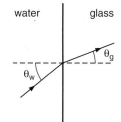

   i) $\sin \theta_w / \sin \theta_g = 0.6$
   ii) $\sin \theta_w / \sin \theta_g = 1.2$
   iii) $\sin \theta_w / \sin \theta_g = 2.4$

2 The diagram shows a ray of light passing from medium 1 into air. What is the refractive index, n, of the medium, in terms of the angles α and β?

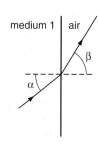

3 Describe the principles of a method for measuring the absolute refractive index of glass for monochromatic light.

4 The diagram shows a ray of light passing through a glass block. The refractive index of the glass is 1.51. Calculate the angle θ.

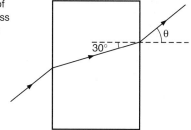

5 For a ray of light passing from a vacuum into glass, does the refractive index of the glass depend on:
   i) the speed of the light in the vacuum;
   ii) the frequency of the light in the vacuum;
   iii) the frequency and the speed of the light in the vacuum;
   iv) neither the speed nor the frequency of the light in the vacuum?

6 When light passes from one medium into another, which of the following quantities will change: frequency; wavelength; speed?

7 The diagram shows a ray of light passing through a layer of ice floating on water.
   a) What equation relates the angles θ_i and θ_w to the wavelengths of the light in ice and water?
   b) What equation relates these angles to the wavelengths of light in ice and water?

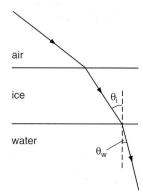

8 The diagram shows a ray of light passing
   from medium 1 to medium 2.
   When it crosses the boundary,
   the wavelength of the light
   changes from 5×10^{-7} m
   to 6×10^{-7} m.
   a) Calculate the angle θ.
   b) If the speed of the light in
       medium 2 is 2.8×10^8 m s^{-1},
       what is its speed in
       medium 1?

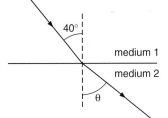

9 The diagram shows a ray of light passing
   through a perspex block. Describe what
   would happen if the block is rotated so
   that the angle of incidence θ increases.

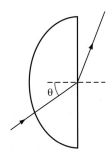

10 For a ray of light in a medium, striking the boundary with air,
    describe what happens if the angle of incidence is:
    a) less than the critical angle for the medium;
    b) greater than the critical angle for the medium.

11 a) What apparatus would you require to measure the critical angle
        for glass?
    b) How would you set up the apparatus?
    c) What measurements would you take?
    d) How would you use these measurements to find the critical
        angle?

12 For a ray of light passing from glass,
    of refractive index n to air the angles
    of incidence and refraction are θ_g and
    θ_a.

       $n = \sin \theta_a / \sin \theta_g$

If the glass block is rotated until the ray
of light only just escapes from the glass:

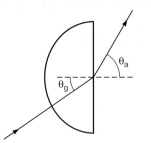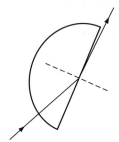

a) What is the value of θ_a?
b) What is the value of $\sin \theta_a$?
c) What is the name given to the
    angle θ_g under these circumstances?
d) Write an equation relating this
    angle to the refractive index of
    the glass.

13 Copy and complete the following table, where the critical angle is
    that for a ray of light striking the boundary with air.

substance	refractive index	critical angle
glass		42°
flint glass	1.66	
water		49°
ice	1.31	

Topic 3.3
Optoelectronics and Semiconductors

Objectives

When you have completed the work of this topic you should be able to:

1 state that the intensity I at a surface on which radiation is incident is the power per unit area;
2 describe the principles of a method for showing that the intensity is inversely proportional to the square of the distance from a point source;
3 carry out calculations involving the relationship $I = k/d^2$;
4 state that the photoelectric emission from a surface occurs only if the frequency of the incident radiation is greater than some threshold frequency f_0 which depends on the nature of the surface;
5 state that for frequencies smaller than the threshold value, an increase in the intensity of the radiation at the surface will not cause photoelectric emission;
6 state that for frequencies greater than the threshold value, the photoelectric current produced by monochromatic radiation is directly proportional to the intensity of the radiation at the surface;
7 state that a beam of radiation can be regarded as a stream of individual energy bundles called photons, each having an energy $E = hf$, where h is Planck's constant and f is the frequency of the radiation;
8 carry out calculations involving the relationship $E = hf$;
9 explain that if N photons per second are incident per unit area on a surface, the intensity at the surface is $I = Nhf$;
10 state that photoelectrons are ejected with a maximum kinetic energy E_k which is given by the difference between the energy of the incident photon hf and the work function hf_0 of the surface: $E_k = hf - hf_0$;
11 state that electrons in a free atom occupy discrete energy levels;
12 draw a diagram which represents qualitatively the energy levels of a hydrogen atom;
13 use the following terms correctly in context: ground state, excited state, ionization level;
14 state that an emission line in a spectrum occurs when an electron makes a transition between an excited energy level W_2 and a lower level W_1, where $W_2 - W_1 = hf$;
15 state that an absorption line in a spectrum occurs when an electron in energy level W_1 absorbs radiation of energy hf and is excited to energy level W_2, where $W_2 = W_1 + hf$;
16 explain the occurrence of absorption lines in the spectrum of sunlight;
17 state that the spontaneous emission of radiation is a random process analogous to the radioactive decay of a nucleus;
18 state that when radiation of energy hf is incident on an excited atom the atom may be stimulated to emit its excess energy hf;

19 state that in stimulated emission the incident radiation and the emitted radiation are in phase and travel in the same direction;

20 state that the conditions in a laser are such that a light beam gains more energy by stimulated emission than it loses by absorption – hence Light Amplification by Stimulated Emission of Radiation;

21 explain the function of the mirrors in a laser;

22 explain why a beam of laser light having a power even as low as 0.1 mW may cause eye damage;

23 state that materials can be divided into three broad categories according to their electrical properties – conductors, insulators and semiconductors;

24 give examples of conductors, insulators and semiconductors;

25 state that the addition of impurity atoms to a pure semiconductor (a process called doping) decreases its resistance;

26 explain how doping can form an n-type semiconductor in which the majority of the charge carriers are negative, or a p-type semiconductor in which the majority of the charge carriers are positive;

27 describe the movement of the charge carriers in a forward/reverse-biased p-n junction diode;

28 state that in the junction region of a forward-biased p-n junction diode, positive and negative charge carriers may recombine to give quanta of radiation;

29 state that a photodiode is a solid-state device in which positive and negative charges are produced by the action of light on a p-n junction;

30 state that in the photovoltaic mode, a photodiode may be used to supply power to a load;

31 state that in the photoconductive mode, a photodiode may be used as a light sensor;

31 state that the leakage current of a reverse-biased photodiode is directly proportional to the light intensity and fairly independent of the reverse-biasing voltage, below the breakdown voltage;

33 state that the switching action of a reverse-biased photodiode is extremely fast;

34 describe the structure of an n-channel MOSFET using the terms: gate, source, drain, substrate, channel implant and oxide layer;

35 explain the electrical ON and OFF states of an n-channel MOSFET;

36 state that the n-channel MOSFET can be used as an amplifier.

3.3 Optoelectronics and Semiconductors

Intensity of illumination

When an object is illuminated, it is receiving light energy. The **intensity** of the illumination of a surface is defined as the amount of light energy per second falling on one square metre of the surface. Since energy per second is power, the intensity of illumination is a measure of the power per unit area and is measured in watts per square metre ($W\,m^{-2}$).

The inverse square law

Figure 1 shows an experimental arrangement that can be used to investigate the relationship between the intensity of illumination on a surface and the distance of the light source from the surface. The experiment must be carried out in a darkened room so that the lamp is the only source of light.

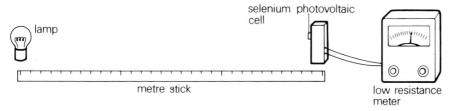

Figure 1 Investigation of the variation of intensity with distance

When light shines on the selenium photovoltaic cell, the cell produces an e.m.f. which is proportional to the intensity of illumination on it. The low resistance meter measures this e.m.f. and the meter reading is directly proportional to the intensity of illumination on the cell. The distance from the lamp to the cell is measured and the reading on the meter is noted. If this is repeated for a number of different distances and a graph of the results is plotted, the graph shown in Figure 2 is obtained.

The relationship between the meter reading and the distance is not apparent from this graph, but an inverse relationship is indicated by the fact that the meter reading decreases as the distance increases. If a graph of the meter reading against $1/(\text{distance})^2$ is plotted, a straight line is obtained which, when extended, passes through the origin, Figure 3.

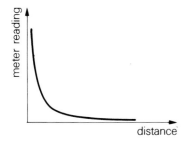

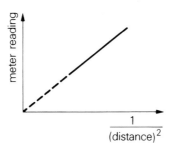

Figure 2 Variation of meter reading with distance between the cell and the lamp

Figure 3 Results of experiment demonstrating inverse square law

Since the meter reading is directly proportional to the intensity of illumination on the cell, this result shows that

$$\text{intensity} \propto \frac{1}{(\text{distance})^2}$$

This is an expression of the **Inverse Square Law**, which states that the intensity of the illumination is inversely proportional to the square of the distance from the light source.

The Inverse Square Law applies only to radiation from a point source, Figure 4.

In the experiment to show the Inverse Square Law, the distances measured are large compared with the size of the lamp filament from which the light is emitted: the lamp is effectively a point source. In a parallel beam of light the energy is not spreading out and the intensity does not decrease with distance from the source, Figure 5.

Figure 4 Light radiated from a point source

Figure 5 A parallel beam of light

Photoelectric effect

There were two conflicting theories of light, the Wave Theory and the Particle Theory. Thomas Young's experiments, producing interference patterns for light, provided strong evidence for the Wave Theory. Evidence supporting the Particle Theory was provided by the photoelectric effect.

In 1887 Heinrich Hertz found that when ultraviolet radiation shines onto two metal spheres, the potential difference required to produce a spark between them is reduced. The following year Hallwachs discovered that a negatively charged zinc plate lost its charge when it was exposed to ultraviolet radiation. In 1899 Lenard carried out further experiments which indicated that the ultraviolet radiation ejects electrons from some metals. These experiments were all demonstrations of what is known as 'the photoelectric effect'.

This effect can be demonstrated by a simple laboratory experiment, Figure 6. An electroscope with a polished zinc plate on its disc is negatively charged. When ultraviolet radiation is shone onto the zinc plate the electroscope rapidly discharges.

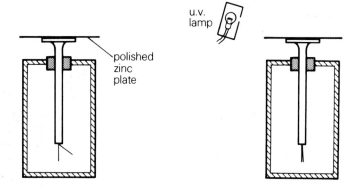

Figure 6 Photoelectric effect

At first this may not appear to be very surprising. Electroscopes are discharged by simply bringing a flame near to them. This happens because the energy of the flame ionizes some of the molecules in the surrounding air, forming negative and positive ions. A negatively charged electroscope attracts the positive ions which collect electrons from the electroscope and cause it to discharge, Figure 7.

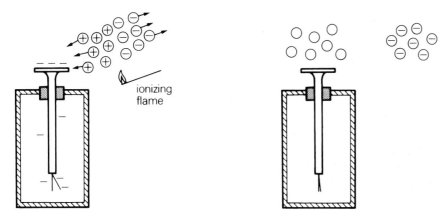

Figure 7 Discharge of a negatively charged electroscope

If the electroscope is initially positively charged, it is the negative ions which are attracted to it and cancel out its charge, Figure 8.

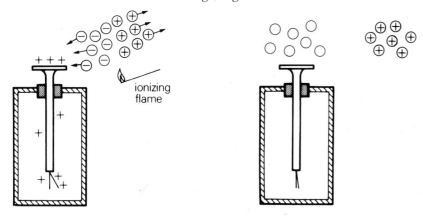

Figure 8 Discharge of a positively charged electroscope

Other ionizing sources such as alpha particles or X-rays discharge electroscopes in the same way. Ultraviolet radiation discharges a negatively charged electroscope with a zinc plate but, if the same electroscope is positively charged, the ultraviolet radiation does not discharge it, Figure 9.

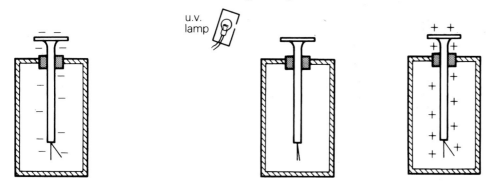
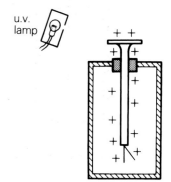

Figure 9 Effect of ultraviolet radiation on charged electroscopes

This shows that the ultraviolet radiation does not discharge the electroscope by ionizing the air.

Ultraviolet radiation discharges the negatively charged zinc plate of an electroscope. Light, which is an electromagnetic radiation of a lower frequency than ultraviolet, does not discharge such an electroscope. It seems that ultraviolet radiation has sufficient energy to eject electrons from the zinc, while visible radiation does not. If the case were that simple, increasing the brightness of the light would increase the total energy supplied and, if the light were bright enough, the electroscope would be discharged. This is not the case. No matter how bright the visible radiation, the electroscope is not discharged. However, a relatively small amount of ultraviolet radiation will cause it to discharge.

The explanation of the photoelectric effect was that electromagnetic radiation consists of small particles or corpuscles.

The radiation will eject electrons only if the corpuscles have sufficient energy. The energy of a corpuscle of visible radiation is less than the energy required to remove an electron from zinc and, no matter how many corpuscles of visible radiation are supplied, no electrons are ejected. The energy of a corpuscle of ultraviolet radiation is sufficient to eject an electron from zinc.

The idea that radiation consists of corpuscles rather than continuous waves is support for the corpuscular theory. The simple demonstration with the gold leaf electroscope provides evidence for this theory. The evidence can be summarized as follows.

evidence	conclusion
1 Ultraviolet radiation discharges the zinc plate of an electroscope which is negatively charged but not of one which is positively charged.	Discharge is a result of ejecting electrons and not a result of ionizing the air about the electroscope.
2 Visible radiation, no matter how bright, does not produce the same effect.	It is *not* simply a case of the total energy supplied, but rather a case of whether each 'bundle' of radiation has sufficient energy to eject an electron.

Young's slits experiment provided strong evidence for the wave theory for electromagnetic radiation. The photoelectric effect provided strong evidence for the corpuscular theory. Einstein provided an explanation which embodied both theories. He suggested that the corpuscles could be thought of as bundles of wave energy, called photons, Figure 10.

The energy E of each photon is proportional to the frequency f of the radiation.

$$E \propto f$$

$$\Rightarrow \quad E = h \times f \qquad \text{where } h \text{ is a constant}$$

The constant h is known as **Planck's constant** and was named after Max Planck who first suggested that the frequency of radiation emitted by an atom was directly proportional to the amount of energy radiated by the atom. The value of h is 6.6×10^{-34} J s.

The intensity of light falling on a surface is equal to the power of light per unit area. N photons of light, of frequency f, have an energy of Nhf.
The intensity of illumination on a surface is given by

$$I = Nhf$$

where N = number of photons per second per unit area and
I = intensity of light on the surface.

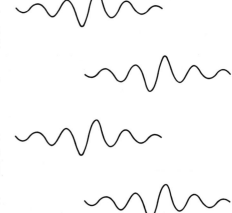

Figure 10 Photons of wave energy

Example 1

The energy required to eject an electron from sodium is 2.9×10^{-19} J. What is the minimum frequency of electromagnetic radiation required to produce the photoelectric effect with sodium?

energy required to eject an electron $= 2.9 \times 10^{-19}$ J

energy of a photon of radiation $= h \times f$

where f = frequency of the radiation
and h = Planck's constant

For the photoelectric effect to occur with sodium

$h \times f = 2.9 \times 10^{-19}$

$\Rightarrow \quad f = \dfrac{2.9 \times 10^{-19}}{h}$

$h = 6.6 \times 10^{-34}$

$\Rightarrow \quad f = \dfrac{2.9 \times 10^{-19}}{6.6 \times 10^{-34}} = 4.4 \times 10^{14}$ Hz

Minimum frequency = 4.4×10^{14} Hz.

Example 2

If the intensity of light of frequency 5×10^{14} Hz falling on a surface of area 1 m^2 is 10 W m^{-2}, how many photons of light are incident on the surface every second?

energy of 1 photon $= hf$

Let the number of photons falling on 1 m^2 each second $= N$

$\Rightarrow \quad$ total energy per second incident on 1 m$^2 = Nhf$

$\Rightarrow \quad$ intensity $I = Nhf$

$\Rightarrow \quad 10 = N \times 6.6 \times 10^{-34} \times 5 \times 10^{14}$

$\Rightarrow \quad N = 10 \div (6.6 \times 10^{-34} \times 5 \times 10^{14})$

$\Rightarrow \quad N = 3.0 \times 10^{19}$

Number of photons incident on the surface per second $= 3.0 \times 10^{19}$.

In 1923, R. A. Millikan won the Nobel prize for his work on the photoelectric effect. He carried out many experiments, finding the minimum frequency of radiation required to produce the photoelectric effect in different metals.

Figure 11 shows a typical apparatus for finding the minimum frequency of radiation to emit electrons from metals and measuring the rate at which electrons are emitted.

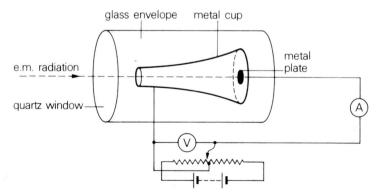

Figure 11 Photoelectric effect apparatus

The electromagnetic radiation passes through a hole in the metal cup onto a metal plate. This plate is made of the metal for which the photoelectric effect is being investigated. Any electrons emitted from the metal plate may cross to the metal cup or return to the metal plate, depending on the potential difference between the plate and the cup. A quartz window is used at the end of the glass tube because quartz allows both light and ultraviolet radiation to pass through it while glass absorbs ultraviolet radiation.

When both the frequency and the intensity of the electromagnetic radiation remain constant and the potential difference between the cup and the plate is varied, the current varies as shown by the graph in Figure 12.

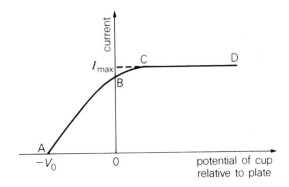

Figure 12 Variation of photoelectric current with potential difference

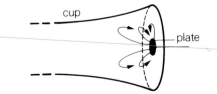

Figure 13 Reverse potential stops current

On the graph, negative values of potential difference represent potential differences which oppose the flow of electrons from the metal plate to the metal cup. The minimum value V_0 of the reverse potential which reduces the photoelectric current to zero, is called the stopping potential, Figure 13.

For the section AB on the graph, the potential difference between the plate and the cup opposes the flow of electrons from the plate to the cup, but is insufficient to overcome the kinetic energy of all the electrons. Thus the current in this section consists of the flow of electrons which have sufficient kinetic energy to overcome the opposing potential difference, Figure 14.

For the section BC on the graph, the potential difference supports the electron flow from plate to cup, but not all of the electrons reach the cup, Figure 15.

For the section CD on the graph, increases in the potential difference supporting the electron flow produced no increase in current. This is because all of the photoelectrons reach the plate and an increase in the potential difference does not increase the current because there are no more electrons available, Figure 16.

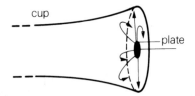

Figure 14 Some of the electrons overcome the reverse potential

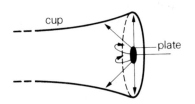

Figure 15 Potential supports the flow of electrons

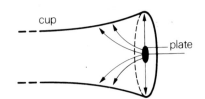

Figure 16 All of the photoelectrons reach the plate

Example 3

If the maximum photoelectric current in the apparatus shown in Figure 11 is $50\,\mu A$, how many electrons are emitted per second?

current $= 50 \times 10^{-6}\,A$

charge flow per second $= 50 \times 10^{-6}\,C$

charge on an electron $= 1.6 \times 10^{-19}\,C$

$\Rightarrow$ number of electrons emitted per second $= \dfrac{50 \times 10^{-6}}{1.6 \times 10^{-19}}$

number of electrons emitted per second $= 3.1 \times 10^{14}$

Number of electrons per second = 3.1×10^{14}.

If the experiment is repeated several times with different intensities of electromagnetic radiation (all with the same frequency), the results produce a set of curves as shown in Figure 17.

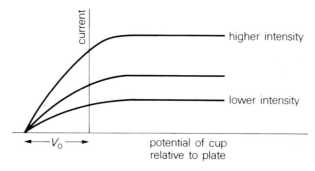

Figure 17 Photoelectric current for different intensities of radiation

These results show that the photoelectric current, which is equal to the maximum current in the circuit, depends on the intensity of the radiation. In fact, the photoelectric current is directly proportional to the intensity of the radiation. Increasing the intensity increases the number of photons per second and hence the number of electrons ejected per second.

The results also show that the stopping potential V_0 is independent of the intensity of the radiation; V_0 is the minimum potential difference required to stop all, including the most energetic, of the electrons emitted from the plate. Thus the fact that V_0 is independent of the intensity of radiation indicates that the energy of the electrons emitted is independent of the intensity of the radiation.

When a charge of Q coulombs moves through a potential difference of V volts, the work done on the charge is QV joules. Thus, if V_0 is the potential difference required to overcome the kinetic energy of the electrons which are emitted with most energy, the work done in stopping those electrons is qV_0 (q = charge on an electron). The work done on the electron is equal to the kinetic energy lost by that electron. Thus the maximum kinetic energy of an emitted electron is given by

$E_{max} = qV_0$ where V_0 = stopping potential

q = charge on an electron

If the experiment is repeated using electromagnetic radiations of different frequencies and V_0 is measured in each case, the results obtained are as illustrated in Figure 18.

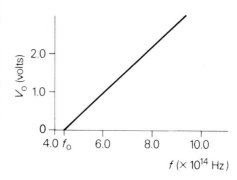

Figure 18 Variation of stopping potential with frequency of radiation

The frequency f_0 is the minimum frequency for which the photoelectric effect occurs and is known as the threshold frequency for the metal being used. The results shown in Figure 18 are those obtained by Millikan for sodium; in that case he found the threshold frequency to be 4.39×10^{14} Hz. For radiations of frequency less than f_0, the individual photons do not have sufficient energy to eject electrons from the metal. The minimum energy required to eject an electron from a metal is called the work function and is given by:

$$E_{min} = hf_0 \qquad \text{where } h = \text{Planck's constant}$$
$$f_0 = \text{threshold frequency for that metal}$$

From the experiments carried out with this apparatus we know that

1   the minimum frequency of radiation required to eject an electron from a metal is given by

$$E_{min} = hf_0 \qquad \text{where } f_0 = \text{threshold frequency;}$$

2   the maximum kinetic energy of an ejected electron is given by

$$E_{max} = qV_0 \qquad \text{where } V_0 = \text{stopping potential}$$
$$q = \text{charge on an electron.}$$

These two energies may be related to the energy of the photons of radiation producing the photoelectric effect since, when a photon is absorbed, its energy ejects the electron with a certain amount of kinetic energy.

$$\begin{array}{ccc} \text{energy of} & = & \text{energy needed to} & + & \text{kinetic energy given} \\ \text{1 photon} & & \text{eject electron} & & \text{to that electron} \end{array}$$

The electron which needs least energy to be ejected will gain the most kinetic energy.

$$\begin{array}{ccc} \text{energy of} & = & \text{minimum energy required} & + & \text{maximum kinetic energy of} \\ \text{1 photon} & & \text{to eject an electron} & & \text{an emitted electron} \end{array}$$

If the frequency of the radiation producing the effect is f,

$$hf = hf_0 + qV_0$$

Example 4

Sodium has a threshold frequency of 4.4×10^{14} Hz. What is the stopping potential when the sodium is irradiated with light of frequency 6.0×10^{14} Hz?

$$f = 6.0 \times 10^{14} \text{ Hz}$$
$$f_0 = 4.4 \times 10^{14} \text{ Hz}$$
$$h = 6.6 \times 10^{-34} \text{ J s}$$
$$q = 1.6 \times 10^{-19} \text{ C}$$
$$hf = hf_0 + qV_0$$

$$\Rightarrow \quad 6.6 \times 10^{-34} \times 6.0 \times 10^{14} = 6.6 \times 10^{-34} \times 4.4 \times 10^{14} + 1.6 \times 10^{-19} \times V_0$$

$$\Rightarrow \qquad V_0 = \frac{6.6 \times 10^{-34}(6.0 - 4.4) \times 10^{14}}{1.6 \times 10^{-19}}$$

$$\Rightarrow \qquad V_0 = \frac{6.6 \times 1.6 \times 10^{-20}}{1.6 \times 10^{-19}}$$

$$\Rightarrow \qquad V_0 = 0.66$$

Stopping potential = 0.66 V.

Spectra

The photoelectric effect provided evidence for the discrete rather than the continuous nature of electromagnetic radiation. This means that the radiation consists of 'bundles' of energy called photons. In the photoelectric effect, photons are absorbed and give energy to electrons in the atoms. The reverse also occurs. This is when electrons in the atoms lose energy and that energy is given off as electromagnetic radiation. The radiation given off when this occurs can be dispersed by a prism or diffracted by a diffraction grating. The spectrum formed in this way is different from that formed from the light from a filament lamp or the Sun.

Emission spectra

When light is given off from a light source, it is split into its different colours by a prism or diffraction grating and forms a spectrum; such a spectrum is called an emission spectrum. Emission spectra are found to be of two types, continuous spectra and line spectra.

Continuous spectra are produced by light from sources which are solids, liquids or high-pressure gases raised to high temperatures. Common examples of such sources are lamp filaments and the Sun. Line spectra (Figure 19) are produced by light from gas discharge tubes, such as those used in neon lights and sodium street lights, or from hot gases and vapours.

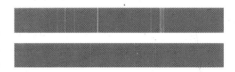

Figure 19 Line spectra

Line emission spectra

A line emission spectrum consists of narrow lines of colour, showing that only radiations of specific frequencies are emitted.

The electric current through the gas gives some energy to the atoms in the gas and this energy gives electrons in the atoms extra energy. When this happens the electrons are said to be 'excited' to higher energy levels and the atoms to be in the 'excited state'.

The atoms in the excited state then tend to return to their original more stable state, giving off their surplus energy. It is this surplus energy that is the radiation given off. In any such light source there are millions of atoms absorbing and emitting energy, yet the emission spectrum consists of a limited number of wavelengths. The reason for this is that, for atoms of a particular element, the electrons can have only a limited number of energy values, known as 'energy levels'. Figure 20 illustrates how an electron which has been excited to a higher energy level W_3 may return to its more stable energy level W_0 either in one step or by a number of steps through other permitted energy levels, W_1 and W_2.

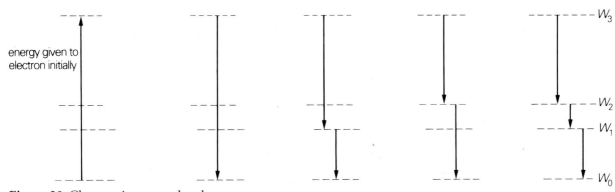

energy given to electron initially

W_3

W_2

W_1

W_0

Figure 20 Changes in energy levels

The most stable level W_0 is known as the 'ground level'. In the example shown in Figure 20, there are four different ways in which the electron can descend from energy level W_3 to the ground level. When an electron descends from one energy level to another, it loses energy and this energy is emitted as a photon of radiation. The energy E of a photon is given by

$E = hf$ where h = Planck's constant
f = frequency of the radiation.

Thus, if the electron descends from energy level W_x to W_y the change in energy E is given by $E = W_x - W_y$

energy of the photon emitted = hf_{xy} where f_{xy} = frequency of the photon

energy of the photon emitted = decrease in the energy of the electron

$hf_{xy} = W_x - W_y$

$\Rightarrow f_{xy} = \dfrac{W_x - W_y}{h}$

Figure 21 shows the four possible ways in which the electron can descend from level W_3 to W_0 and the frequency of each photon emitted (the higher the wavelength the smaller the frequency).

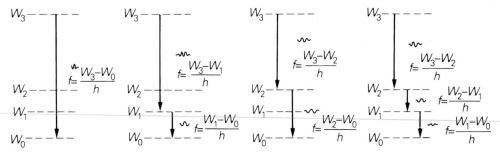

Figure 21 Photons of emitted radiation

An electron may descend by one of these ways only, but, with millions of atoms in the light source, electrons in different atoms will descend in different ways and the light emitted will contain the full range of frequencies shown in Figure 21. There are six different frequencies in this example. Not all of the frequencies are necessarily in the visible range of the electromagnetic spectrum.

In a line spectrum, the frequency of each radiation corresponds to the frequency of photons emitted by electrons descending between two definite energy levels.

Study of line spectra shows that some lines are brighter than others. This is because the electrons are more likely to occupy some energy levels than others. If in the example illustrated in Figure 21, W_1 is an energy level which is less likely to be occupied, the number of atoms in which the electrons descend by steps involving level W_1 will be less. This means that, in the spectrum, the lines produced by these steps would be less bright because there would be fewer photons of the energy corresponding to these steps.

In the example given, the frequencies of the lines that would be less bright if level W_1 is less likely to be occupied are: $\dfrac{W_3 - W_1}{h}$; $\dfrac{W_1 - W_0}{h}$; $\dfrac{W_2 - W_1}{h}$

The fact that line spectra are produced by radiations from millions of atoms in the source shows that the permitted energy levels are the same in the many atoms of the element. In fact, these permitted energy levels are a characteristic of an element, and can be used to identify the element. Chemists use this fact to analyse very small samples. The sample is excited by an electric spark or simply by heating in a flame, and the light given off is dispersed to form a spectrum which is photographed. The photograph is compared with those of the spectra of different elements to see which elements are present in the sample.

By studying the spectra produced from the light emitted by stars, astronomers can determine which elements are present in the stars.

When an electron is not attached to an atom, it is said to be at an energy level of zero. When the electron becomes attached to the atom, energy is given off and this means that the energy of the electron is reduced below zero and is, therefore, negative. Since energy levels in an atom are the possible electron energies, energy levels must have negative values.

Example 5

The diagram represents three possible energy levels of an atom of hydrogen.

When the energy of an electron changes from a higher to a lower energy level, a quantum of electromagnetic radiation is emitted. The frequency f of the radiation emitted in a transition between energy levels W_1 and W_2 is given by

$W_2 - W_1 = hf$ where h is Planck's constant.

a) How many lines in the hydrogen spectrum are produced as a result of transitions between the energy levels shown in the diagram?

b) Calculate the wavelength of one of these hydrogen spectrum lines.

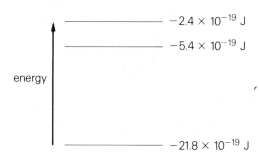

a) The possible ways that electrons might descend from the highest energy level to the lowest are shown in the diagram.

This shows that there are three possible changes in energy levels and this means that these changes will produce three lines in the hydrogen spectrum.

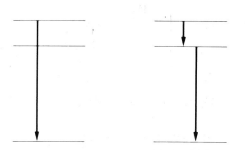

b) For the change from the highest energy level to the lowest,

$$W_2 = -2.4 \times 10^{-19}\,\text{J}$$
$$W_1 = -21.8 \times 10^{-19}\,\text{J}$$
$$h = 6.63 \times 10^{-34}\,\text{J s}$$
$$W_2 - W_1 = hf \quad \text{where } f = \text{frequency of emitted photon}$$
$$\Rightarrow \quad -2.4 \times 10^{-19} - (-21.8 \times 10^{-19}) = 6.63 \times 10^{-34} \times f$$
$$\Rightarrow \quad f = \frac{19.4 \times 10^{-19}}{6.63 \times 10^{-34}}$$
$$\Rightarrow \quad f = 2.93 \times 10^{15}$$
$$v = f \times \lambda$$

For electromagnetic radiation in air $v = 3.0 \times 10^8\,\text{m s}^{-1}$

$$3 \times 10^8 = 2.93 \times 10^{15} \times \lambda$$
$$\Rightarrow \quad \lambda = \frac{3 \times 10^8}{2.93 \times 10^{15}}$$
$$\Rightarrow \quad \lambda = 1.02 \times 10^{-7}\,\text{m}$$

Wavelength of emitted radiation = 1.02×10^{-7} m.

Continuous emission spectra

In a solid, liquid or high-pressure gas, the atoms are much closer than in a normal gas. Under these circumstances, some of the outer electrons in the atoms experience forces from the neighbouring atoms as well as from the nucleus of the atom containing the electrons. At high temperatures the high energy of the atoms combined with these interatomic forces result in some of the electrons being able to take on a wide range of energies rather than being confined to the small number of energy levels within one atom. Since the electrons may now occupy a wide range of energy values, and may therefore undergo a wide range of energy changes, the radiation emitted contains a range of frequencies. In this way, light emitted by hot sources of radiation in which the atoms are relatively close together, contains the range of frequencies that produces a continuous spectrum.

Absorption spectra

White light emitted by a hot source produces a continuous spectrum when viewed through a spectroscope. If the white light is passed through a gas before entering the spectroscope, some dark lines are seen in the spectrum, Figure 22. The dark lines show that the gas absorbs some of the light, but only at certain definite frequencies. The spectrum formed in this way is called the absorption spectrum of the gas which absorbed the light.

The frequencies of absorbed light are identical to those in the line emission spectrum of the same gas, Figure 23.

The absorption spectrum is a result of photons of energy being absorbed by the atoms and exciting the electrons to higher energy levels. Only those photons with exactly the energy required to excite the electrons are absorbed.

Thus the process that is occurring is the reverse of that described for the production of a line emission spectrum, Figure 24.

Figure 22 Absorption spectrum of mercury

Figure 23 Emission and absorption spectra of sodium

(Examples of these in colour are shown on the back cover of this book)

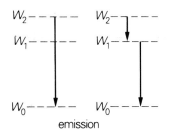

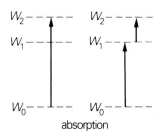

Figure 24 Transitions for line emission and absorption spectra

When an atom has absorbed a photon, it is in the excited state and is likely to return to the stable state by re-emitting the photon. At first sight it might seem that, since the photons are re-emitted, there should be no dark lines and hence no absorption spectrum; yet experiment shows this is not true. The reason for this is that the light beam from which the light is absorbed is directed towards the spectroscope. When the light is re-emitted it is emitted in all directions, and only a small percentage of it will reach the spectroscope.

Absorption spectra can be used to analyse a gas through which light has passed.

Dark lines are observed in the spectrum of light produced from the Sun's rays. These are due to absorption by gases in the outer atmosphere of the Sun and study of these spectra has enabled astronomers to analyse the composition of this outer atmosphere. Similarly, absorption spectra of light which has passed through the atmospheres of some of the planets have produced evidence of the compositions of these atmospheres.

Lasers

Lasers are one of the more modern applications of physics, of great importance with uses ranging from delicate eye surgery to navigation in aircraft and the guidance of missiles. The absorption of photons, raising electrons to higher energy levels, and the emission of photons when the electrons return to lower energy levels, are important processes in the production of laser beams.

Spontaneous emission of radiation

Different energy levels in atoms have different stabilities. If an electron is raised to an unstable level, it will immediately descend to a lower level with the emission of a photon. On average, the time for which the electron remains in the higher energy level is in the order of a one hundred millionth of a second (10^{-8} s). This is called **spontaneous emission** of radiation.

Stimulated emission of radiation

Other upper energy levels are more stable, and the electron may stay there for a short time before descending. Electrons in these levels may stay there on average for in the order of 1 s, and they are said to be in the metastable state. The length of time for which the electron remains in the higher level varies from one atom to another, and there is no way of predicting how long it will do so. Some may descend just as rapidly as those in unstable energy levels, while others may stay in the higher level for well over 1 s. This can be compared with the process of radioactive decay, when nuclei of radioactive atoms emit radiation. In this case, some atoms will emit radiation immediately while others may remain unchanged for some time.

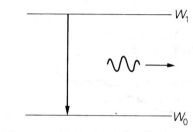

Figure 25 Emission of radiation

When an electron is in a relatively stable energy level, it may be 'encouraged' or stimulated to descend to a lower level, Figure 25.

If an electron in a higher energy level W_1 falls down to the ground state energy level W_0 a photon of radiation is emitted of frequency f and

$$hf = W_1 - W_0$$

If an atom in the excited state that has an electron in the energy level W_1 receives a photon of energy hf equal to the difference between the energy levels, it causes the electron to descend to the lower energy level with the emission of a photon of the same energy, Figure 26. This is called **stimulated emission** of radiation; the first photon stimulates the electron to descend to the lower level, emitting the second photon.

The emitted photon in stimulated emission of radiation has important properties. It is emitted **in phase** with, and **parallel** to the stimulating photon. If this occurs in a substance with a large number of excited atoms, the process starts a chain reaction. Emitted photons become stimulating photons, the number of photons rapidly increases, and the amount of radiation in the beam is amplified. In this way a concentrated beam of photons, all in phase and all moving parallel to each other is produced. This amplification of the beam of photons as a result of the stimulated emission led to the naming of the **laser** which stands for 'Light Amplification by Stimulated Emission of Radiation'.

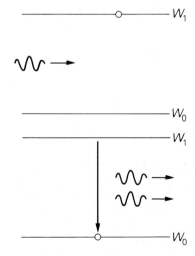

Figure 26 Stimulated emission of radiation

Amplification in the laser

In a laser, the substance containing the excited atoms is held in a tube with a mirror at one end and a half-silvered mirror at the other end. The half-silvered

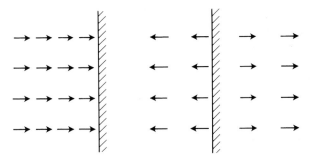

Figure 27 Half-silvered mirror

mirror is one with a very thin layer of silvering so that half of the light striking its surface is reflected and half passes through, Figure 27.

The light is reflected backwards and forwards between the ends, causing a rapidly increasing number of photons to be produced, Figure 28. In this way the intensity of the beam increases until the beam escaping through the half-silvered mirror is very intense.

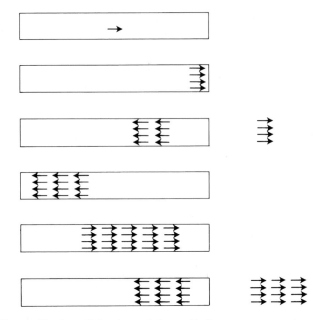

Figure 28 Amplification of the radiation

Since the light travels at a speed of over $2 \times 10^8 \, \text{m s}^{-1}$ through the material in the laser tube, this build-up takes well under a ten millionth of a second. The transmitted light is the laser beam consisting of a narrow, parallel beam of photons which are all in phase.

The fact that the photons are all in phase results in the laser delivering high energy, since all the photons reinforce each other. The fact that all the photons move parallel to each other results in another important laser property that the beam does not spread out and does not, therefore, decrease in intensity over large distances.

Exciting the atoms

In a laser, the photons of light have energy exactly equal to the difference between two permitted energy levels in the atoms of the substance. When a photon meets one of these atoms, one of two things may happen.

If the atom is in the ground state, the photon of light may be absorbed, resulting in an electron being raised to the higher energy level. Whenever this happens, a photon is absorbed and the intensity of the beam is decreased, Figure 29.

If the atom is already in the excited state, the photon of light may stimulate the emission of a second photon, causing the electron to descend to the ground state. Whenever this happens, there is an increase in the number of photons and hence in the intensity of the beam, Figure 30.

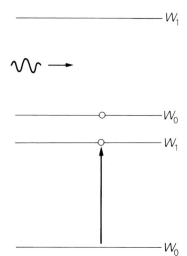

Figure 29 Absorption of radiation

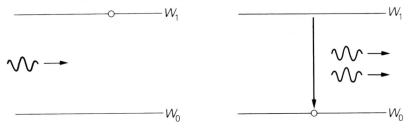

Figure 30 Stimulated emission

If the laser is to amplify the radiation, there must be a greater number of photons meeting excited atoms than meeting atoms in the ground state. If this is so, the amplification of radiation by stimulated emission will be greater than the decrease in radiation by the absorption of photons.

One way of exciting electrons from energy level W_0 to energy level W_1 would be to radiate the atoms with light of frequency f so that

$$hf = W_1 - W_0.$$

This is not a practical way of creating large numbers of atoms in the excited state, because these photons are also of the correct energy to stimulate the electrons to descend back to the lower energy level. Other ways of building up the number of excited atoms are needed, and different methods are used with different laser materials.

The ruby laser

Artificial ruby is one material used in lasers. The ruby is illuminated with flashes of yellow-green light from a flash tube surrounding the ruby rod. The photons of this light have the correct energy to excite the electrons in the ruby atoms to a higher energy level W_2. This is an unstable energy level, and the electrons immediately descend to a lower energy level W_1 between W_2 and the ground state energy level W_0. In this way a large number of atoms with electrons in energy level W_1 is built up, and these are the excited atoms necessary for the production of the laser beam.

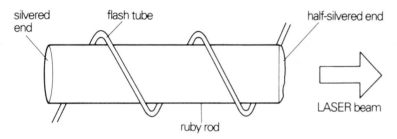

Figure 31 Ruby laser

In the ruby laser, a rod of artificial ruby is surrounded by a flash tube. The mirrors are made by silvering the ends of the rod, one end with a thick layer of silver to provide total reflection, and the other end with a thin layer to provide partial reflection, Figure 31. A flash of light from the flash tube provides a population of excited atoms in the ruby rod, Figure 32.

Some of the atoms will emit photons by spontaneous emission. These photons will then go on to cause stimulated emission in other excited atoms, and the laser process takes place. Photons which are not moving parallel to the sides of the rod will soon pass through the sides of the rod. Only beams of photons which are moving parallel to the sides will continue to move to and fro between the mirrors, without being lost.

In this way a pulse of radiation results from the population of excited atoms produced by the flash of light from the surrounding tube. Another flash of light from the tube starts the process again. The ruby laser is a pulsed laser, producing a large number of pulses of radiation.

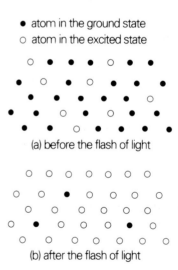

Figure 32 Excitation of the atoms

The helium-neon laser

In a helium-neon laser, a mixture of the two inert gases, helium and neon, at a very low pressure, is held in a sealed glass tube with two electrodes in contact with the gases. When a high voltage is placed across these electrodes, a current flows through the gases producing light. This is the way in which the more familiar neon lights work. This flow of electricity through the gases produces ions (charged particles produced by removing electrons from atoms) and atoms in excited energy states. When helium atoms which have been excited to a metastable state collide with neon atoms, they transfer energy to electrons in the neon atoms. In this way a population of excited neon atoms is produced, and the laser action can take place.

The power of the laser

The power output of lasers can range from 0.1 mW to several million watts. The effectiveness of the laser results largely from its ability to deliver energy in a concentrated form. This can be demonstrated by considering the intensity of radiation delivered by a 100 W bulb with that delivered by a 0.1 mW laser at a range of 1 m.

If the light from the 100 W light bulb is radiated in all directions, at a range of 1 m the power output will be spread over an area represented by a sphere of radius 1 m. The surface area of such a sphere is approximately 12 m^2, Figure 33.

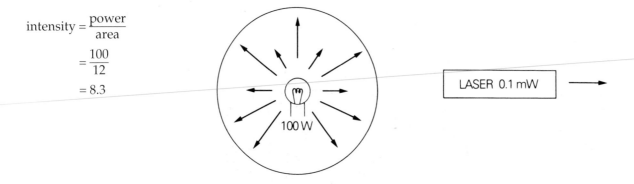

$$intensity = \frac{power}{area}$$

$$= \frac{100}{12}$$

$$= 8.3$$

LASER 0.1 mW

Figure 33 Light bulb and laser

At a range of 1 m the light intensity delivered by a 100 W bulb is about 8 W m^{-2}.

The radiation from a laser is in a parallel beam which is very narrow and has a cross section in the order of 1 mm^2. Since it is parallel, the laser beam does not spread out, and the energy is just as concentrated 1 m from the source, as it is very close to the source. For a 0.1 mW laser with a beam of cross-section 1 mm^2

power $= 0.1 \times 10^{-3}$ W

area $= 1 \times 10^{-6}$ m^2

$$intensity = \frac{0.1 \times 10^{-3}}{1 \times 10^{-6}}$$

$$= 10^2 \text{ W m}^{-2}$$

At a range of 1 m the light intensity delivered by a 0.1 mW laser is about 100 W m^{-2}.

The laser is using one millionth of the power of the light bulb, but, at a range of 1 m, delivers ten times the intensity of light.

Safety with lasers

The properties of lasers which make them useful in a wide range of applications also contribute to the dangers that can result from their use. The laser supplies a concentrated beam of light, in which the photons are in phase. The energy of this light is capable of burning and, if it should enter the eye it will damage the sensitive material at the back of the eye. For this reason, even laser with a power as low as 0.1 MW, the laser beam should never be allowed to shine directly into the eye. Care should also be taken to ensure that the beam is not reflected into the eye. Operators should always wear laser safety goggles to reduce the intensity of the laser beam should it happen to be directed towards the eye. The goggles act in much the same way as sun glasses in that they only allow a very small part of the light to pass through, Figure 34.

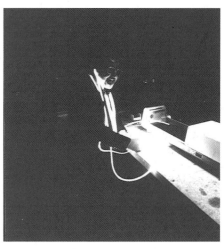

Figure 34 Safety goggles with a laser

Uses of lasers

Lasers in medicine

Lasers can be used by surgeons to perform very delicate operations. The fact that the laser beam can be very concentrated means that it can be used to deliver energy to a very small area. An example of such use is in operations on the inside of the eye. Where the sensitive lining in the back of the eye comes adrift from the inside of the eyeball, a laser can be used to fuse the retina back in place. The

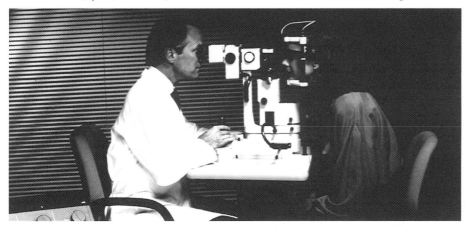

Figure 35 Photograph of surgeon operating on eye

beauty of this operation is that it can be carried out inside the eye without having to cut into the eye. The laser beam can be directed through the lens into the eye, to supply the energy needed to fuse the retina into place. Another similar use is in treating burst blood vessels inside the eye. The heat from laser light directed onto such blood vessels seals them and prevents further bleeding, Figure 35.

Another example of the use of lasers in carrying out delicate surgery is in operations inside the body using an endoscope. Since a laser beam is a beam of light, it can be directed along an optical fibre. An endoscope is a bundle of optical fibres and controls, less than 1 cm across, Figure 36.

It can be fed into a patient via the mouth and throat, and directed through the internal vessels to the area where surgery is needed. The controls are used to guide and direct the fibres inside the body of the patient. Ordinary light fed through the optical fibres illuminates the inside of the body and reflected light

Figure 36 An endoscope

transmitted back through other fibres allows the surgeon to see inside the patient. When the endoscope reaches the diseased part inside the patient, the surgeon sends pulses of laser light down a separate optical fibre system. The energy of the beam is sufficient to cut away diseased parts. Such operations avoid having to cut open the patient to reach the diseased areas; therefore much less damage is caused and recovery time after the operation is considerably reduced.

Not all medical use of lasers is for internal operations. Laser light of different colours is absorbed in different amounts by different colours of skin. Laser light of a colour absorbed by coloured skin can be used to burn off birthmarks, warts and tattoos from the skin. Since the laser light does not penetrate the skin, only a thin layer of skin is burnt off, and it is quickly replaced by new skin growing over the area.

Lasers and metals

The ability of a laser to deliver a concentrated beam of energy has several uses in engineering when working with metal. A high-powered laser beam provides a very efficient cutting tool which will cut through thick pieces of metal. It has the added advantage over more traditional cutting tools and drills that it does not throw up pieces of metal as it cuts, Figure 37.

As well as cutting metal, lasers can be used to join pieces of metal together by welding. The heat produced by the concentrated laser beam is used to melt the edges of two pieces of metal in contact with each other. When the metal is allowed to cool, it solidifies and the two pieces of metal are welded together, Figure 38.

Figure 37 Laser cutting (left) and drill cutting (above)

Figure 38 Welding by laser

Another use of lasers in treating metal is the hardening of metal. If the surface of a metal is heated with a high power laser and then rapidly cooled, the surface is hardened. This makes it more resistant to wear and tear, and is useful for metal used to make moving parts of machinery.

The laser and other materials

Lasers are not only used for cutting metal where high power is needed. The laser beam is easily manipulated, either by moving the laser, by reflecting it with mirrors or by directing it down flexible optical fibres. The beam can be moved easily and with great precision by computer controlled mirrors or optical fibres. An example of such use is in the clothing trade. Lasers are used to cut several layers of cloth to a pattern. An added benefit is that the laser beam cuts the cloth with a neat edge. The heat from the laser seals off the cloth. This makes the cloth less likely to fray than cloth cut by scissors. Similar benefits are obtained by using lasers for cutting other materials such as plastics.

The laser as a distance measuring instrument

The laser beam is used in the measurement of great distances. Light travels at a speed of $3 \times 10^8 \, \text{m s}^{-1}$. If the time taken for a laser beam to travel to a certain object is measured, the distance to that object can be calculated using the equation

distance = speed × time

Perhaps the most spectacular example of this is in the measurement of the distance to the Moon. Apollo II astronauts placed a mirror on the Moon. Scientists are able to shine a laser beam onto this mirror and time how long it takes the light to travel to the Moon and back, Figure 39. Using this method, they have been able to calculate the distance to the Moon to an accuracy of 5 cm. It is the fact that the laser beam is perfectly parallel that enables it to travel such great distances without spreading out and becoming too faint to be detected that makes this possible.

Meteorologists are able to measure the height of clouds by reflecting laser beams off the water droplets in the clouds. Inspectors can monitor the smoke output of factory chimneys by reflecting laser beams off the smoke. Surveyors use laser beams when measuring distances on the Earth's surface, by reflecting the beam off conveniently placed mirrors.

Figure 39 Mirror on the Moon for reflecting a laser beam

As well as measuring these very large distances, lasers are used in the measurement of very small distances. If a laser beam is split by mirrors, the two parts of the beam can be brought together again to form an interference pattern, Figure 40.

If one of the mirrors is then moved a very small distance, this can cause a change in the interference pattern which can be used to measure distances in the order of 10^{-5} m. One use of this method is in measuring small shifts in the surface of the Earth, a valuable aid in monitoring and predicting earthquakes.

Military uses of lasers

Lasers have a wide and increasing range of uses in weaponry and guidance systems. Their use for measuring distances makes them useful rangefinders for setting missiles and guns on target. Targets can be pinpointed by laser beams. If the laser beam is directed onto the target, detectors on a missile can pick up the reflected laser light and home in on the target. Not only can lasers be used to direct and aim other weapons, they can be powerful weapons in themselves. The concentrated energy in a laser beam can be enough to shoot down missiles or aircraft.

Lasers in communications

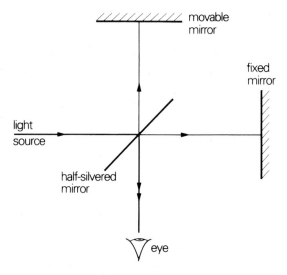

Figure 40 Interferometer

Information can be transmitted by directing laser beams along optical fibres. This has a number of advantages over radio and telephone. The laser beam is confined to the optical fibre until it reaches the receiver. The only way to tap into the signal is to cut the fibre; this is immediately detectable, making it a much safer method of sending confidential information than the radio or the telephone which can be 'tapped'.

In order to transmit information using a laser beam, sound, electronic output from a computer or T.V. signals are converted into electric signals which control pulses sent out by the laser. At the receiving end, these pulses of laser light are converted back into electrical signals which then reproduce the original signal at the other end.

Optical fibres are much cheaper to make than telephone wires, and a single fibre is capable of carrying much more information than a telephone wire.

In space, where there are no clouds or objects to get in the way, lasers are used for communicating with astronauts and for sending control signals to the equipment contained in the satellites.

Lasers in the future

Lasers have many and varied uses. It is likely that scientists will continue to find further uses for the laser. One exciting development is in the field of nuclear fusion. If hydrogen nuclei are made to fuse together, vast amounts of energy are released. This is the power which makes the hydrogen bomb such an awesome weapon. The difficulty in using this potentially great source of energy is the problem of controlling it and the fact that large amounts of energy are required to start the fusion process. Scientists are experimenting with controlled thermonuclear explosions, using lasers to produce the high temperatures needed to start the fusion process.

Semiconductors

Conductors, semiconductors and insulators

If a potential difference is set up across a conductor, a current will flow in it. If a potential difference is set up across an insulator, no current will flow.

However, if the potential difference across the insulator is increased sufficiently, a point will be reached where the insulation breaks down and a current will flow. A dramatic example of this is lightning, Figure 41. Air is an insulator, but friction on the clouds can build up the potential difference between earth and the cloud sufficiently for a current to flow as shown by a flash of lightning.

Generally speaking, conductors are substances which require only a small potential difference across them to cause a current to flow, while insulators are substances which do not normally allow a current to flow unless very high potential differences develop across them.

A group of substances, called **semiconductors**, fall into a category between conductors and insulators. When a potential difference is set up across a semiconductor, a current will flow but this current will be less than for the same potential difference across a conductor of the same dimensions, Figure 42.

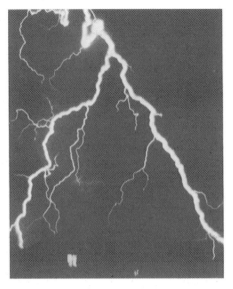

Figure 41 Lightning

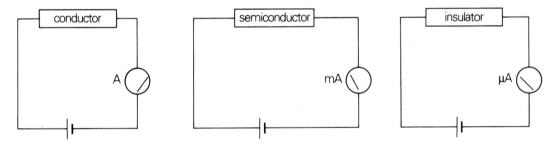

Figure 42 Conductors, semiconductors and insulators

What determines whether a substance is a good conductor, a semiconductor or an insulator is the ease with which the electrons in the substance can be made to move. In a good conductor, the outer electrons in the atoms of the substance are easily removed from the atom. A potential difference placed across the conductor will result in these easily moved electrons moving towards the more positive end of the conductor, and a flow of current is produced. In a semiconductor, more energy is required to release the outer electrons from the atom, and this means that the current flow produced is less than in a conductor. In insulators, the electrons are tightly bound to the atoms and only very high potential differences can release the electrons to produce a current flow.

Comparison of the resistance of conductors, semiconductors and insulators can be made by measuring the resistance of samples of different materials. Since the resistance depends on the length of the sample and the area of cross section, then samples used must be of the same dimensions. Table 1 shows some typical resistances of samples of different substances of length 1 m and area of cross section 0.01 mm^2.

conductor	resistance (Ω)	semiconductor	resistance (Ω)	insulator	resistance (Ω)
copper	1.72	carbon	3.5×10^3	glass	1.0×10^{20}
steel	20	germanium	6.0×10^7	wood	1.0×10^{18}
nichrome	100	silicon	2.3×10^{11}	sulphur	1.0×10^{23}

Table 1

In a semiconductor there are electrons that are relatively free to move, allowing current to flow when a potential difference across the semiconductor sets up an electric field in it. Additions of very small amounts of certain impurities can increase the conductivity of the semiconductor. For example, the addition of 1 part of the impurity arsenic to 10^{10} parts of the semiconductor germanium increases its conductivity greatly. The reason for this is based on the electronic structure of the atoms of the two substances. The germanium atoms form a lattice structure bonded together by a sharing of their outer electrons. Each germanium atom has four outer electrons which take part in the bonding, so that each atom is linked to four neighbouring atoms, Figure 43.

While all of the electrons are bound in this way, the energy required to release them is not very great, and an electric field in the semiconductor will release some of them to flow as an electric current. The introduction of a minute quantity of arsenic greatly increases the conductivity, because it increases the number of electrons which are free to move. The arsenic atom has five outer electrons. When it replaces a germanium atom in the lattice, only four of these electrons are used to bond to neighbouring atoms, and the fifth outer electron is easily removed by an electric field. Thus the conductivity is increased by the availability of free electrons which can be made to flow by the application of an electric field. A semiconductor which has its conductivity increased by the addition of a small amount of impurity is said to have been **doped**. When the doping increases the conductivity by releasing electrons, which are negatively charged, the semiconductor is called an **n-type semiconductor**.

Doping a semiconductor with an impurity which has only three outer electrons in each atom can also increase the conductivity. For example, germanium can be doped with gallium. The gallium atom has only three outer electrons to bond with the four neighbouring germanium atoms in the lattice. Thus one of the four bonds is not complete, but an electron from another germanium atom can easily be moved in to complete this bond. The germanium atom that has lost an electron in this way can then readily accept an electron from its neighbour and the process is repeated. In this way, atoms with only three outer electrons act as if they are short of electrons and are called **positive holes**. When an electric field is applied, electrons are made to move into these holes and the effect is that the hole moves in the opposite direction to the movement of the electrons as if a positive charge is flowing towards the negative side of the electric field, Figure 44.

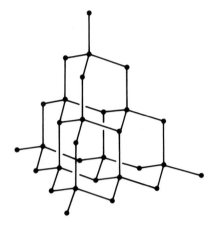

Figure 43 Model of a germanium lattice

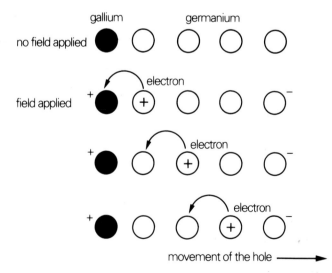

Figure 44 Movement of charge in germanium doped with gallium

The apparent effect of the movement of electrons through a semiconductor doped with an impurity with less outer electrons than the semiconductor is the movement of positive holes. A semiconductor in which this occurs is called a **p-type semiconductor**.

When the temperature of a semiconductor is increased, the heat energy excites the atoms so that more electrons are released, creating pairs of electrons and positive holes. This increase in the number of charge carriers decreases the resistance of the semiconductor.

p-n junctions

A semiconductor diode consists of a small semiconductor, part of which is n-type and part p-type. The boundary between the two types is called a junction. The effect of such a junction can be demonstrated by the experiments illustrated in Figure 45.

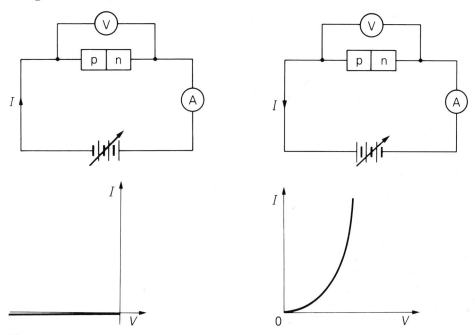

Figure 45

The results of these two experiments can be summarized as in Figure 46.

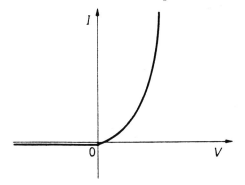

Figure 46 Variation of current with potential difference across a p-n junction

The p-n junction is a good conductor when the p-type semiconductor is more positive than the n-type. In this case the junction is said to be **forward-biased**. When the p-type is more negative than the n-type, the junction is a poor conductor, allowing a negligible current to flow, and the junction is said to be

reverse-biased. The overall effect is that the p-n junction allows current to flow in one direction only. A device which allows current to flow in one direction only is called a **diode**, and this type of diode is called a **junction diode**, Figure 47.

The p-type semiconductor conducts mainly by the movement of positive holes while the n-type conducts by the movement of electrons. In a junction between the two types, free electrons from the n-type cross the boundary and occupy positive holes in the p-type. This creates a layer at the junction where the effective availability of charge carriers is depleted. This is called the **depletion layer**. The movement of the charge carriers between the n-type and the p-type semiconductor sets up a small potential difference, called the junction voltage, across the depletion layer. The junction voltage is about 0.1 V for germanium and 0.6 V for silicon.

When the junction is reverse biased, the applied voltage is in the same direction as the junction voltage, increasing its effect, and widening the depletion layer. In this state the junction will not conduct.

When the junction is forward biased, the applied voltage opposes the junction voltage, reducing the width of the depletion layer. When the applied voltage exceeds the junction voltage, the charge carriers are able to cross the junction and the junction conducts.

The p-n junction diode is one of the basic electronic components. Its main use is in the rectification of alternating current, based on its property of only allowing an appreciable current to flow in one direction, Figure 48.

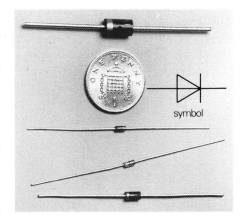

Figure 47 Junction diodes

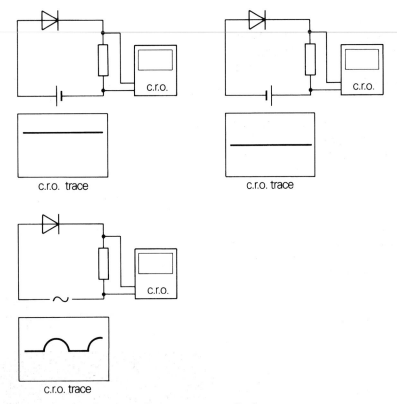

Figure 48 Rectification of a p-n junction diode

Rectification converts alternating current, which flows alternately in two directions, into direct current which flows in one direction only. While a simple diode converts alternating current into direct current, the current still varies between 0 and the peak value.

Often, when supplying direct current, a steady current is required. A capacitor can be used to reduce the variations of the current. The capacitor used to reduce the variations in current is called a **smoothing capacitor**. The capacitor is connected in parallel across the load in the circuit, Figure 49.

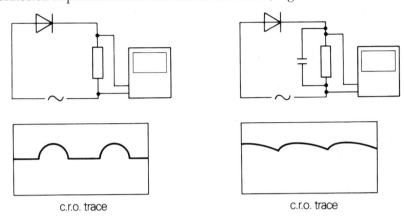

c.r.o. trace   c.r.o. trace

Figure 49

Light emitting diodes

When a current flows in a forward-biased junction diode, electrons are continually combining with and being separated from positive holes. Energy is required to separate the electrons from positive holes. This energy is supplied by the power supply which sets up the potential difference across the diode. When an electron combines with a positive hole, a photon of energy is released. In a light emitting diode, the energy W of this photon is such that its frequency f falls in the range of the frequencies of visible light, given by the equation:

$$W = hf$$

In this way, a current flowing through this diode causes electrons and positive holes continually to recombine, giving off photons: the diode gives off light. Whether or not a diode emits light when forward biased depends on the semiconductor from which the diode is made, and on the impurity with which it is doped.

Example 6

In a junction diode, made from the semiconductor gallium arsenide phosphide, the energy released when an electron combines with a positive hole is 2.8×10^{-19} J. Calculate whether this diode is a light emitting diode.

Energy of photon released is given by $W = hf$

$$\Rightarrow \qquad 2.8 \times 10^{-19} = 6.6 \times 10^{-34} \times f$$

$$\Rightarrow \qquad f = \frac{2.8 \times 10^{-19}}{6.6 \times 10^{-34}}$$

$$\Rightarrow \qquad f = 4.2 \times 10^{14}\,\text{Hz}$$

This frequency is the frequency of red light, which means that the diode will emit red light when it is forward biased.

The diode as a light emitting diode.

Light emitting diodes are often used for digital displays on electronic equipment, Figure 50. They have the advantage over normal light bulbs that they require very little energy to cause them to light; choice of the right semiconductor and doping impurities can give different colours, as required.

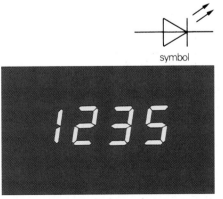

symbol

Figure 50 Light emitting diodes in digital display

231

Photodiodes

Common practice has been to use a light dependent resistor (LDR) for the measurement of intensity of light. An LDR is normally constructed of cadmium sulphide whose electrical resistance varies with the intensity of light falling on the material. Modern practice is now to use a photodiode having a p-n junction.

Figure 51 shows an example of a photodiode and the symbol used to represent it. The p-n junction is connected in the **reverse bias** in a circuit; if no light is falling on the junction, there is negligible current in the circuit. With an increase in the light falling on the p-n junction, this **leakage** current from the n-type to the p-type layer increases in direct proportion to the light intensity.

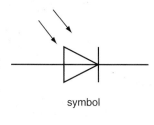

symbol

Figure 51 Photodiode

The photons of light cause electrons to be released in the depletion layer of the junction; this has the effect of changing the number of positive holes and electrons in the p-type and n-type layers on either side of the depletion layer, so creating more charge carriers. The device is then said to be in the **photoconductive mode**. Because the leakage current depends only on the number of charge carriers created, this current is independent of the voltage across the diode. The creation of charge carriers in a photodiode by the light falling on it is virtually instantaneous.

This device therefore has immense advantages over the LDR in that variations of current with light intensity are also instantaneous. The photodiode may be regarded as an extremely fast electrical switch. As such, the device, connected in a reverse bias circuit, finds many uses in high speed timing applications. It is also used for measuring the intensity of light in the light meter of a camera where a cell is required for other purposes such as automatic focusing.

One of the most significant developments is the use of the device in fibre optics applied to telecommunications. Here a digital light signal containing the message is sent along an extremely thin glass fibre. The message itself is secure because the signals produce no electromagnetic field and any break in the fibre is immediately detectable.

The photovoltaic cell

In this device, no outside source of electricity is required. The photovoltaic cell contains photodiodes; light falls on the p-n junction of these and produces an e.m.f. in the circuit. The p-type layer of the junction is thin enough to allow light energy to reach the junction. The light energy separates electrons from atoms in the depletion layer, creating positive holes in the p-type side and extra electrons in the n-type side. Thus a potential difference is set up across the cell; if a circuit is connected between its sides, a current will flow from the n-type to the p-type layer. The photodiode used is said to be in the **photovoltaic mode**.

Photovoltaic cells are used to convert sunlight to electrical energy. Solar powered calculators, Figure 52, use such cells to avoid the need for batteries. On a larger scale, the solar panels on satellites, Figure 53, are constructed of a number of photovoltaic cells which convert the energy from the Sun's rays into electrical energy to power the electrical and electronic equipment in the satellites.

Figure 52 Solar calculator

Figure 53 Satellite solar panels

Field effect transistor

The field effect transistor is an electronic component in which the current is controlled by an applied voltage. Figure 54 shows the basic structure of a metal-oxide-silicon field effect transistor (MOSFET).

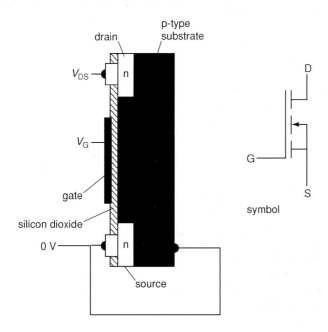

Figure 54 MOSFET

The substrate consists of a p-type semiconductor which is only lightly doped and is not therefore a good conductor. The substrate is covered by a layer of silicon dioxide which is an insulator. The source and drain are two heavily doped n-type regions that have been diffused, through etched spaces in the silicon dioxide, into the substrate. Electrical connection to the source and the drain is made through a thin layer of aluminium deposited on the surface. The gate is a layer of aluminium separated from the substrate by the insulating layer.

The substrate and the source are connected together and a potential difference V_{DS} is applied between the drain and the source so that the drain is more positive than the source. When no voltage is applied to the gate, the MOSFET will not conduct electricity because the substrate is a poor conductor. The conductivity is reduced even further since there is a reverse biased junction between the substrate and the drain. When the device is in this non-conducting mode it is said to be in the OFF state, Figure 55, and the potential difference, V_{DS}, between the drain and the source, does not produce a current.

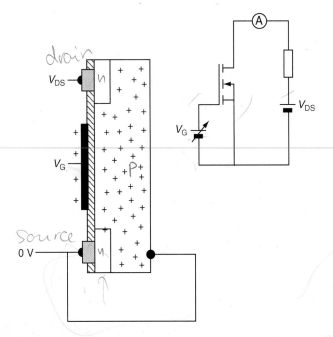

Figure 55   MOSFET in the OFF state: $V_{G} < 2$ V

If a potential V_{G} is applied to the gate, making it more positive, it will attract electrons from the substrate towards the gate. When V_{G} rises above the threshold voltage of about 2 V the increase in electrons overcomes the slight p-type nature of the substrate near the gate and it will gain a surplus of electrons becoming, in effect, an n-type area. Thus the n-type source and drain will become connected by an n-type channel, known as a channel insert, and the device will conduct. The potential difference, V_{DS}, between the drain and the source, causes a current to flow in the device. It is then said to be in the ON state, Figure 56.

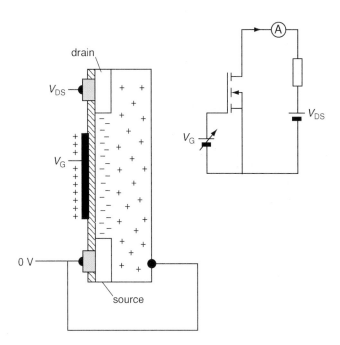

Figure 56 MOSFET in the ON state: $V_G > 2$ V

When in the ON state, the potential of the gate controls the width of the conducting layer of the induced n-type semiconductor and, hence, the conductivity of the transistor. Increasing the potential of the gate increases the width of the conducting layer and more current will flow between the drain and the source. In this situation the device acts as an amplifier, with variations in the potential applied to the gate producing variations in the current flowing through the device.

Summary

The intensity of illumination of a surface is the amount of light energy falling on one square metre of the surface in one second, and is measured in watts per square metre ($W\,m^{-2}$).

The intensity of illumination on a surface is given by

$$I = Nhf$$

where N = number of photons per second per unit area
h = Planck's constant
I = intensity of light on the surface.

The Inverse Square Law states that the intensity I produced on a surface by a point source of light is inversely proportional to the square of the distance d between the surface and the light source.

This can be written

$$Id^2 = \text{constant}$$

The photoelectric effect is demonstrated by the fact that ultraviolet light discharges a negatively charged zinc plate on an electroscope.

Electromagnetic radiation is made up of photons of wave energy and the energy E of a single photon of radiation is given by:

$$E = h \times f \qquad \text{where } h = \text{Planck's constant}$$
$$f = \text{frequency of the radiation.}$$

In the photoelectric effect the maximum kinetic energy of an emitted electron is given by:

$$E_{max} = qV_0 \qquad \text{where } V_0 = \text{stopping potential}$$
$$q = \text{charge on an electron.}$$

In the photoelectric effect, the minimum frequency of radiation required to eject an electron from the metal is given by:

$$E_{min} = hf_0 \qquad \text{where } f_0 = \text{threshold frequency}$$
$$h = \text{Planck's constant.}$$

A line emission spectrum consists of lines of specific frequencies of light. Each frequency corresponds to the energy of a photon equal to the energy emitted by an electron descending from one permitted energy level to another.

For an electron descending from energy level W_x to W_y the frequency f_{xy} of the emitted photon is given by:

$$f_{xy} = \frac{W_x - W_y}{h}$$

An absorption spectrum is formed when white light is passed through a gas or vapour and lines of specific frequencies of light are absorbed. Each frequency absorbed corresponds to the energy of a photon equal to the energy of an electron ascending from one permitted energy level to another.

In a laser, the light beam gains more energy by stimulated emission than it loses by absorption.

In stimulated emission, the incident radiation and the emitted radiation are in phase and travel in the same direction.

Materials can be divided into three broad categories according to their electrical properties: conductors, insulators and semiconductors.

Adding atoms of another element to a pure semiconductor increases its conductivity. This process is called **doping**.

The conductivity of a semiconductor increases with temperature rise.

In a light emitting diode (LED), positive and negative charge carriers recombine to give quanta of radiation.

In a photodiode, the action of light on the p-n junction causes electrons to be released in the depletion layer. This changes the leakage current in a reverse bias circuit in proportion to the intensity of illumination.

A photovoltaic cell is a p-n junction which can convert light energy into electrical energy. When light falls on the junction, an e.m.f. is set up across the cell.

In an n-channel MOSFET the conductivity between the source and the drain is controlled by the potential applied to the gate.

When the gate potential is below the threshold value the MOSFET is in the OFF state.

When the gate potential is above the threshold value the MOSFET is in the ON state.

The n-channel MOSFET can be used as an amplifier

Questions

1 A set of readings I on a light meter at various distances d from a point source of light is shown in the table.

I/units	15	48	116	249	442	761
d/cm	114	64	41	28	21	16

Using these results, develop a relationship between I and d.

2 An experimenter investigated the effect of shining different electromagnetic radiations on the polished zinc plates of charged electroscopes. He found that ultraviolet radiation discharged the negatively charged electroscope but not the positively charged electroscope. Visible radiation, no matter how bright, did not discharge any electroscope.

a) How does this experimental evidence support the following statements?

   i) The process by which the ultraviolet radiation discharges the electroscope is not the ionization of the surrounding air.

   ii) Whether or not the electroscope is discharged does not depend on the total amount of energy supplied by the electromagnetic radiation.

b) What is the name of the 'effect' by which ultraviolet radiation can eject electrons from zinc?

c) For which theory did this effect provide strong support?

3 For a certain metal, the energy required to eject an electron from an atom is 3.3×10^{-19} J.

a) What is the minimum frequency of electromagnetic radiation required to produce the photoelectric effect with this metal?

b) Would the photoelectric effect occur when this metal is illuminated with light of:

   i) frequency 4×10^{14} Hz;   **ii)** wavelength 5×10^{-7} m?

   (Planck's constant $= 6.63 \times 10^{-34}$ J s)

4 The power for a space probe is produced by an array of photodiodes. Each photodiode in the array acts as a photovoltaic cell. Under certain conditions the power output of the array is 150 W at 34 V.

a) Calculate the current produced by the array.

b) Explain how a photovoltaic cell can produce a small voltage.

c) What happens to the intensity of the solar radiation falling on the array if the probe moves to a position twice as far as the Sun?

Justify your answer.

SQA

5 The diagram represents four possible energy levels of an atom of a metal.

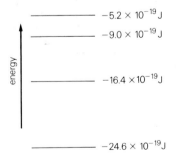

a) How many lines in the spectrum of this metal are produced as the result of transitions between the energy levels shown in the diagram?

b) Calculate the wavelengths of the spectrum lines representing the greatest and the least energy transitions.

(Planck's constant = 6.63×10^{-34} J s)

6 A beam of ultraviolet radiation falls on a suitable metal plate Y, which lies on the axis of a hollow metal cylinder X. X and Y are connected in an electric circuit including a battery and a milliammeter as shown in the diagram.

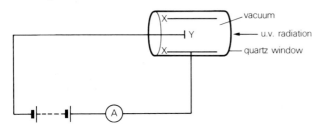

a) Explain why a small current is registered.

b) What would happen to the current if the intensity of the light were increased?

SQA

7 The diagram shows part of the emission spectrum of an element.

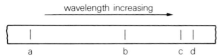

Light of frequency corresponding to each of the above spectral lines is allowed to strike a metal plate in turn and in some cases electrons are ejected from the metal.

i) Light from which of the above spectral lines is most likely to eject electrons from the plate? Give a reason for your answer.

ii) Light of frequency 5.08×10^{14} Hz, corresponding to one of the above lines, can eject electrons with a kinetic energy of 0.45×10^{-19} J from the metal plate. How much energy is required just to release electrons from the metal?

iii) Show whether light of frequency 4.29×10^{14} Hz, corresponding to line c, is capable of ejecting electrons from the metal.

(Planck's constant $h = 6.63 \times 10^{-34}$ J s)

SQA

8 a) Explain what is meant by the photoelectric effect. Indicate how it depends on:

i) the frequency of the light;

ii) the intensity of the light.

Explain how your answers to **i)** and **ii)** are related to a theory of the nature of light.

b) A clean zinc plate is mounted in an ionization chamber, just below a wire mesh as shown. The chamber is connected in series with a d.c. supply and a sensitive current meter. The current meter amplifies any small current in the circuit by a factor of 10^6 and displays the amplified current on a microammeter. The zinc plate is illuminated by an ultraviolet lamp.

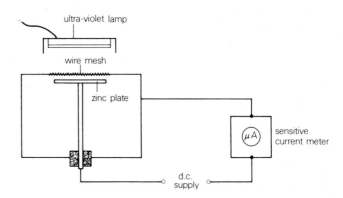

Describe how you would use the apparatus to show that any small current in the circuit was due to the photoelectric effect.

SQA

9 The diagram shows a simplified view of a laser tube used in a gas laser.

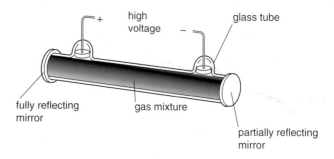

a) The name LASER stands for Light Amplification by Stimulated Emission of Radiation.

i) What is meant by 'stimulated emission'?

ii) Explain the purpose of each mirror in the laser tube.

b) In the experiment shown below, a laser beam is directed at a diffraction grating.

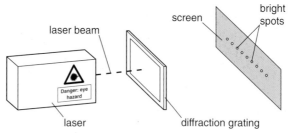

A pattern of bright spots is observed on the screen. Explain in terms of the wave nature of light, how this pattern is formed.

c) The laser is marked with the warning 'Danger : Eye Hazard'. Why does this laser, which has a power output of only 0.20 mW, present a greater potential eye hazard than a 100 W lamp?

d) In hospitals, pulsed lasers may be used to repair damage to the retina of the eye. The specification of a typical pulsed laser is given below:

      gas used in the laser   : argon
      duration of pulse   : 0.50 ms
      energy of one pulse   : 0.10 J
      wavelengths of laser light emitted : 88 and 514 nm.

The cross-sectional area of the laser beam at the retina is 1.5 × 10^{-9} m².

Calculate the light intensity produced at the retina during a pulse of light from this laser.

SQA

10 a) The diagram below represents the p-n junction of a light emitting diode (LED).

    i) Draw a diagram showing the above p-n junction connected to a battery so that the junction is forward biased.

    ii) When the junction is forward biased, there is a current in the diode. Describe the movement of the charge carriers which produces this current.

    iii) Describe how the charge carriers in the light emitting diode enable light to be produced.

b) The following graph shows the variation of current with voltage for a diode when it is forward biased.

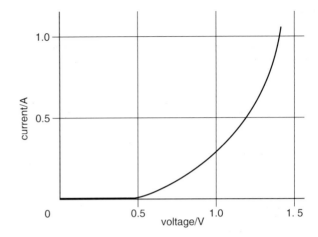

i) What is the minimum voltage required for this diode to conduct?

ii) What happens to the resistance of the diode as the voltage is increased above this minimum value?

Use information from the graph to justify your answer.

SQA

Topic 3.3 Test 1

1 What is the relationship between the intensity of radiation on a surface, the power of the radiation falling on the surface and the area of that surface?

2 a) What apparatus could be used to find the relationship between the intensity of radiation from a point source and the distance from that source?
b) How would you set up the apparatus?
c) What readings would you take?
d) How would you use these readings to demonstrate the relationship.

3 A light meter gives a reading of 128 units when placed 1 metre from a small light source.
What readings would it give at distances of: **a)** 80 cm, **b)** 120 cm?

4 a) If a metal has a threshold frequency of 5×10^{14} Hz, what does this tell you about the frequencies of light that can produce photoelectric emission?
b) Do all metals have the same threshold frequency?

5 A negatively charged electroscope is illuminated by light of frequency 4×10^{14} Hz and intensity 10 W m^{-2}. It is not discharged by photoelectric emission.
What change in the light would be required to produce photoelectric emission from the electroscope?

6 In Millikan's experiment on photoelectric emission, he measured the photoelectric current produced by illuminating a metal cup with electromagnetic radiation. If the radiation is of high enough frequency to cause photoemission, what would happen to the current if the intensity of the illumination were doubled?

7 What is a photon of electromagnetic radiation?
What is the equation relating the energy E of a photon to the frequency f of the radiation. Name any other symbol in the equation.

8 A photon of light has energy 3.3×10^{-19} J. What is the frequency of the light? (Planck's constant $= 6.6 \times 10^{-34}$ J s.)

9 If N photons of electromagnetic radiation are falling on a unit area of a surface, how is the intensity of radiation falling on that surface related to the frequency of the radiation?

10 When an electron is ejected by a photon of radiation it has a maximum kinetic energy of E_k. How is this related to the work function hf_0 of the surface and the energy hf of the photon?

11 Electrons in a free atom have a range of energies. What can you say about the values of energy that these electrons might have?

12 Draw a diagram to show how an electron in an upper energy level in a hydrogen atom might descend to two lower energy levels.

13 Copy out the following definitions and write after each one the appropriate name from 'ground state', 'excited state' and 'ionization level':
a) an electron with sufficient energy to escape from the atom;
b) an electron with more than its minimum permitted energy in an atom;
c) an electron with its minimum permitted energy in an atom.

14 In an emission spectrum light of frequency f is emitted when an electron descends from level W_2 to a lower level W_1. Write an equation relating these terms.

15 In an absorption spectrum, light of a particular frequency f is absorbed by the atoms of a substance. What changes does this absorption of energy produce in electrons of the atoms of the substance?
Write an equation relating the frequency of absorbed radiation to energy levels in the atom.

16 The spectrum of sunlight contains absorption lines. What absorbs these frequencies from the sunlight?

17 Compare the rate at which atoms in an excited state emit radiation with the rate of decay of radioactive nuclei.

18 An electron in an atom is excited to a higher energy state with excess energy hf. If a photon of energy with energy hf is incident on this atom, what is likely to happen?

19 What process is able to produce two photons with the same phase and travelling in the same direction?

20 For a laser to operate, what must be the relationship between the stimulated emission and the absorption within it? What do the letters LASER stand for.

21 Explain the function of the mirrors in a laser.

22 A laser of energy as low as 0.1 mW can cause eye damage. Explain how such a low power of radiation can be dangerous.

23 State briefly the difference between materials which are conductors, insulators and semiconductors.

24 Name one example each of a conductor, an insulator and a semiconductor.

25 What is the name given to the addition of an impurity to a semiconductor? What effect does this process have on the conductivity of the material?

26 Addition of different impurities to semiconductors can result in n-type or p-type semiconductors.
a) What are the majority charge carriers in an n-type semiconductor?
b) What are the majority charge carriers in a p-type semiconductor?

27 In a p-n junction diode, describe with the aid of a diagram the movement of the charge carriers when the diode is:
a) forward biased;
b) reverse biased.

28 In the junction region of a forward biased p-n junction diode what may be produced when positive and negative charge carriers recombine?

29 What is a photodiode and what is the effect of the action of light on it?

30 A resistor is connected across a photodiode in the photovoltaic mode. State what would happen in the resistor if the photodiode is then illuminated with light.

31 Explain, using a diagram, the use of a photodiode in the photoconductive mode.

32 Which of the following is true of the leakage current in a reverse biased photodiode?
  i) It is directly proportional to the light intensity and directly proportional to the reverse-biasing voltage below the breakdown voltage.
  ii) It is directly proportional to the light intensity and fairly independent of the reverse-biasing voltage below the breakdown voltage.
  iii) It is fairly independent of the light intensity and fairly independent of the reverse-biasing voltage below the breakdown voltage.
  iv) It is fairly independent of the light intensity and directly proportional to the reverse-biasing voltage below the breakdown voltage.

33 What type of diode would be useful as a switch in a circuit for high speed timing applications? Would it be forward or reverse-biased in such a circuit?

34 Sketch an n-channel MOSFET and label its different parts.

35 a) In an n-channel MOSFET explain whether it will be in the ON state or the OFF state in the following circumstances:
  i) the gate is 3 V more positive than the substrate;
  ii) the gate is at the same potential as the substrate;
  iii) the gate is 3 V more negative than the substrate.
  b) Explain why the ON and OFF states occur in each of the above cases.

36 For which of the following can an n-channel MOSFET be used:
  i) production of light energy;
  ii) measurement of heat energy;
  iii) amplification of electrical signals?

Topic 3.3 Test 2

1 Define the intensity of radiation in terms of the power of the radiation and the area of the surface on which it falls.

2 Describe an experiment to demonstrate the inverse square law for radiation from a point source.

3 A light meter gives a reading of 64 units when placed 120 cm from a small light source.
What readings would it give at distances of: **a)** 60 cm, **b)** 30cm?

4 Define the threshold frequency for a surface.

5 In an experiment to investigate photoelectric emission from a metal surface, a student finds that the light she is using produces no photoelectric emission. If she were to change her light source, what change would be necessary to result in photoelectric emission? Could she have produced the change by changing the material? If so, what property of the surface would need to be different and would it need to be greater or less?

6 If a monochromatic radiation is able to produce a photoelectric current, what is the relationship between the current and the intensity of that radiation?

7 Electromagnetic radiation is made up of bundles of energy. What is the name given to these bundles of energy?
Write an equation for the energy E of one of these bundles, defining any symbols used.

8 What is the energy of a single bundle of electromagnetic radiation of frequency 4.0×10^{14} Hz? (Planck's constant = 6.6×10^{34} J s.)

9 Define the intensity of electromagnetic radiation falling on a surface in terms of the number of bundles of energy falling on a unit area and the frequency of the radiation.

10 A surface has a work function hf_0. If a photon of electromagnetic radiation of frequency f ejects an electron from the surface, what is the equation giving E_k, the maximum kinetic energy of the ejected electron?

11 Can electrons in a free atom have a range of values?

12 Draw a sketch to show how an electron in a hydrogen atom might move between the lowest energy level and two higher energy levels.

13 For an electron in a free atom define:
  a) ground state;
  b) excited state;
  c) ionization level.

14 When an electron in a free atom descends from energy level W_2 to energy level W_1 what happens to the energy? Write an equation relating this energy loss to W_2 and W_1.

15 A beam of white light is passed through a diffraction grating to form a spectrum. When a clear container full of a particular gas is placed in the path of the beam of white light, the gas absorbs blue light.
  a) What effect will this have on the spectrum?
  b) What happens to the blue light in terms of energy levels W_2 and W_1 in the atoms of the gas and how is this related to the frequency f of the blue light?

16 Why are there absorption lines in a spectrum produced from sunlight?

17 If a number of atoms are excited to a higher energy state by a burst of energy, will they all emit their surplus energy at the same time? Compare the emission of energy with the rate of decay of radioactive nuclei.

18 If an electron in an atom is in a level of energy hf greater than the ground state, is it most likely to emit this excess energy if it is radiated by a photon with energy:
  i) less than hf;
  ii) equal to hf;
  iii) greater than hf?

19 When a photon of energy is incident on an atom, causing the emission of a second photon from the atom, what can be said about the direction and phase of the two photons?

20 State where the word 'laser' comes from. State briefly how the laser produces a high energy beam by comparing the absorption and the stimulated emission of radiation within the laser.

21 In a laser there are mirrors at both ends. How does the mirror at the emitting end differ from that at the other end and why are they necessary for the production of a laser beam?

22 A laser beam of power 0.1 mW is capable of causing eye damage but a beam of ordinary light of much greater power is harmless. Explain why this is.

23 When a potential difference is applied across a material it may produce a current in that material. Name the three categories of materials described below:
a) a material in which a small potential difference produces an appreciable current;
b) a material in which a small potential difference produces a small current;
c) a material in which a small potential difference produces no current.

24 For each of the following materials state whether it is a conductor, an insulator or a semiconductor:
a) silicon,   **b)** copper,   **c** rubber.

25 What is meant by 'doping' a semiconductor? What effect does this have on the electrical properties of the semiconductor?

26 There are two types of semiconductors, n-type and p-type. Explain how they are formed from a pure semiconductor. What are the majority charge carriers in each type?

27 a) In a forward biased p-n junction diode which side is more positive, the n-type or the p-type? Under these conditions what movement of charge carriers takes place in the diode?
b) In a reverse biased p-n junction diode which side is more positive, the n-type or the p-type? Under these conditions what movement of charge carriers takes place in the diode?

28 In the junction region of a forward biased p-n junction diode explain the process by which quanta of radiation might be produced.

29 How is the junction in a photodiode affected by the action of light?

30 What is meant by the statement that a photodiode is in the photovoltaic mode?

31 When a photodiode is in the photovoltaic mode what can it be used for?

32 for a reverse biased photodiode how does the leakage current relate to:
a) the light intensity;
b) the reverse biasing voltage below breakdown voltage?

33 What property makes a reverse biased photodiode particularly useful as a switch in a circuit?

34 The diagram shows a sketch of the structure of a MOSFET. What are the parts labelled A, B, C, D, E, F?

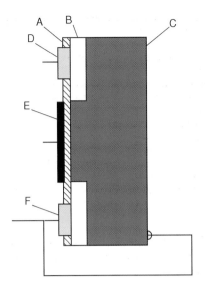

35 a) Describe how an n-channel MOSFET behaves in the ON state and in the OFF state.
b) How is it switched from one state to the other?
c) Explain why this produces the different behaviour in each state.

36 Which of the following can be used as an amplifier:
i) photodiode;
ii) photovoltaic cell;
iii) n-channel MOSFET?

Topic 3.3 Test 3

1 Radiation falls on a surface area A.
The intensity of radiation on a surface is I.
The power of the radiation falling on the surface is P.
What is the equation relating these three quantities?

2 The equipment shown in the diagram can be used to demonstrate the relationship between the intensity of radiation from a point source and the distance from the source.

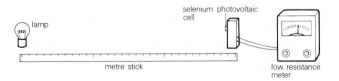

Describe how you would do this, what readings you would take and how you would use these readings.

3   A light meter gives a reading of 64 units when placed 100 cm from a small light source.
    What readings would it give at distances of: **a)** 50 cm, **b)** 200 cm?

4   For photoelectric emission to occur what is the relationship between the threshold frequency for a surface and the frequency of the incident radiation?

5   In an experiment to investigate photoelectric emission from a metal surface, the surface is illuminated by light of frequency 4×10^{14} Hz and intensity 15 W m^{-2}. Photoelectric emission does not occur. The experimenter decides to change the source of illumination.
    Which of the incident illuminations in the table below is/are more likely to produce photoelectric emission?

radiation	frequency	intensity
A	4×10^{14} Hz	10 W m^{-2}
B	4×10^{14} Hz	20 W m^{-2}
C	3×10^{14} Hz	20 W m^{-2}
D	5×10^{14} Hz	10 W m^{-2}

6   What is the relationship between a photoelectric current and the intensity of the radiation producing it?

7   A beam of radiation acts as a stream of individual energy bundles. What are these called? What is the equation relating the energy E of a single bundle of energy to the frequency f of the radiation and Planck's constant h?

8   A single bundle of electromagnetic energy has an energy of 2.9×10^{-19} J. What is the frequency of the radiation? (Planck's constant $= 6.6 \times 10^{-34}$ J s.)

9   Write down an equation relating the following quantities:
    I = the intensity of radiation falling on a surface
    f = the frequency of the radiation
    N = the number of bundles of energy falling on unit area of the surface per second
    h = Planck's constant.

10 The symbol for the maximum kinetic energy with which a photoelectron is emitted is E_k.
    How is E_k related to the work function hf_0 and the energy hf of the incident photon?

11 If an electron in a free atom is given increased energy, can it increase its energy continuously until it is ejected from the atom? Explain your answer.

12 An electron in a hydrogen atom can occupy one of three possible energy levels. Draw a diagram to show these levels and the possible energy transitions between these levels.

13 For an electron in a free atom, describe what would happen if its energy is increased. Your description should include the terms 'ground state', 'excited state' and 'ionization level'.

14 An emission line in a spectrum has a frequency f. How is this frequency related to an upper energy level W_2 and a lower level W_1 in the atoms from which the light is emitted?

15 Describe how a line in an absorption spectrum is produced and write an equation relating the frequency f of the absorbed energy to upper energy level W_2 and lower energy level W_1 in the atoms of the absorbing substance.

16 A spectrum produced from sunlight contains absorption lines. How does this come about?

17 Is it possible to predict how long it will take for an atom in an excited state to emit radiation?

18 What is likely to occur when radiation of energy hf is incident on an excited atom with excess energy hf?

19 In stimulated emission of radiation, what can be said about the direction of travel and the phase of the incident and emitted radiation?

20 In a laser, photons may be absorbed or may produce more photons by stimulated emission. Which process must dominate if the laser is to operate? What is the full name for laser?

21 A laser contains two mirrors. How do they differ and what is their function in the laser?

22 Why can a laser beam of power as low as 0.1 mW cause damage to the eyes?

23 What are the names given to the following categories of materials which react in the following way when a potential difference is applied across them:
    a) materials that readily allow a current to flow;
    b) materials which do not normally allow a current to flow unless the potential difference is very high;
    c) materials that allow a current to flow, but not as readily as the first group.

24 **a)** Which of the following is **not** a conductor?
        copper;   germanium;   aluminium.
    b) Which of the following is **not** an insulator?
        copper;   plastic;   rubber.
    c) Which of the following is **not** a semiconductor?
        silicon;   germanium;   aluminium.

25 How can the conductivity of a pure semiconductor be increased?

26 **a)** Explain how doping can form an n-type semiconductor and state what the charge carriers are.
    b) Explain how doping can form a p-type semiconductor and state what the charge carriers are.

27 **a)** In a p-n junction diode the p-type semiconductor is more positive than the n-type semiconductor.
        i) Is the junction forward or reverse biased?
        ii) Will the diode conduct?
        iii) Explain your answer by stating what happens to the charge carriers at the junction.
    b) In a p-n junction diode the p-type semiconductor is more negative than the n-type semiconductor.
        i) Is the junction forward or reverse biased?
        ii) Will the diode conduct?
        iii) Explain your answer by stating what happens to the charge carriers at the junction.

28 Explain how in the junction region of a forward biased p-n junction diode the charge carriers may produce quanta of radiation.

29 In a photodiode, how does the action of light affect the charges in a p-n junction?

30 In what mode can a photodiode be used to supply power to a load resistor?

31 In what mode can a photodiode be used as a light sensor.

32 A potential difference is applied across an electronic component in a circuit. It is found that the current in the circuit is directly proportional to the light intensity on this component. The current is not affected by variations in the potential difference across the component.
Name the component and say which end must be made more positive by the applied voltage.

33 Which of the following is an important property of a reverse biased photodiode?
  i) It produces light.
  ii) It has a very fast switching action.
  iii) It amplifies electric current.

34 Describe the structure of an n-channel MOSFET using the terms: gate, source, drain, substrate, channel implant and oxide layer.

35 **a)** Will an n-channel MOSFET be in the ON or OFF state when the potential difference between the gate and the substrate is zero?
    b) To change this state, should the gate be made more positive or negative?
    In each case explain how this comes about.

36 As which of the following can an n-channel MOSFET be used:
  i) amplifier;
  ii) power meter;
  iii) light detector;
  iv) load resistor.

Topic 3.4
Nuclear Reactions

Objectives

When you have completed the work of this topic you should be able to:

1 describe how Rutherford showed that:
   a) the nucleus has a relatively small diameter compared with that of the atom;
   b) most of the mass of the atom is concentrated in the nucleus;
2 explain what is meant by alpha, beta and gamma decay of radionuclides;
3 identify the processes occurring in nuclear reactions written in symbolic form;
4 state that, in fission, a nucleus of large mass number splits into two nuclei of smaller mass numbers, usually along with several neutrons;
5 state that fission may be spontaneous or induced by neutron bombardment;
6 state that, in fusion, two nuclei combine to form a nucleus of larger mass number;
7 explain, using $E = mc^2$, how the products of fission and fusion acquire large amounts of kinetic energy;
8 carry out calculations, using $E = mc^2$, for fission and fusion reactions.

3.4 Nuclear Reactions

Models of the atom

At the beginning of the nineteenth century John Dalton put forward a theory which assumed that matter consisted of solid indivisible particles called atoms. At the start of the twentieth century, experimental evidence had suggested the existence of even smaller particles. It was recognized that atoms contain positive and negative charges; J. J. Thomson suggested a model in which the positive charge is distributed evenly throughout the volume of the atom with negative charges fixed at various points, like 'currants in a plum pudding', Figure 1.

On the basis of this model, a stream of charged particles fired at the atom would be deflected through only fairly small angles.

In 1908 Geiger and Marsden, two assistants of Ernest Rutherford, started to investigate the deflection of alpha particles which they fired at a thin metal foil, Figure 2.

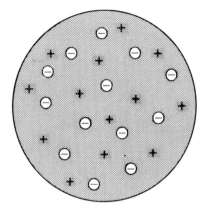

Figure 1 Model of the atom suggested by J. J. Thomson

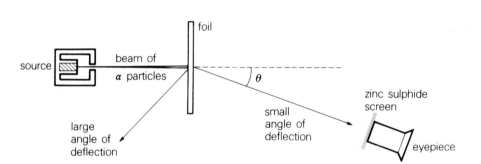

Figure 2

In 1909 they made the surprising discovery that a few of the particles bounced back from the foil. When Geiger reported to Rutherford, he expressed his surprise by saying that 'it was almost as incredible as if you had fired a 15-inch shell at a piece of tissue paper and it came back and hit you'.

Rutherford showed that these results could only be explained if the positive charge was concentrated into a very small volume. Making this assumption Rutherford applied the rules of electrostatic force between charges and predicted the number of particles which would be deflected along a given direction.

Geiger and Marsden then tested Rutherford's theory using the apparatus shown in Figure 3.

In the experiments, a beam of alpha particles from a radon source was fired at a metal foil. After deflection the particles were observed through the eyepiece which was set at different positions round the rotating table.

The presence of the alpha particles was detected by a zinc sulphide screen. Every time an alpha particle hit the screen, a minute flash of light (a scintillation) was seen through the microscope. By counting the number of flashes, it was possible to determine the number of particles arriving at the screen. The screen could be moved to detect alpha particles which had been deflected at various angles. The chamber was evacuated to prevent the absorption of the particles by the air.

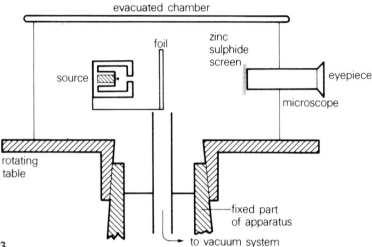

Figure 3

In his theory Rutherford predicted four factors upon which the number of particles hitting the zinc sulphide screen would depend:

1   the magnitude of the positive charge on the nucleus;

2   the angle of deflection θ;

3   the velocity of the particles;

4   the thickness of the metal foil.

The experimental results confirmed that these four factors determined the number of particles hitting the screen. On the basis of these findings Rutherford proposed a model of the atom in which the mass and positive charge are concentrated in the nucleus surrounded by a space containing the negative charge.

To appreciate the relative sizes, if the diameter of the nucleus were a few millimetres the whole of the atom would be about the same size as a football stadium. Figure 4 gives a simple picture of the model.

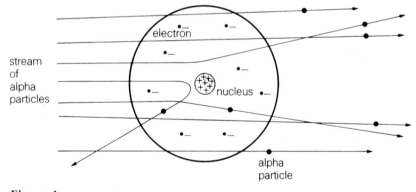

Figure 4

The particles in the nucleus were called protons by Rutherford (after the Greek *protos* meaning 'first'). This was taken up by Niels Bohr (among others) who proposed that the negative charges, the electrons, were confined to strictly defined orbits round the nucleus. The charge on an electron is -1.6×10^{-19} C and the charge on a proton is $+1.6 \times 10^{-19}$ C. Since the atom is electrically neutral, the total negative charge is equal to the total positive charge. Thus, for a neutral atom, the total number of electrons must be the same as the total number of positive charges. All the atoms of any one element contain the same number of protons; this number is called the **atomic number**.

Isotopes

A mass spectrometer is used to determine accurately the mass of the atoms of an element. A simplified diagram of the apparatus is shown in Figure 5.

Positive ions of the element under test are produced at an anode and accelerated through a hollow cathode. They then pass through an electric field which produces a deflection away from the positive plate (plate A in Figure 5).

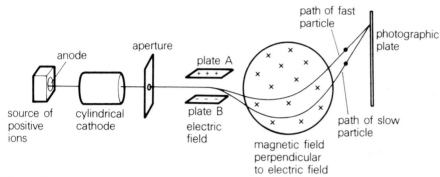

Figure 5

The positive ions are then deflected by a magnetic field which causes the particles to hit a photographic plate and form an image. By using these two fields, it is possible to eliminate the effects of varying speeds in the particle stream so that all particles of the same mass are focused at one point only on the screen. It is possible to determine accurately the mass of any particle by measurements taken from the mark on the photographic plate.

Data obtained on the mass of atoms indicated that atoms of the same element can have different masses. Such atoms are called isotopes. It is possible for an atom to have more than one isotope; for example, the element tin has as many as ten isotopes. An explanation for the existence of isotopes was finally provided in 1932 by James Chadwick. He bombarded a beryllium target with alpha particles, Figure 6.

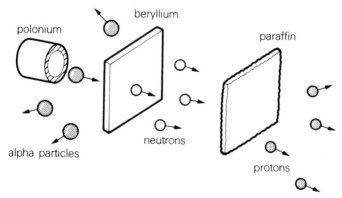

Figure 6

The beryllium target gave off radiation which was found to be able to penetrate several centimetres of lead. If however, this radiation is used to bombard paraffin wax the radiation is absorbed and protons are ejected from the slab. By considering conservation of momentum and energy, Chadwick was able to show that a neutral particle was emitted by the beryllium. He called this particle a neutron, symbol $_0^1\text{n}$, which has the same mass as a proton but no charge. It is the presence of the neutron in the nucleus which accounts for isotopes. Isotopes of an element have the same number of protons but different numbers of neutrons.

Most elements have several isotopes; many isotopes occur naturally, but others can be made artificially. Often isotopes are stable, but those that are unstable are radioactive and are known as **radioisotopes**, Table 1.

Protons and neutrons are known collectively as **nucleons**.
When specifying an atomic nucleus, it is necessary to give some numbers:

A = mass number or nucleon number
= number of nucleons (protons + neutrons) in nucleus;
Z = atomic number or proton number
= number of protons in the nucleus;
N = neutron number
= number of neutrons in the nucleus.

These are related by $N = A - Z$.

For example:

$$A \longrightarrow {}^{208}_{82}\text{Pb}$$
$$Z \longrightarrow {}_{82}$$

$N = 208 - 82 = 126$

For example a beryllium nucleus has the symbol ${}^{9}_{4}\text{Be}$ where the number of protons is 4 and the number of neutrons is 5.
   These symbols are used in an equation to describe a nuclear reaction. For example, when an alpha particle bombards a beryllium nucleus, a neutron and a carbon nucleus are formed.

$$
{}^{9}_{4}\text{Be} \quad + \quad {}^{4}_{2}\text{He} \quad \longrightarrow \quad {}^{12}_{6}\text{C} \quad + \quad {}^{1}_{0}\text{n}
$$
beryllium   alpha particle   carbon   neutron

A specific nucleus of an element is termed a **nuclide**. If the nuclide is radioactive it is called a **radionuclide**. For nuclei of greater mass, greater numbers of nucleons are packed together. For example, the hydrogen nucleus ${}^{1}_{1}\text{H}$ contains 1 proton and no neutrons, but a uranium nucleus ${}^{238}_{92}\text{U}$ contains 92 protons and 146 neutrons. Since protons are positive, they exert an electrostatic force of repulsion on each other, yet are contained tightly packed together in the nucleus without flying apart. Part of the reason for this lies in the presence of the neutrons.

	stable isotope	radioactive isotope
carbon	${}^{12}_{6}\text{C}$	${}^{14}_{6}\text{C}$
strontium	${}^{88}_{38}\text{Sr}$	${}^{90}_{38}\text{Sr}$
iodine	${}^{127}_{53}\text{I}$	${}^{131}_{53}\text{I}$
gold*	${}^{197}_{79}\text{Au}$	
einsteinium	–	${}^{254}_{99}\text{Es}$

* has no naturally occurring isotopes

Table 1

Nuclear radiation

When a nucleus disintegrates forming the nucleus of a new element, it emits radiation. The emissions can be alpha, beta or gamma radiation.

Alpha particles

Alpha (α) particles are nuclei of helium and contain two protons and two neutrons.

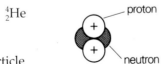

${}^{4}_{2}\text{He}$

Figure 7 Alpha particle

They have a mass number of 4 and a charge of +2e.

Beta particles

Beta (β) particles are high energy electrons which have a very small mass and a charge of $-e$.

$^{0}_{-1}e$

Figure 8 Beta particle

Gamma-rays

Gamma-rays (γ-rays) are bursts of electromagnetic radiation.

When a nucleus disintegrates emitting either an α-particle or a β-particle, the resulting nucleus is often in a highly excited state. In a very short time, usually less than a microsecond, the nucleons re-arrange themselves into a more stable configuration and energy is released in the form of gamma radiation.

The properties of each of these radiations is given in Table 2.

name	nature	velocity	ionization in air	cloud chamber tracks	absorption	deflection
alpha	helium nucleus	5% of speed of light	produces a large number of ions	dense tracks	can be stopped by paper	deflected by a magnetic field
beta	high energy electron	90% of speed of light	produces some ions	less dense tracks than alpha particles	can be stopped by aluminium	deflected by a magnetic field
gamma	electro-magnetic radiation	speed of light	produces very few ions	very few tracks	not easily absorbed even by lead	not deflected by a magnetic field

Table 2

Equations of decay

When a nucleus disintegrates, it usually undergoes several stages before a stable nucleus is formed. This series of disintegrations is termed a **radioactive decay** series. At each stage, radiation is emitted and a new nuclide is formed.

An example is the decay of uranium to protactinium during which alpha, beta and gamma radiation is emitted.

Uranium-238 decays to thorium-234 emitting alpha particles and gamma radiation.

The thorium-234 decays to protactinium-234 emitting beta particles and gamma radiation.

These processes are taking place at the same time within the same sample of original uranium-238.

The disintegrations can be described using equations of nuclide symbols.

α emission $\qquad ^{238}_{92}U \longrightarrow\ ^{234}_{90}Th + ^{4}_{2}He + \gamma$

When alpha particles are given out the mass (nucleon) number decreases by 4 and the proton (atomic) number decreases by 2.

β emission $\qquad ^{234}_{90}Th \longrightarrow\ ^{234}_{91}Pa + ^{0}_{-1}e + \gamma$

When beta particles are given off the mass (nucleon) number is unchanged, but the proton number increases by 1. This occurs because a neutron in the nucleus of thorium-234 splits up into a beta particle which is radiated and a proton which forms the nucleus of protactinium-234.

The process can also be described by omitting the gamma rays and writing the symbols α and β above the arrow:

$$^{238}_{92}\text{U} \xrightarrow{\ \alpha\ } \ ^{234}_{90}\text{Th} \xrightarrow{\ \beta\ } \ ^{234}_{91}\text{Pa}$$

Example 1

The symbol $^{194}_{78}\text{Pt}$ represents an isotope of platinum.

What is the neutron number?

$$\begin{aligned}
\text{neutron number } N &= \text{nucleon number} - \text{proton number} \\
&= 194 - 78 \\
&= 116
\end{aligned}$$

There are 116 neutrons in the nucleus.

Example 2

An isotope of lead disintegrates as shown below.

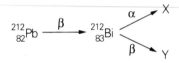

Find the nucleon and proton number for the nuclides X and Y and from the Periodic Table find which elements they represent. Write the symbols for each of these nuclides.

When bismuth decays emitting an alpha particle, the nucleon number decreases by 4 giving

$$212 - 4 = 208$$

The proton number decreases by 2 giving

$$83 - 2 = 81.$$

From the Periodic Table, this represents the element thallium.

Nuclide X is therefore

$$^{208}_{81}\text{Tl.}$$

When bismuth decays emitting a beta particle, the nucleon number remains the same but the proton number increases by 1 giving

$$83 + 1 = 84.$$

From the Periodic Table this represents polonium.

Nuclide Y is therefore

$$^{212}_{84}\text{Po.}$$

Radioactive series

When a nuclide disintegrates, it forms a daughter nucleus which in turn disintegrates forming another nucleus. This process continues and a series of new nuclei is formed.

This can be illustrated by using a diagram listing elements in boxes. Each box has a nucleon number on the vertical axis and a proton number on the horizontal axis. These correspond to the numbers A and Z in the nuclide symbol $^A_Z X$. This is shown in the diagram, Figure 9.

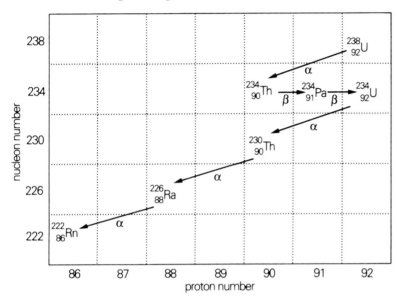

Figure 9

Notice that, when uranium-238 decays emitting an alpha particle, the arrow indicates the new nuclide, thorium-234; this is one row down and two columns to the left.

In a similar way, beta emission is indicated by a movement of one column to the right in the same row. Thorium-234 becomes protactinium-234.

Example 3

The diagram shows part of a radioactive decay series.

a) Give two examples of pairs of isotopes.
b) Write down in equation form one example of alpha decay.
c) Write down in equation form one example of beta decay.

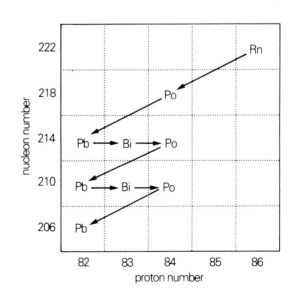

a) Isotopes have the same proton number but different nucleon numbers.
From the diagram, examples are $^{218}_{84}Po$ and $^{214}_{84}Po$; $^{214}_{82}Pb$ and $^{210}_{82}Pb$.

b) Radon decays to polonium emitting an α-particle.
$$^{222}_{86}Rn \xrightarrow{\alpha} {}^{218}_{84}Po$$

c) Lead decays to bismuth emitting a β-particle.
$$^{210}_{82}Pb \xrightarrow{\beta} {}^{210}_{83}Bi$$

Unstable nuclei

When the number of protons in a nucleus is small, an equal number of neutrons results in a stable nucleus. For example helium has 2 protons and 2 neutrons; oxygen has 8 protons and 8 neutrons. As the number of protons increases, a greater proportion of neutrons is required to ensure stability. This can be seen with iron (26 protons, 28 neutrons), tin (50 protons, 62 neutrons), lead (82 protons, 126 neutrons), and bismuth (83 protons, 126 neutrons). In fact, no nucleus with 84 protons or more is stable. These massive nuclei disintegrate producing radiation.

The disintegration of uranium results in the following radioactive series (Table 3). In the series each element is formed when the preceding one disintegrates.

element	isotope	radiation	
uranium	$^{238}_{92}U$	α	γ
thorium	$^{234}_{90}Th$	β	γ
protactinium	$^{234}_{91}Pa$	β	γ
uranium	$^{234}_{92}U$	α	γ
thorium	$^{230}_{90}Th$	α	γ
radium	$^{226}_{88}Ra$	α	γ
radon	$^{222}_{86}Rn$	α	
polonium	$^{218}_{84}Po$	α	
lead	$^{214}_{82}Pb$	β	γ
bismuth	$^{214}_{83}Bi$	β	γ
polonium	$^{214}_{84}Po$	α	
lead	$^{210}_{82}Pb$	β	γ
bismuth	$^{210}_{83}Bi$	β	
polonium	$^{214}_{84}Po$	α	
lead	$^{210}_{82}Pb$	STABLE	

Table 3

The disintegration of the nuclei in such a series will continue until a stable nuclide (usually lead or bismuth) is produced and no more disintegrations take place. Although nuclei with more than 83 protons are unstable, they do exist because all of the nuclei do not disintegrate at the same time.

Nuclear fission

Nuclear fission is the splitting of a nucleus of large mass into two nuclei of smaller mass. The process may be accompanied by the release of energy, and of neutrons or gamma-rays, or both.

Fission is usually caused by neutron bombardment and this is known as **induced** fission; however it is possible for fission to be **spontaneous**, particularly in the case of the heavier elements.

Nuclear fission was first discovered in 1938 by two Germans, Hahn and Strassman. They bombarded uranium with neutrons and found that the products of the reaction had a proton number of about 56. A number of different reactions are possible, including the following.

$$_{0}^{1}\text{n} + {}_{92}^{238}\text{U} \longrightarrow {}_{56}^{145}\text{Ba} + {}_{36}^{94}\text{Kr}$$

$$_{0}^{1}\text{n} + {}_{92}^{235}\text{U} \longrightarrow {}_{56}^{138}\text{Ba} + {}_{36}^{95}\text{Kr} + 3{}_{0}^{1}\text{n} + \text{energy}$$

The reaction with the production of neutrons and energy is shown diagrammatically in Figure 10.

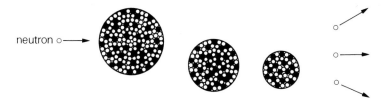

Figure 10

To describe how the nucleus splits in this way George Gamow, a Russian working in America, proposed a liquid drop model, Figure 11. First the neutron penetrates the 'nuclear liquid' to form the isotope uranium-239. The extra energy causes the nucleus to oscillate. If the energy is sufficient the drop becomes elongated and eventually splits into two separate parts.

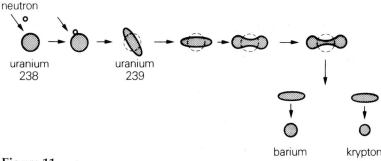

Figure 11

If the energy is not sufficient the nucleus vibrates but eventually settles down again releasing a neutron and returning to its original form, Figure 12.

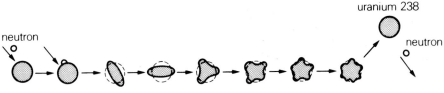

Figure 12

Energy release

The amount of energy released in a fission reaction can be found from Einstein's equation of mass–energy equivalence:

$$E = mc^2 \quad \text{where } E = \text{energy released (J)}$$
$$m = \text{mass defect, or loss in mass after the reaction (kg)}$$
$$c = \text{velocity of light (m s}^{-1})$$

Example 4

Consider the fission reaction of uranium-235 that results in the formation of the stable elements molybdenum and xenon.

$$^{235}_{92}U + ^1_0n \longrightarrow ^{98}_{42}Mo + ^{136}_{54}Xe + 2^1_0n + 4^{\ 0}_{-1}\beta$$

before		after	
$^{235}_{92}U$	234.993 u	$^{98}_{42}Mo$	97.883 u
^1_0n	1.009 u	$^{136}_{54}Xe$	135.878 u
		2^1_0n	2.018 u
		$4^{\ 0}_{-1}\beta$	0.002 u
total mass 236.002 u		total mass 235.781 u	

(1 u = 1 unified atomic mass unit = 1.660×10^{-27} kg)

$$\text{mass defect} = 0.221 \text{ u} = 0.221 \times 1.660 \times 10^{-27}$$
$$= 0.369 \times 10^{-27} \text{ kg}$$

energy equivalence:
$$E = mc^2 = 0.369 \times 10^{-27} \times (3 \times 10^8)^2$$
$$= 3.32 \times 10^{-11}$$

Energy released = 3.32×10^{-11} J.

Chain reactions and the atomic bomb

Uranium-238 does not easily undergo fission, but the isotope uranium-235 is suited to the capture of a neutron and the production of two, or sometimes three further neutrons. These neutrons in turn are able to continue the fission process, given the right conditions. Under these conditions, a reaction known as a **chain reaction** is started; this provides its own conditions for continuation with the additional neutrons released and enables the rapid release of an enormous amount of energy.

However, the isotope uranium-235 comprises only 0.7% of the total naturally occurring uranium. It is possible to concentrate the isotope in one sample by a process of enrichment and this was made possible in 1945, resulting in the explosion on 16 July of the first atomic bomb at Alamogordo in New Mexico, Figure 13.

Figure 13

When the nucleus of uranium splits up, it releases further neutrons which are capable of bombarding neighbouring nuclei producing further fission. If there are sufficient nuclei of uranium-235 available there is a build-up of nuclei being split until there is a large release of energy all at once. In order for this to happen a critical mass must be present and when this happens the chain reaction goes ahead and an atomic explosion takes place releasing a huge amount of energy, equivalent to thousands of tonnes of conventional explosive. This is shown diagrammatically in Figure 14.

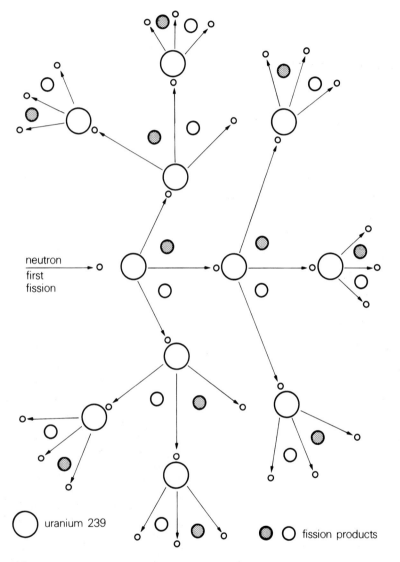

Figure 14

When an atomic explosion takes place there are three damaging effects.

Blast – the explosion forces air outward in huge shock waves and the earth trembles. This combination of wind and earthquake has a devastating effect on houses and structures

Heat – a huge release of heat produces very high temperatures and sets up widespread fires

Radiation – very energetic rays, gamma-rays and X-rays, are released which can damage living tissue.

The products of the explosion which are highly radioactive are released and carried by wind and air currents and spread over a large area. These products are known as fallout and are highly dangerous. One of the most dangerous is strontium-90 which does not occur naturally but can be absorbed into the body in much the same way as calcium. This radioactive material persists throughout the lifetime of a human being and increases the risk of cancer.

Nuclear reactors

In an atomic explosion a chain reaction occurs and a huge uncontrollable release of energy takes place. Fortunately the fission reaction can be controlled so that it produces useful heat energy without the explosion.

For a fission process to continue the following conditions must be satisfied.

1   There are enough heavy nuclei of the fuel material packed together to capture released neutrons. There must be enough fissions to start the reaction.

2   These neutrons must have the correct energy to cause fission in other nuclei before they escape from the material.

There are three essential parts in a reactor:
a)   the rods of fuel which provide heavy nuclei and neutrons;
b)   control rods which absorb some of the neutrons and so regulate the number of neutrons in the system;
c)   a moderator which slows down the neutrons.

The first type of operating reactor used natural uranium as the fuel, in the form of rods, with rods of cadmium or boron fitted to control the number of neutrons. Graphite was used as the moderator, all three parts forming the **core** of the reactor.

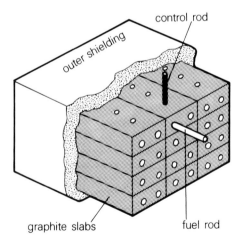

Figure 15 Reactor core

The fuel, containing the isotope uranium-235, captures the neutrons and releases a large amount of energy. In order for this to happen, the fast neutrons which are released during fission must be slowed down to increase the chance of capture by the nuclei. Graphite does not capture neutrons but successive collisions with the graphite nuclei result in loss of energy which slows the neutrons down.

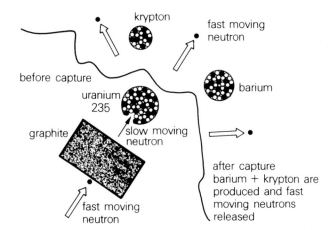

Figure 16

The speed of the neutrons must be correct to ensure efficient capturing. Another important aspect is the means of controlling the number of neutrons; this is achieved by using control rods to absorb the neutrons. The control rods are let down into the core and contain a material, such as boron, which has a strong affinity for neutrons. Boron captures neutrons, forming the stable elements helium ($^4_2$He) and lithium ($^7_3$Li) so that the captured neutrons are lost for ever.

In practice, the number of neutrons produced in the reaction is monitored continuously and when it rises above a predetermined level, the control rods are pushed a little further into the core. This additional absorption of neutrons causes the reaction to proceed at a lower rate. If the rods are withdrawn slightly, the reaction proceeds at a higher rate.

The nuclear reactor produces heat. This heat raises the temperature of a liquid or gas which circulates round the reactor core. The hot liquid or gas is then used to produce steam which operates a turbine generating electricity, Figure 17.

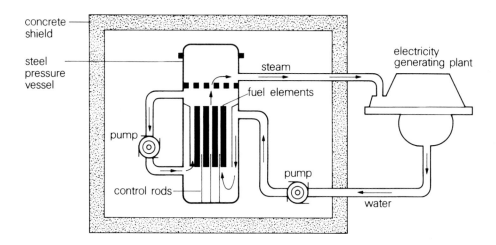

Figure 17 Boiling water reactor (BWR)

Plutonium has been produced in large quantities as a by-product of some reactors and when used in fast breeder reactors (so called because fast neutrons are used), it is possible to convert natural uranium into additional plutonium which can be used as fuel. It thus 'breeds' additional fuel for use in reactors. Figure 18 shows the first fast breeder reactor which was set up in Dounreay in 1960. Due to difficulties it has been shut down.

Figure 18(a) Fast breeder reactor at Dounreay

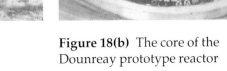

Figure 18(b) The core of the Dounreay prototype reactor

Radioactive materials can cause cancer and produce genetic damage so they must be safely stored in an isolated place. The storage and disposal of the waste from power stations is a major problem and has not yet been adequately solved.

Nuclear fusion

We have seen that when a heavy nucleus such as uranium splits up forming two new elements, energy is released either in an uncontrolled manner in the atomic bomb or in a carefully controlled process in a nuclear reactor.

It is also possible to release energy by joining two light nuclei together to form a new nucleus in a process known as nuclear fusion.

In order to explain how energy is released by fusion, the average mass per nucleon, measured in unified atomic mass units, must be considered. This is found by dividing the mass of the nucleus by the number of nucleons in the nucleus.

$$\text{average mass per nucleon} = \frac{\text{total mass of nucleus}}{\text{number of nucleons in the nucleus}}$$

Table 7 shows the calculations for some elements.

element	mass of nucleus (u)	no. of nucleons	average mass per nucleon (u)
hydrogen	1.008	1	1.0080
helium	4.002	4	1.0005
potassium	38.953	39	0.9988
tin	119.875	120	0.9990
platinum	193.920	195	0.9945
uranium	234.993	235	1.0000

Table 4

If similar calculations are carried out for all elements, a graph of average mass per nucleon against number of nucleons can be drawn, Figure 19.

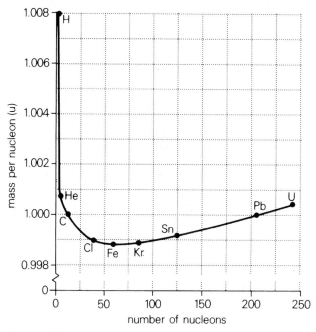

Figure 19

Figure 20

From the graph it can be seen that if two nuclei of hydrogen are combined to form a helium nucleus, the average mass per nucleon of the single helium nucleus is less than the average mass per nucleon for the original hydrogen nuclei. This deficit in mass is converted into energy.

A number of possible fusion reactions exist and many involve two isotopes of hydrogen, deuterium and tritium, Figure 20.

Deuterium, usually called heavy hydrogen, contains an additional neutron and can be written either $_1^2H$ or $_1^2D$. It is in plentiful supply existing in 'heavy water' which makes up about 1 part in 5000 of all water. Another isotope, tritium, contains two additional neutrons and can be written $_1^3H$ or $_1^3T$.

In one possible reaction, two nuclei of deuterium combine to form a single nucleus of an isotope of helium plus one neutron.

$$_1^2D \; + \; _1^2D \; \rightarrow \; _2^3He \; + \; _0^1n$$
$$2.013\,u + 2.013\,u \quad 3.015\,u + 1.009\,u$$

There is a mass defect which releases energy

$$\text{mass defect} = 4.026 - 4.024$$
$$= 0.002\,u$$

But 1 u releases about 931 MeV (1 MeV = 1.6×10^{-13} J)

Therefore the energy released = $0.002 \times 931 = 1.9$ MeV

A fusion reaction requires very high temperatures in order to provide enough kinetic energy to overcome the forces of electrostatic repulsion between the positive nuclei. Temperatures of one hundred million degrees Celsius are necessary to fuse a large number of nuclei together at the same time so that a thermonuclear explosion can take place: this is the principle of the hydrogen bomb. In the H-bomb the high temperatures are provided by an atomic explosion which is used to initiate the reaction. The high temperatures produce a stream of positive ions and electrons called a plasma.

One possible reaction which can take place in the plasma is described by the following equation

$$_1^2D + _1^3T \rightarrow _2^4He + _0^1n + 17.6\,MeV$$

The energy released, 17.6 MeV, is very much less than that obtained by a fission reaction (200 MeV) but it must be remembered that the nucleus of uranium has a mass of about 235 u whereas the mass of one deuterium nuclei is about 2 u. The energy yield per kilogram for a fusion reaction is very much larger than the energy per kilogram for a fission reaction. There is also no requirement for a critical mass as there is for a fission reaction.

The possibility of producing energy from a controlled fusion reaction is very attractive because of the plentiful supply of deuterium and also because the radioactive waste produced is small.

In order to achieve a controlled thermonuclear (fusion) reaction four conditions must be satisfied:

a)   suitable material which will undergo fusion must be available;

b)   material must be heated to the required high temperature;

c)   hot plasma must be contained sufficiently long to allow the energy produced by fusion to exceed the input energy;

d)   fusion energy must be converted into electricity.

A possible practical arrangement is illustrated in Figure 21. This shows the Tokamak system first developed in the USSR in the late 1960's.

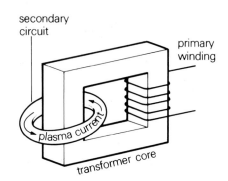

Figure 21

A current is produced in the primary circuit, usually by some kind of discharge. Transformer action causes a very large current to be induced in the secondary. This current heats the plasma and temperatures of 70 million degrees have been attained.

The most difficult problem is to contain the plasma because if the plasma touches the walls of the container the high temperatures would destroy the container material. Present methods use strong magnetic fields which are designed to confine the stream of plasma. The magnetic field produced by the plasma current itself tends to hold the particles of the plasma together. The streams of ions moving in the same direction produce magnetic fields which tend to draw the streams together in the same way that two conductors lying side by side will be pulled towards each other by the magnetic fields (Figure 22). This is known as the **pinch effect** (Figure 23).

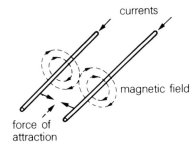

Figure 22

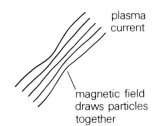

Figure 23

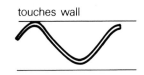

Figure 24

Unfortunately the plasma does not remain stable and starts to twist and eventually touches the walls, Figure 24.

The plasma can be stabilized for short periods by applying a large magnetic field by means of a coil wrapped round the container walls, Figure 25.

This and other methods are not entirely satisfactory and a great deal of further research is needed to produce a working system. The first attempt at a

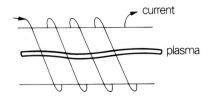

Figure 25

Figure 26

thermonuclear reactor in the United Kingdom was completed at Harwell in 1958, Figure 26. It was known as ZETA.

A circular aluminium tube, known as a torus, contains deuterium. The tube has a diameter of about 1 metre and the circle is about 4 metres across, Figure 27.

To start up the process a radio frequency oscillator is used to produce a spark discharge inside the torus which ionizes the deuterium gas. This oscillator is turned off and a large bank of capacitors is discharged through the primary winding of a transformer. This causes a large pulse of deuterium ions to flow round the torus which forms the secondary winding of the transformer. Currents of 250 000 amperes existing for 2 milliseconds have been recorded.

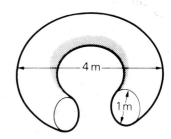

Figure 27

However the plasma cannot be easily stabilized in the circular-shaped torus and research is at present progressing using different methods. Eventually a commercially successful thermonuclear reactor may be built but it will not provide cheap power. There are formidable engineering difficulties and the capital cost of such a reactor is high because of the equipment needed for magnets, cooling systems and ancillary equipment. As supplies of conventional fuel begin to run out the cost of a thermonuclear reactor will become competitive. The exciting aspect of the system is the fact that the deuterium fuel is in such plentiful supply in the oceans of the world.

Summary

Rutherford's scattering experiments showed that most of an atom is empty space and that all the positive charge and practically all the mass of an atom is concentrated in a tiny nucleus.

The nucleus of an atom contains protons and neutrons.

A nucleus can be described using a symbol such as $^A_Z X$ where X denotes the element and

A = number of nucleons
Z = number of protons
$A–Z$ = number of neutrons.

Isotopes contain the same number of protons but different numbers of neutrons.

An element can have more than one isotope.

An alpha particle is a helium nucleus (charge + 2).
A beta particle is a fast moving electron (charge – 1).
A gamma ray is a high frequency electromagnetic radiation (no charge) and travels at the speed of light.

Alpha emission can be represented by:

$$^A_Z X \rightarrow ^{A-4}_{Z-2} Y + ^4_2 He$$

The mass number falls by 4 and the atomic number falls by 2.

Beta emission can be represented by:

$$^A_Z X \rightarrow ^A_{Z+1} Y + ^{\ 0}_{-1} He$$

The mass number is unchanged and the atomic number increases by 1.

Gamma emission does not affect either the mass number or the atomic number.

Einstein showed that mass and energy are related by the equation $E = mc^2$.

In nuclear fission a nucleus splits forming two new elements and releasing energy.

A critical mass is required before a chain reaction can take place.

In nuclear fusion two nuclei join together forming a single nucleus and releasing energy.

Questions

1   In a historically important experiment a stream of alpha particles directed at a metal target produced a set of results which led to the development of a model of the atom suggested by Rutherford. Draw a diagram of the apparatus used, describe how observations were taken and indicate how the results were interpreted to explain the structure of an atom.

2   A decay process is described by the symbolic equation

$$^{14}_6 C \rightarrow ^A_Z \ ? \ + ^{\ 0}_{-1} e$$

   a)   What particle is emitted?
   b)   Copy the equation, filling in the missing element indicated by the box and put in the missing numbers A and Z.

3   Energy is released when the reaction described below takes place.

$$^{239}_{94} Pu + ^1_0 n \rightarrow ^{137}_{52} Te + ^{100}_{42} Mo + 3^1_0 n$$

   a)   Name the type of reaction taking place.
   b)   Using the figures in the table below, estimate the energy released for each nucleus of plutonium.

nuclide/particle	mass (u)
$^{239}_{94} Pu$	239.0512
$^1_0 n$	1.0087
$^{137}_{52} Te$	137.0000
$^{100}_{42} Mo$	99.9066

4   When radium decays, the nucleus of another element is formed and a particle released.

$$^{226}_{88} Ra \rightarrow ^{222}_{86} Rn + \boxed{\text{particle}}$$

   What particle is produced?

5   In certain circumstances two nuclei can combine to form a more massive nucleus with the release of energy.

$$^2_1 H + ^2_1 H \rightarrow ^4_2 He$$

   a)   What type of reaction is taking place?
   b)   Using the figures given below, calculate the energy released for each helium nucleus formed.

$^2_1 H$	2.0141 u
$^4_2 He$	4.0026 u

6   a)   In the symbol X^m_n what do m and n signify?
   b)   The nuclide X^m_n is radioactive, decaying by emitting in succession alpha, gamma, beta, gamma, beta radiation. What symbol would denote the nuclide at this stage in its decay?
   c)   In an experiment involving plants, a radioactive isotope is to be used as a tracer. Which type, or types, of isotope radiation would be suitable?
   Justify your choice very briefly.

time in days	total count rate in counts per min.
0	66
3	57
6	49
9	43
12	39

From the data:
i) determine which of the following isotopes had been used in the experiment:

Na^{24} — half life 5.6 days
I^{131} — half life 8.1 days
P^{32} — half life 45 days
Sr^{89} — half life 53 days

ii) Find when the sample can be safely thrown away, if this is possible, when its activity is less than that which would give a count rate of 10 counts per minute in the apparatus used. The apparatus used has a background count of 23 counts per minute.

SQA

7 a) A radioactivity kit includes three closed sources made up as shown.

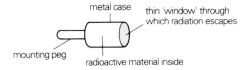

Description of closed sources

type of radiation given out	name of radioactive nucleus	number of protons	number of neutrons
alpha	americium 241	95	146
beta	strontium 90	38	52
gamma	cobalt 60	27	33

i) Describe how to find out, experimentally, which is the alpha source.
ii) When an alpha particle is emitted from an americium nucleus, state the number of protons and the number of neutrons in the new nucleus formed.
iii) Cobalt 60 emits beta and gamma radiations. Explain how the case is designed so that the closed source gives out gamma rays only.

b) The discharge of waste solutions from a factory into a bay is to be investigated.
i) Describe how a radioactive liquid could be used to map the spread of the solution in the bay.
ii) Suggest whether a liquid would be chosen with a half-life of a few seconds, a few minutes, a few days, a few years or many years. Justify your choice.

8 The following reaction takes place in the Sun:

$$^{3}_{1}H + ^{2}_{1}H \rightarrow ^{4}_{2}He + ^{1}_{0}n$$

a) State the name given to this type of reaction.
b) Calculate the energy available from the above reaction, given the following information.
Rest mass of $^{3}_{1}H = 5.005 \times 10^{-27}$ kg
Rest mass of $^{2}_{1}H = 3.342 \times 10^{-27}$ kg
Rest mass of $^{4}_{2}He = 6.642 \times 10^{-27}$ kg
Rest mass of $^{1}_{0}n = 1.674 \times 10^{-27}$ kg.

SQA

9 a) A girl sets up a Geiger–Müller tube and scaler in front of a radioactive source which emits two types of radiation. Pieces of aluminium, of different thicknesses, are placed between the source and detector and the count rate determined in each case.

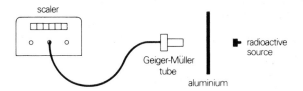

The results obtained were used to plot a graph of count rate, corrected for background, against thickness and this is shown below.

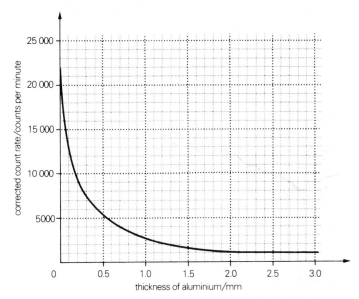

This source is to be stored in an aluminium box and the count rate, measured outside the box, must not be greater than 2000 counts per minute.
Use the graph to estimate:
i) the minimum thickness of aluminium required for the box;
ii) the count rate when the thickness of aluminium is 3 mm.
What types of radiation are emitted from the source? Give reasons for your answer.

b) A water engineer wishes to locate leakage from a long sewage pipe buried under a field. Suggest how he could do this using a Geiger counter and a radioactive liquid. Which of the liquids listed on the right would be most suitable for use? Why?

liquid	half-life	type of emission
A	10 ms	alpha
B	6 hours	gamma
C	10 hours	beta
D	24 days	alpha
E	1000 years	gamma

SQA

Topic 3.4 Test 1

1 The essential parts of a particle scattering experiment carried out by Geiger and Marsden are shown in the plan view diagram.

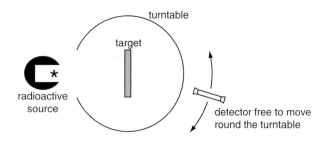

What kind of particles were emitted by the source? State the material used for the target. Explain how the results of this experiment were used by Rutherford to develop a model of the atom.

2 **i)** When a thorium nucleus disintegrates it forms radium and emits a particle.

$$^{232}_{90}\text{Th} \rightarrow \,^{228}_{88}\text{Ra} + \boxed{\text{particle}}$$

What particle is produced?
 i) Explain how a beta particle is produced by a radionuclide.
 ii) Describe the circumstances under which gamma radiation is produced by a radionuclide.

3 **i)** A neptunium nucleus disintegrates and emits an alpha particle.

The symbol for neptunium is $^{237}_{93}\text{Np}$.

Write down this decay process in symbolic form.
 ii) A nuclear reaction is described by the equation below.

$$^{235}_{92}\text{U} + \,^{1}_{0}\text{n} \rightarrow \,^{95}_{X}\text{Kr} + \,^{Y}_{56}\text{Ba} + 3\,^{1}_{0}\text{n}$$

Write down the missing numbers X and Y.

4 Describe what is meant by nuclear fission.

5 Explain the difference between induced and spontaneous fission.

6 Describe the process of nuclear fusion.

7 In fission and fusion processes large amounts of energy are produced.
  Explain how this arises.

8 **i)** A nuclear reaction is described by the equation below.

$$^{235}_{92}\text{U} + \,^{1}_{0}\text{n} \rightarrow \,^{98}_{42}\text{Mo} + \,^{136}_{54}\text{Xe} + 2\,^{1}_{0}\text{n} + 2\,^{0}_{-1}\text{e}$$

What kind of reaction is this?
Using figures in the table calculate the energy released by one uranium nucleus. (Ignore any mass associated with electrons.)

nucleus/particle	mass
uranium-235	235.043 u
molybdenum-98	97.905 u
xenon - 136	135.907 u
neutron	1.009 u

$(1 \text{ u} = 1.660 \times 10^{-27} \text{ kg})$

ii) The equation describes a nuclear reaction.

$$^{1}_{1}\text{H} + \,^{2}_{1}\text{H} \rightarrow \,^{3}_{2}\text{He}$$

What kind of reaction is this?
Using the masses given calculate the energy released when one helium nucleus is formed.

$$^{1}_{1}\text{H} = 1.008 \text{ u} \qquad ^{2}_{1}\text{H} = 2.014 \text{ u}$$
$$^{3}_{2}\text{He} = 3.016 \text{ u} \qquad 1 \, \mu = 1.660 \times 10^{-27} \text{ kg}$$

Topic 3.4 Test 2

1 A computer simulation is used to illustrate the scattering of particles fired at a metal target.

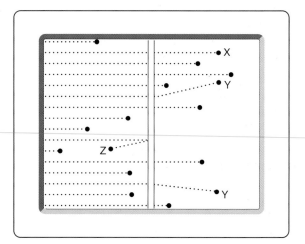

Most particles go straight through as shown at X. Some are deflected by a small amount as at Y. Very few are deflected backwards as at Z.
In the actual experiment carried out by Geiger and Marsden what particles were used?
What metal was used for the target?
Explain how, using the results of this experiment, Rutherford put forward a new model of the atom.

2 Describe the particles or radiation released in the following processes.
 i) A nucleus with nucleon number A and proton number Z, disintegrates forming a daughter nucleus with numbers $(A - 4)$ and $(Z - 2)$.
 ii) A nucleus, nucleon number A and proton number Z, disintegrates forming a new nucleus with numbers A and $(Z + 1)$.
 iii) A daughter nucleus produced after a nucleus disintegrates rearranges its nucleons releasing a burst of radiation.

3 The following equation describes a process used to detect neutrons.

$$^{10}_{5}\text{B} + \,^{1}_{0}\text{n} \rightarrow \,^{7}_{3}\text{Li} + \,^{4}_{2}\text{He}$$

Explain what is happening during this process.

4 A nuclear process is described by the equation below.

$$^{235}_{92} + ^{1}_{0}n \rightarrow ^{140}_{58}Ce + ^{94}_{40}Zr + 1^{1}_{0}n + 6^{0}_{-1}e$$

What is this process called?

5 A nucleus can break into two new nuclei when it captures a neutron.
A very heavy nucleus may, very rarely, split up forming two lighter nuclei of approximately similar mass.
Name the nuclear processes described by these statements.

6 Write down an equation to illustrate nuclear fusion.

7 The following statements are in a textbook.

'A large nucleus can split into two smaller neuclei when it captures a neutron and releases a large amount of energy'.

'Two hydrogen nuclei can fuse together forming a helium nucleus and releasing a large amount of energy'.

Explain how each of these processes is able to release large amounts of energy.

8 Plutonium splits into two nuclei plus other particles.

$$^{239}_{94}Pu + ^{1}_{0}n \rightarrow ^{141}_{58}Ce + ^{96}_{42}Mo + 3^{1}_{0}n + 6^{0}_{-1}e$$

Using the masses given and ignoring the mass of the electrons produced determine the energy released during this process by one plutonium nucleus.

plutonium-239	$=3.968 \times 10^{-25}$ kg
caesium-141	$=2.330 \times 10^{-25}$ kg
molybdenum-96	$=1.592 \times 10^{-25}$ kg
neutron	$=1.674 \times 10^{-27}$ kg

9 Two nuclei of a hydrogen isotope fuse together to form helium and the equation of the process is given below.

$$^{2}_{1}H + ^{2}_{1}H \rightarrow ^{3}_{2}He + ^{1}_{0}n$$

The masses of the isotopes and of the neutron are as follows:

$$^{2}_{1}H = 3.34 \times 10^{-27} \text{ kg}$$
$$^{3}_{2}He = 5.01 \times 10^{-27} \text{ kg}$$
$$^{1}n = 1.67 \times 10^{-27} \text{ kg}$$

Determine the energy released during this process for each helium nucleus formed.

Topic 3.4 Test 3

1 Rutherford suggested that an atom consists of a very small nucleus, positively charged, which contains most of the mass of the atom within itself.
Describe the experiment which was used to illustrate these conclusions.

2 a) When a nucleus disintegrates releasing an alpha particle a process of transmutation takes place.
What happens to the proton number and the nucleon number of the original nucleus?

b) A radionuclide disintegrates and the equation describes this using symbols.

$$^{90}_{38}Sr \rightarrow ^{90}_{39}Y + \boxed{\text{particle}}$$

What is the particle which is released?

c) Often when a nucleus is in an excited state (i.e. it possesses more energy than it can hold on to) during a decay process it emits a quantum of electromagnetic energy.
What is this radiation called?

3 The equation shows a nuclear reaction.

$$^{27}_{13}Al + ^{4}_{2}He \rightarrow ^{30}_{15}P + ^{1}_{0}n$$

Describe what is taking place during this process.

4 Name the process described by the following

'the disintegration of a nucleus of large mass number into two nuclei with much smaller mass number.'

5 Nuclear fission can take place due to neutron bombardment or on its own accord.
Write down the words which describe these two processes.

6 Name the process described as

'the combination of two nuclei to form a single nucleus of larger mass number'.

7 a) In a nuclear reactor heavy nuclei split releasing large amounts of energy.
Explain how such large quantities of energy are produced.

b) In the hydrogen bomb a huge release of energy takes place.
Briefly describe the process involved and explain how a large quantity of energy is produced.

8 Calculate the energy released in joules when one nucleus of an isotope of plutonium undergoes fission as indicated in the equation.
Ignore the mass of the beta particle.

$$^{239}_{94}Pu + ^{1}_{0}n \rightarrow ^{108}_{46}Pd + ^{129}_{54}Xe + 3^{1}_{0}n + 6^{0}_{-1}$$

plutonium-239	$= 3.968 \times 10^{-25}$ kg
palladium-108	$= 1.791 \times 10^{-25}$ kg
xenon-129	$= 2.140 \times 10^{-25}$ kg
neutron	$= 1.674 \times 10^{-25}$ kg

b) A series of fusion reactions take place in the Sun.
These can be summarized by the equation

$$4^{1}_{1}H \rightarrow ^{4}_{2}He + 2^{0}_{1}e \text{ (positron)}$$

Using the masses given calculate the energy released during this process by the formation of one helium nucleus.

$$^{1}_{1}H = 1.673 \times 10^{-27} \text{ kg}$$
$$^{4}_{2}He = 6.644 \times 10^{-27} \text{ kg}$$
$$^{0}_{1}e = 9.11 \times 10^{-31} \text{ kg}$$

Topic 3.5
Dosimetry and Safety

Objectives

When you have completed the work of this topic you should be able to:

1 state that the average activity A of a quantity of radioactive substance is N/t where N is the number of nuclei decaying in time t;
2 state that one becquerel is one decay per second;
3 carry out calculations involving the relationship $A = N/t$;
4 state that the absorbed dose D is the energy absorbed per unit mass of the absorbing material;
5 state that the gray Gy is the unit of absorbed dose and that one gray is one joule per kilogram;
6 state that the risk of biological harm from an exposure to radiation depends on:
    a   the absorbed dose;
    b   the kind of radiations, e.g. slow neutrons;
    c   the body organs or tissues exposed;
7 state that a quality factor Q is given to each kind of radiation as a measure of its biological effect;
8 state that the dose equivalent H is the product of D and Q and is measured in sieverts (Sv);
9 carry out calculations involving the relationship $H = DQ$;
10 state that dose equivalent rate = H/t;
11 state that the effective dose equivalent takes account of different susceptibilities to harm of the tissues being irradiated and is used to indicate the risk to health from exposure to ionizing radiation;
12 describe the factors affecting the background radiation level;
13 state that the average annual effective dose equivalent which a person in the UK receives due to natural sources (cosmic, terrestrial and industrial radiation) is approximately 2 mSv;
14 state that annual effective dose equivalent limits have been set for exposure to radiation for the general public and higher limits for workers in certain occupations;
15 sketch a graph to show how the intensity of a beam of gamma radiation varies with the thickness of an absorber;
16 describe the principles of a method for measuring the half-value thickness of an absorber;
17 carry out calculations involving half-value thickness;
18 state that the dose equivalent rate is reduced by shielding or by increasing the distance from a source.

3.5 Dosimetry and Safety

Hazards

Serious damage can occur when living cells are exposed to ionizing radiation such as X-rays, alpha, beta or gamma radiation.

A hazard warning sign (Figure 1) is used to indicate the presence of ionizing radiation and all containers and storage areas are clearly marked with it.

Figure 1

The energy absorbed by the cell tissue may remove electrons in the organic molecules of the tissue so that ionization takes place.

The main serious effect is ionization of the water in the cells. This upsets the chemical reactions taking place and can lead to injury or death. Exposure to radiation increases the incidence of cancer in cells. Doses of radiation cause nausea, vomiting, radiation burns, changes in blood cells, loss of weight and loss of hair. Death can follow within hours or days of a massive exposure.

Henri Becquerel first discovered radioactivity in 1897, and since then a large amount of data on the effects of radiation on the human body has been collected. Various quantities and units relating to radiation exposure are in use, described below.

The ionizing effects of alpha, beta and gamma radiation are different and for comparison it is useful to consider the ionizing effect that they have on air at atmospheric pressure.

Alpha particles have a short range (about 5 cm) but produce a large number of ions. Beta particles produce a much smaller amount of ionization than alpha particles. Gamma radiation passes readily through the air and produces very few ions.

Therefore alpha particles are potentially harmful because of their ionizing properties. However, another factor to be taken into account is how the various radiations are absorbed into the body. Figure 2 illustrates how α, β and γ radiation are absorbed.

Gamma radiation passes straight through the hand transferring some energy to the cells. Beta particles are absorbed when they have travelled about 1 cm below the surface of the skin. Alpha particles are absorbed at the skin surface. This means that radionuclides, such as radon gas, which emit alpha particles are dangerous only when they are inhaled into the lungs or enter the body in some other way.

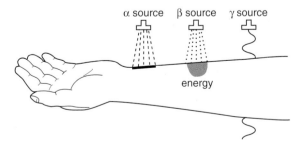

Figure 2

Measuring the dose

Activity

The activity A of a sample of radioactive material is the number of disintegrations of nuclei which occur per second. It is measured in becquerels (Bq) where

   1 Bq = 1 disintegration per second

1 gram of radium has an activity of 3×10^{10} Bq while the activity of sea water is about 11 Bq per litre. The radioactive sources which are used in schools have activities of around 185 kBq.

Absorbed dose

Damage can result due to the transfer of radiation energy to a body. The greater the transfer of energy, the more likely it is that damage will occur.
The absorbed dose D is the energy absorbed per kilogram and is measured in grays (Gy).

   1 Gy = 1 joule per kilogram

Absorbed dose rate

The absorbed dose rate $\dot{D}$ (pronounced D *dot*) is the absorbed dose divided by the time during which it is absorbed.
It is measured in grays per hour or grays per minute.

   absorbed dose = absorbed dose rate × time
$$D = \dot{D} \times t$$

Dose equivalent

In biological systems, the damage depends on the radiation type and how it is distributed. To take account of this a quality factor is introduced; this is a number and indicates the ability of the particular radiation to cause damage.
Table 1 gives some typical figures for quality factor Q.
Having defined the quality factor Q, the dose equivalent H is given by

   dose equivalent = absorbed dose × quality factor
$$H = D \times Q$$
The dose equivalent is measured in sieverts (Sv).

   sieverts = grays × quality factor.

type of radiation	quality factor Q
X-rays	1
γ-rays	1
β-particles	1
thermal neutrons	3
fast neutrons	10
α-particles	20

Table 1

Example 1

A worker operates in a workplace over a whole year where he receives the following

   25 mGy from beta radiation $Q = 1$

   300 µGy from fast neutrons $Q = 10$

Calculate his dose equivalent for the year.

   dose equivalent = absorbed dose × quality factor

   for betas $H = 25 \times 10^{-3} \times 1 = 2.5 \times 10^{-2}\,\text{Sv}$

   for neutrons $H = 300 \times 10^{-6} \times 10 = 3.0 \times 10^{-3}\,\text{Sv}$

   total $H = 2.5 \times 10^{-2} + 3.0 \times 10^{-3} = 28 \times 10^{-3}\,\text{Sv}$

The dose equivalent for the year is 28 mSv.

Dose equivalent rate

The dose equivalent rate $\dot{H}$ (pronounced *H dot*) is the dose equivalent absorbed divided by the time during which it is absorbed.
It is measured in sieverts per hour or sieverts per minute.

dose equivalent = dose equivalent rate × time
$$H = \dot{H} \times t$$

Also the dose equivalent rate = absorbed dose rate × quality factor
$$\dot{H} = \dot{D} \times Q$$

Example 2

A person spends 5 hours in an area where the absorbed dose rate for thermal neutrons is 36 µGy per hour; the quality factor is 3.
What is the dose equivalent rate and the dose equivalent?

dose equivalent rate = absorbed dose rate × quality factor
$$\dot{H} = 36 \times 10^{-6} \times 3$$
$$= 108 \times 10^{-6}$$

The dose equivalent rate is 108 µSv per hour

dose equivalent = dose equivalent rate × time
$$= 108 \times 10^{-6} \times 5$$
$$= 540 \text{ µSv}$$

The dose equivalent received in 5 hours in 540 µSv.

Background radiation

Everyone is exposed to radiation from natural sources and from man-made radioactive material – Table 2.

source	radiation
cosmic rays	– the earth is bombarded by very high energy particles, mostly protons, from outer space.
rocks	– soil and rocks contain traces of radioactive material.
buildings	– building materials are radioactive and the gas radon accumulates in buildings due to seepage from the ground. Insulating a house by reducing the ventilation and flow of air causes a build up of radon gas.
industrial	– many industries use radioactive material for monitoring purposes – nuclear reactors contribute to the amount of radiation received.
medical	– X-rays and radioactive tracers are used in diagnosis.
human body	– the human body is itself radioactive. This is due to the presence of potassium-40 in all cells and traces of radioactive material from fruit, vegetables and meat which have been eaten.

Table 2

The average dose equivalent received over a period of one year by members of the public is shown in Table 3.

source	dose equivalent
cosmic rays	0.3 mSv
rocks, soil, buildings	0.3 mSv
present in body	0.4 mSv
industry	1.0 mSv
dental X-ray	0.3 mSv
chest X-ray	2.0 mSv
one flight over the Atlantic	50 μSv

Table 3

A maximum dose equivalent for members of the public has been established at 5 mSv. Radiation workers and those working in certain parts of industry are allowed much higher amounts; this is set at 50 mSv.

The dose equivalent rate for a person standing 1 metre away from a typical school experimental source (185 kBq strontium-90 source) is approximately 130 μSv h^{-1}.

In cancer therapy, the radiation is used to kill the cancer cells so that very high doses are used. A typical cobalt-60 treatment will involve a dose equivalent of 30 000 mSv.

Example 3

A radiation worker receives a total dose equivalent of 450 μSv during a working week of 30 hours.
    Calculate the average dose equivalent rate.

$$\text{dose equivalent rate} = \frac{\text{dose equivalent}}{\text{time}}$$

$$\dot{H} = \frac{450 \times 10^{-6}}{30} = 15 \times 10^{-6}$$

The dose equivalent rate is 15 μSv per hour.

Example 4

A monitoring device aboard an aircraft registers a dose equivalent rate of 6 μSv h^{-1}.
    Calculate the dose equivalent during a 7-hour flight.

$$\text{dose equivalent} = \text{dose equivalent rate} \times \text{time}$$

$$H = 6 \times 10^{-6} \times 7 = 42 \times 10^{-6}$$

The dose equivalent is 42 μSv.

Absorption of gamma-rays

Lead is a very effective absorber of gamma-rays. An experimental arrangement to show this is given in Figure 3. As greater thicknesses of lead are used, the count rate decreases. Throughout the experiment, the distance between the source and the detector is kept constant.

A graph of a typical set of results is shown in Figure 4. This shows count rate N in counts per minute against the thickness of lead t in millimetres.

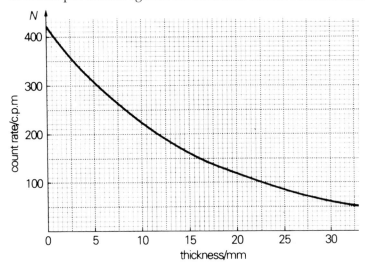

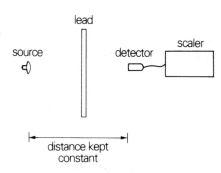

Figure 3

Figure 4 Graph of count rate against thickness of lead absorber

The thickness of lead required to reduce the count rate to half its original value is known as the **half-value**, $t_{1/2}$. This can be determined from the graph above and shown more clearly in Figure 5.

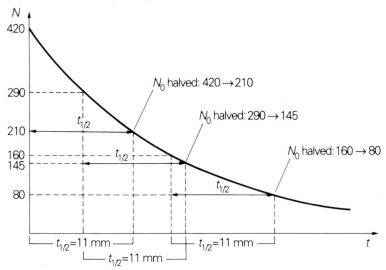

Figure 5

It can be seen that the value of $t_{1/2}$ remains constant each time the count rate is halved fron N_0 to $\frac{1}{2}N_0$. The half-value thickness is about 11 mm.

The half-value thickness for absorption depends on the nature of the source and on the energy of the particles emitted. When storing or transporting radioactive material, use is made of the absorption properties of lead, concrete and other materials to reduce the risk of exposure to personnel. These materials have a shielding effect.

Example 5

The dose equivalent rate due to a gamma source is 12 Sv per hour.
If the half-value thickness of lead for this source is 16 mm, what would be the
dose equivalent rate with the source placed behind 48 mm of lead shielding?

half-value thickness = 16 mm

thickness = 0	$12\,\mathrm{Sv\,h^{-1}}$
thickness = 16 mm	$\frac{1}{2} \times 12 = 6.0\ \mathrm{Sv\,h^{-1}}$
thickness = 32 mm	$\frac{1}{2} \times 6\ = 3.0\ \mathrm{Sv\,h^{-1}}$
thickness = 48 mm	$\frac{1}{2} \times 3\ = 1.5\ \mathrm{Sv\,h^{-1}}$

The 48 mm of lead will reduce the dose equivalent rate to 1.5 Sv per hour.

Example 6

A cobalt-60 source emits gamma-rays and, at a point some distance away,
produces a dose equivalent rate of 6 µSv per hour.
If the half-value thickness of lead for this source is 11 mm, what thickness of lead
would reduce the dose equivalent rate to 1.5 µSv per hour?

desired rate = $1.5\ \mathrm{\mu Sv\,h^{-1}}$

initial rate = $6\ \mathrm{\mu Sv\,h^{-1}}$

The rate has to be cut to one quarter of the original.
One half-value thickness will reduce the rate to $\frac{1}{2}$ of the original; this means that
two half-value thicknesses are required ($\frac{1}{4} = \frac{1}{2} \times \frac{1}{2}$)

A thickness of 22 mm will reduce the dose equivalent rate to 1.5 µSv per hour.

Inverse Square Law for γ-radiation

Just as with other sources of radiation like light or heat, we would expect the
intensity of radiation from a gamma source to reduce as the distance from it is
increased. To investigate this, a source is placed in line with a Geiger-Müller
tube which measures the count rate at various distances, Figure 6.

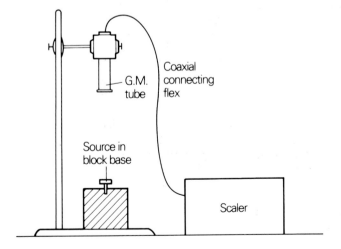

Figure 6

A graph of results from a typical experiment is shown in Figure 7.

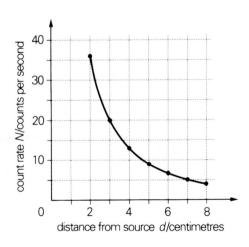

Figure 7 Graph of count rate against
distance from source

If, as is expected, the count rate is inversely proportional to the distance squared, then

$$N = k \times \frac{1}{d^2} \qquad \text{where } N = \text{count rate}$$
$$d = \text{distance}$$
$$k = \text{constant}$$

$$\Rightarrow \quad N \times d^2 = k$$

When this is done with the results, a constant value is not obtained, Table 4.

distance d (cm)	count rate N (counts per second)	$N \times d^2$
2	36	144
3	20	180
4	13	208
5	9	225
6	7	252
7	5	245
8	4	256

Table 4

The non-constant results arise because there is an uncertainty in the distance measurement, Figure 8.

The exact position of the source is not known and the point at which the Geiger-Müller tube detects the radiation is also uncertain. The correct distance should be increased by a small constant amount because of this.

The extra distance can be found by drawing a suitable graph.
When this is done for the results given in Table 4, a length of 1 cm is added to each distance to give the corrected value.

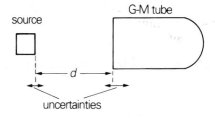

Figure 8

Table 5 gives the corrected results which produce a constant value for the product $N \times d^2$.

d (cm)	N (c/s)	$N \times d^2$
3	36	324
4	20	320
5	13	325
6	9	324
7	7	343
8	5	320
9	4	324

Table 5

These results show that $N \times d^2$ gives a constant value for all the readings.
It can therefore be concluded that the intensity of radiation from a gamma-ray source is inversely proportional to the square of the distance from the source.

For a given source, if the dose equivalent rate is $\dot{H}_1$ at a distance d_1 from the source and $\dot{H}_2$ at a distance of d_2, the inverse square law means that:

$$\dot{H}_1 \propto \frac{1}{d_1^2} \qquad \text{and} \qquad \dot{H}_2 \propto \frac{1}{d_2^2}$$
$$\Rightarrow \quad \dot{H}_1 \times d_1^2 \quad = \quad \dot{H}_2 \times d_2^2$$

Example 7

The dose equivalent rate at a distance of 3 m from a source of gamma radiation is 750 μSv per hour.
What is the dose equivalent rate at 5 m from the source?

The inverse square law gives

$$\dot{H}_1 \times d_1^2 = \dot{H}_2 \times d_2^2$$
$$\Rightarrow \quad 750 \times 10^{-6} \times 3^2 = \dot{H}_2 \times 5^2$$
$$\Rightarrow \quad \dot{H}_2 = 750 \times 10^{-6} \times \frac{9}{25} = 270 \times 10^{-6}$$

The dose equivalent rate is 270 μSv h^{-1} at a distance of 5 m from the source.

Example 8

A detector is placed 10 cm from a point source of gamma rays. A count rate of 600 c.p.m. is recorded.
   What count rate would be obtained at a distance of 20 cm from the source?

The distance has doubled, therefore the count rate will be $\frac{1}{2^2}$ of the original reading.

$$\text{The new count rate is } 600 \times \frac{1}{2^2} = \frac{1}{4} \times 600 = 150$$

The new count rate will be 150 counts per minute.

Summary

Activity, $A = \dfrac{N}{t}$ where N = number of disintegrations which occur in time t.

Absorbed dose, $D = \dfrac{\text{energy absorbed}}{\text{mass of absorbing material}}$.

Absorbed dose rate, $\dot{D} = \dfrac{D}{t}$ where D = absorbed dose in time t.

Ionizing radiations from a radioactive source can damage living cells. The risk of biological damage depends on the type of radiation, the amount of absorbed dose and the organ exposed to the radiation.

Quality factor, Q   Different radiations pose different degrees of risk of biological damage to living cells.
To take account of this each type of radiation is given a number called the **quality factor**.

Dose equivalent, $H = D \times Q$.

Dose equivalent rate, $\dot{D} = \dfrac{H}{t}$.

The dose equivalent received from a point source of radiation is inversely proportional to the square of the distance from the source:

$$H \propto \frac{1}{d^2}$$

As various thicknesses of lead absorber are placed between a source of gamma radiation and a detector the intensity of the radiation received for increasing thicknesses of absorber gives a curved graph.

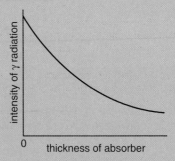

When radiation is absorbed, the half-value thickness of the absorber is the thickness which reduces the dose equivalent to half of its original value.

The dose equivalent rate due to a source can be reduced by increasing the distance from the source or by putting a shield around the source.

Questions

1 A technician receives a dose equivalent rate of 3.0 μSv per hour when standing 1 metre away from a gamma ray source. Calculate the dose equivalent rate that he would receive when standing 0.5 metre from this source.

2 An experiment is carried out to find the half-value thickness for an absorber of gamma radiation.
The results are given in the table.

corrected count rate N (c/m)	thickness of absorber d (mm)
120	5
76	10
49	15
32	20
20	25
14	30

Draw a graph of the count rate against the thickness for these results and use it to determine the half-value thickness for this absorber.

3 A worker spends 5 hours in an area where absorbed dose rates are:

thermal neutrons 36 mGy h^{-1}
fast neutrons 20 μGy h^{-1}

Calculate the dose equivalent rates for each type of neutron. What is the total dose equivalent for the 5 hours?

4 In a year a fitter working in a nuclear power station receives:

20 mGy of gamma radiation
300 μGy of thermal neutrons.

Determine the dose equivalent for the year.

5 In the course of a 35-hour week an industrial worker receives a dose equivalent of 400 μSv.
Determine the dose equivalent rate for this week.

6 The dose equivalent rate from a source is 1200 μSv h^{-1} at a distance of 2 m. Calculate the distance at which this will fall below a rate of 600 μSv h^{-1}.

7 A businessman receives radiation at the rate of 12 μSv h^{-1} while flying in an aircraft. His total flying time per annum is 250 hours. Calculate his total dose equivalent for the year.

8 In investigating the effect of different types of radiation on the human body, the data in the table below were obtained for one particular type of body tissue.

radiation	absorbed dose rate	quality factor
γ-rays	100 μGy h^{-1}	1
fast neutrons	400 μGy h^{-1}	10
α-particles	50 μGy h^{-1}	20

a) Show, using the data in the table, which radiation is likely to be most harmful to this tissue.

b) **i)** The maximum permitted dose equivalent for this tissue is 5 mSv. Calculate the time the tissue can be exposed to fast neutrons without exceeding this limit.
ii) A sample of this tissure has a mass of 25 grams. How much energy will it absorb from fast neutrons in 2 hours?

c) The effect of radiation on this tissue can be reduced by putting shield material between the source of radiation and the tissue. the effectiveness of this shielding material can be described by the half-value thickness of the material.
i) Explain the meaning of 'half-value thickness'.
ii) The half-value thickness for a particular material is 7mm. A block of this material of thickness 3.5cm is inserted between the source and the tissue.
What fraction of the radiation which is directed at the tissue is received by the tissue?

SQA

9 A nuclear medicine laboratory contains a small radioactive source in a sealed container. The following information is displayed on the label.

Radionuclide: ^{131}I
Date: 23rd Feb. '93 (12 noon)
Activity: 300 MBq
Half-life: 8 days
Radiation emitted: gamma (quality factor 1)
Dose equivalent rate at a distance of 1 m: 16 μSv h^{-1}
Half value thickness of lead: 3.3 mm

a) When the source has the activity stated on the label, how many nuclei decay in one minute?

b) A technician needs to work at a distance of 1 m from a freshly prepared source.
For what period of time can the technician work at this distance so that the absorbed dose does not exceed 50 μGy?

c) Lead shielding is used around the source to reduce the dose equivalent rate at a distance of 1 m to 2.5 μSv h^{-1}.
i) On graph paper, draw a graph to show how the dose equivalent rate at a distance of one metre varies with the thickness of lead shielding.
ii) Use your graph to estimate the thickness of lead needed to provide the required level of shielding.

d) A gamma ray source is often transported in a cardboard container carried by two porters. The source is inside a small lead pot surrounded by a large volume of polystyrene packaging.

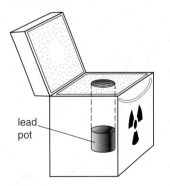

lead pot

The lead pot provides shielding.
What other features of this packaging system reduces the dose equivalent rate for the porters?
Give a reason for your answer.

SQA

10 a) A certain radioactive source emits only gamma radiation.
A technician is asked to determine the half-value thickness of lead for the radiation from this source.
The technician sets up the apparatus shown below and keeps the distance between the source and the gamma ray detector the same throughout the experiment.

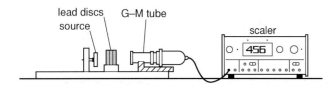

The technician measures the count rate several times for a certain thickness of lead sheet, and obtains an average value for the count rate.
The measurements are repeated with several different thickness of lead sheet and also with no lead present.
The source and the lead are then removed and the background count rate is measured.
The technician corrects each average count rate for background and records the results as shown in the table.

Thickness of lead sheet (mm)	Corrected average count rate (counts/minute)
0	520
5	390
10	280
15	200
20	145
25	110

  i) Draw a graph of corrected average count rate against thickness of lead sheet, using graph paper.
  Find the half-value thickness of lead for this source.
  ii) On the same axes, sketch a graph which might be obtained if the average count rate was not corrected for background radiation.

b) 21 years later, another technician repeats the experiment with the same source.
The gamma ray source has a half-life of 5.25 years
What corrected average count rate would be recorded with no lead sheet between the source and the detector?

SQA

11 a) The diagram shows the apparatus used by Rutherford to investigate the scattering of alpha particles by a gold foil.

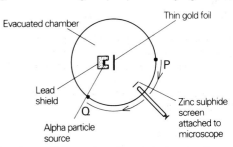

From the observations made as the microscope and screen were moved from P to Q Rutherford deduced that an atom has a nucleus which is:
  i) positively charged;
  ii) massive;
  iii) much smaller that the value of the atom.
Explain how the observations from the scattering experiment led to these three deductions.

b) A pupil reads in a textbook about the possible effects of a source of gamma rays and neutrons on one type of body tissue. A table in the textbook provided information relating to the radiations and absorbed doses this body tissue. This table is shown below.

Type of radiation	Quality factor	Absorbed dose (μ Gy)
gamma	1	200
neutrons	3	100

  i) Calculate the total dose equivalent received by the body tissue.
  ii) Calculate the thickness of lead which would have to surround the above source to reduce the absorbed dose from the gamma rays to 25 μ Gy.
  The half-value thickness of lead for the gamma radiation is 8 mm.

SQA

Topic 3.5 Test 1

1 State the meaning of activity with reference to radioactive substances.

2 Define the becquerel.

3 In a sample of radioactive material, 3.7×10^8 atoms disintegrate in 1 minute.
What is the activity of this sample?

4 When ionizing radiation passes into living cells in an organ of the body a dose of radiation is experienced.
What is the exact definition of the **absorbed dose**?

5 Which of the following is equivalent to the gray?
  i) watts per kilogram
  ii) joules
  iii) joules per kilogram
  iv) becquerel per kilogram
  v) watts per square metre

6 List **three** factors which affect the risk of biological damage due to exposure to ionizing radiation.

7 What does the **quality factor** measure?

8 Write down an expression for the dose equivalent H and state the unit in which it is measured.

9 The absorbed dose from a source is 15 μGy. If the radiation producing this is composed of alpha particles, calculate the dose equivalent.

10 Define the dose equivalent rate.

11 State **two** factors which the **effective dose equivalent** takes into account.

12 List **three** factors which contribute to background radiation.

13 What is the recommended maximum permissible dose equivalent limit due to natural causes for a person in the UK in one year?

14 State the maximum annual dose equivalent limit in the UK due to all sources except background for an office worker and a radiation worker.

15 A source of gamma radiation is placed a fixed distance from a G-M tube which is connected to a scaler.
Lead sheets of various thickness are placed in turn between the source and detector.

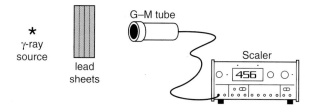

Sketch the graph you would expect to obtain if the results were plotted.
Use count rate: y-axis, thickness of absorber: x-axis.

16 Describe an experiment you would carry out to find the half-value thickness of a lead absorber which is used to absorb radiation from a gamma ray source.

17 A worker experiences an absorbed dose equivalent rate of 40 μSv h^{-1} when operating near a source.
If the half-value thickness for an absorbing material is 13 mm, what thickness would be needed to bring the dose equivalent rate to 5 μSv h^{-1}?

18 The absorbed dose rate 1 metre away from a radioactive source is 400 μGy h^{-1}.

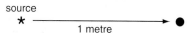

State **two** ways in which the absorbed dose rate could be reduced.

Topic 3.5 Test 2

1 A radionuclide in the form of a disc fitted with a small handle is used for experiments in radioactivity.

In this disc N nucleons disintegrate in a time of t seconds and for each disintegration one beta particle is emitted.
What is the quantity N/t called?

2 A laboratory source of alpha particles is labelled 185 kBq.
Approximately how many atoms disintegrate, on average, in one second?

3 In 1 gram of natural uranium 4.3×10^7 nuclei disintegrate in 1 hour.
Determine the activity of this sample.

4 When ionizing radiation passes through an organ in the human body it transfers some energy which is absorbed by the organ.
If E = energy absorbed and m = mass of absorbing organ
  what does the ratio E/m represent?

5 An organ in a laboratory animal has a mass of 18 g.
When exposed to ionizing radiation the absorbed dose is 120 Gy.
Determine the energy absorbed by the organ.

6 Certain organs of the body are more susceptible to damage when exposed to ionizing radiation than others. State **two** other factors which affect the risk of biological damage to cells when they are exposed to ionizing radiation?

7 When living tissue is exposed to ionizing radiation the total effect is a combination of the type of radiation and the total amount of energy absorbed. The following table can be used to compare the damage likely to be inflicted by each type of radiation.

type of radiation	?
X-rays	1
β particles	1
γ-rays	1
α particles	20
slow neutrons	3
fast neutrons	10

What is the missing heading in the table?

8 Which physical quantity is measured in sieverts and how is it defined?

9 A source of alpha particles produces an absorbed dose rate of $15\,\mu Gy\,h^{-1}$.
Determine the dose equivalent over a working day of 8 hours.

10 A radiation worker receives 2.5 mSv over a period of 180 hours. What is the dose equivalent rate per second?

11 Which quantity is used to indicate the risk to health from exposure to ionizing radiations?

12 Background radiation to which everyone is exposed can arise from natural sources or be due to human activity.
State **two** sources in each category.

13 The annual effective dose equivalent which a person in the UK receives due to natural sources is approximately which of the following?

i) 2 Sv   iv) 2 mSv
ii) 50 mSv   v) 2 μSv
iii) 5 mSv

14 Most workers in the UK are allowed to have an annual dose equivalent limit of 1 mSv (formerly 5 mSv).
Name **one** category of worker allowed a higher limit and state what this limit is.

15 Which of the following graphs illustrates how the corrected count rate measured at a fixed distance from a gamma ray source changes when various thicknesses of lead absorber are placed between the sources and the G-M tube.

d = thickness of absorber. N = corrected count rate

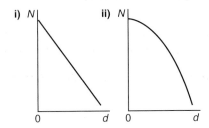

16 The apparatus shown below is used to determine the half-value thickness for lead which absorbs gamma radiation.

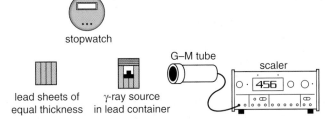

a) How would you determine the corrected count rate from the source?
b) Why should the distance between the source and the G-M tube be kept constant during the experiment?
c) Describe the procedure you would use to obtain a set of results stating the measurements taken.
d) Explain how you would use the results to obtain a value for the half-value thickness for the lead and this source.

17 A used fuel element from a nuclear reactor provides an absorbed dose rate of $10\,Sv\,h^{-1}$ at a distance of 1 metre away in air.
What would the absorbed dose rate be, at the surface, if the element were submerged 1 metre under water?

Half-value thickness for water in these circumstances is 200 mm.

18 A radioactive liquid which emits gamma-radiation is sealed in a plastic bottle.
The bottle is stored in a box made of 3 mm thick lead walls and door.

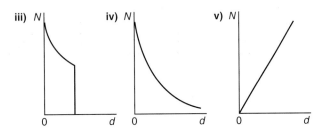

A technician opens the door and stands behind the box at a distance of 0.5 m from the source of radiation.
A student stands 2 m from the source and receives a dose equivalent rate of $9\,\mu Sv\,h^{-1}$ from exposure to the gamma radiation.
Discuss how the dose equivalent rate experienced by the technician will compare with that of the student.

Topic 3.5 Test 3

1 In a radionuclide the number of disintegrations which take place per second in a sample is called which of the following?
  i) absorbed dose per second
  ii) activity
  iii) dose equivalent rate
  iv) exposure rate
  v) decay constant

2 Each time a strontium-90 nucleus splits up a beta particle is emitted. If the activity of the strontium source is 40 kBq how many beta particles are produced in 1 second?

3 A certain quantity of a radionuclide is used in an experiment. Approximately 3×10^8 atoms disintegrate in 1 hour. What is the activity of this nuclide?

4 When living tissue is exposed to a source of ionizing radiation a useful quantity is found by dividing the energy absorbed during the exposure by the mass of the tissue involved.
  What is this quantity termed?
  i) exposure
  ii) activity
  iii) quality factor
  iv) dose equivalent
  v) absorbed dose

5 A gland in the human body has a mass of 36 g and absorbs 18 J of energy when exposed to ionizing radiation.
  Express the absorbed dose in grays.

6 When living cells absorb energy from ionizing radiation there is a risk of biological damage.
  Which of the following has/have an effect on the risk?
  I energy absorbed per kilogram of exposed tissue
  II nature of the radiation
  III the temperature of the surroundings
    i) I only
    ii) II only
    iii) I and II only
    iv) II and III only
    v) I, II and III

7 A number, called the quality factor, is used as a measure of the amount of risk certain radiations pose to living cells.
  The quality factor is equal to which of the following?
  i) $\dfrac{\text{dose equivalent rate}}{\text{absorbed dose}}$

  ii) $\dfrac{\text{dose equivalent}}{\text{absorbed dose}}$

  iii) $\dfrac{\text{absorbed dose} \times \text{mass of absorbing tissue}}{\text{absorbed dose}}$

  iv) dose equivalent

  v) $\dfrac{\text{dose equivalent}}{\text{absorbed dose rate}}$

8 The table lists some possible expressions for the **dose equivalent** and the unit in which it could be measured. Which entry in the table is correct?

	dose equivalent (H)	unit
i)	absorbed dose $\times Q$	Gy
ii)	$\dfrac{\text{absorbed dose}}{Q}$	Gy^{-1}
iii)	dose rate $\times Q$	Sv
iv)	absorbed dose $\times Q$	Sv
v)	$\dfrac{Q}{\text{absorbed dose}}$	$Gy\ s^{-1}$

9 The table lists some sources and gives the quality factor and the absorbed dose for each.

source	type of radiation	Q	absorbed dose (μGy)
W	slow neutrons	3	120
X	gamma rays	1	100
Y	alpha particles	20	80
Z	fast neutrons	10	150

Which source has a dose equivelent of 1.5 mSv?

10 A radiation worker is exposed to $3\ \mu Sv\ h^{-1}$ during working hours. State the total dose equivalent which he experiences in one month (140 hours).

11 The effective dose equivalent gives useful information regarding ionizing radiation.
  What information does it provide?

12 Sources contributing to natural background radiation to which everyone is exposed can be classified under three headings – cosmic, terrestrial and internal.
  Cosmic radiation is caused by particles coming from outside the solar system.
  Give **one** example for each of the other two categories.

13 What is the approximate annual dose equivalent for a member of the public in the UK due to exposure to background ionizing radiation not connected with their employment?

14 For a worker in the UK the maximum annual dose equivalent due to exposure to radiation at work is set at 1 mSv. Name **one** category of worker who can be exposed to a higher limit and state the value of this limit.

15 An experiment is carried out to investigate how the corrected count rate from a gamma-ray source N is reduced by various thicknesses of lead absorber d.
  Which graph(s) show(s) the correct relationship between N and d?

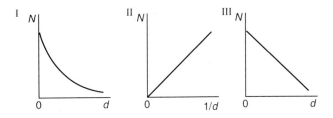

i) I only
ii) II only
iii) III only
iv) I and II only
v) I and III only

16 An experiment is carried out to determine the half-value thickness of a lead absorber which is placed between a gamma-ray source and the detector.
Lead sheets with various thicknesses are used to absorb the radiation and the count rate is observed each time. The average background count rate during the experiment was 45 counts per minute.

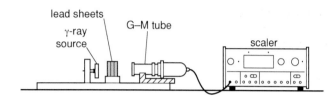

The results are listed in the table.

thickness of lead (mm)	observed count rate (counts/minute)
0	360
10	237
20	163
30	117
40	99
50	72

Describe how these results would be used to find the half-value thickness for the lead absorber.

Appendix
Measurements and Uncertainty

Random errors

When a physical quantity is measured, there is always some doubt about the exact value of the reading. This may be due to the person taking the measurement, the apparatus being used or some random variation which is unpredictable.

It is important to realise the limitations of any measurement and to allow for these when stating the final value for the measurement.

If a sheet of paper is passed round a group of people who are asked to find the width, there will be a variation in the answers given. Some typical examples are given in Table 1. There is a spread of results from the lowest of 208 mm to the highest of 212 mm.

person making reading	reading stated (mm)
A	209
B	210
C	210
D	211
E	212
F	210
G	209
H	208
I	210
J	211

Table 1

In general, the spread of readings in an experiment could be due to a number of factors.

1. Wrong use of equipment.
2. Mis-reading of the scale, either from mistaken interpretation of scale divisions, or from a parallax error where the scale is incorrectly lined up with the pointer of the instrument or the object being measured, Figures 1 and 2.
3. Variation in the dimensions of the object being measured.

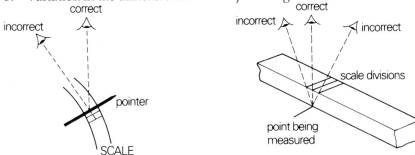

Figure 1

Figure 2

To illustrate the spread of readings, consider the count rate due to background radiation in a laboratory; a Geiger-Müller tube and a scaler are used, Figure 3. The scaler is started and the count recorded at the end of each minute. The results are listed in Table 2.

$$\text{mean count rate} = \frac{\text{total count}}{\text{time taken}} = \frac{563}{10}$$
$$= 56.3$$

The mean count rate is 56 counts per minute. There is a spread of values above and below this so that a random error is present.

Figure 3

Approximate random error

There are a number of ways of estimating the random error: computer software and programmable calculators allow this to be done using certain mathematical relationships. The final answer is achieved with the minimum of effort.

For most experimental work at this stage, a much simpler approach can be used but the random error can still be estimated reasonably well using the formula:

$$\text{approximate random error in the mean} = \frac{\text{maximum value} - \text{minimum value}}{\text{number of measurements taken}}$$

In the case of the count rate in Table 2:

$$\text{approximate random error in the mean} = \frac{64 - 46}{10} = \frac{18}{10} = 1.8$$

The approximate random error in the mean count rate is ± 2 counts. The final value of count rate would be stated: 56 ± 2 counts per minute

count	time (minutes)
0	0
60	1
50	2
61	3
46	4
47	5
61	6
64	7
57	8
55	9
62	10

Table 2

Significant figures

The way in which a value is stated is used to indicate the precision of the measurement.

A length may be given as 12.7 cm. This indicates that the value lies between 12.65 and 12.75 cm. In this case the result has been given to 3 significant figures.

A statement of length of 12 cm has only 2 significant figures and indicates that the length lies between 11.5 cm and 12.5 cm.

The number of significant figures used when stating experimental results will depend on the sensitivity of the instrument and the procedure used. A voltage of two volts can be expressed with different numbers of significant figures.

The range setting on the instrument allows different degrees of precision to be obtained. Although the reading is still two volts in each case, the presence of the three zeros indicates 4 significant figures in the result, Figure 4.

When scientific notation is used, the number of digits indicates the number of significant figures.

2 significant figures 1.2×10^5
3 significant figures 5.78×10^3
4 significant figures 3.560×10^6

   2.000 V

4 significant figures

   2.0 V

2 significant figures

Figure 4 A digital voltmeter

Example 1

Some measurements are given in the table. State the upper and lower limits in the value indicated by the significant figures.

current	2.60 A
voltage	9.4 V
length	12.27 mm
time	3.0 s
temperature	10° C

Current is stated to two decimal places i.e. to the nearest 0.01 A.
Taking half of this allows the limits to be set.
This gives $\frac{1}{2} \times 0.01 = 0.005$ A.
The lower limit is taken to be $2.60 - 0.005 = 2.595$.
By convention, the upper limit is taken to be 2.604.
This avoids the overlap with $2.61 - 0.005 = 2.605$ A.

The voltage lies between 9.35 and 9.44 V.

The length lies between 12.265 and 12.274 mm.

The time lies between 2.95 and 3.04 seconds.

The temperature lies between 9.5 and 10.4° C.

Percentage error

When taking a measurement, the absolute error does not by itself indicate how precise the stated value might be. A more useful error is the fractional or percentage error.
    A stop clock for example can measure to the nearest half second (0.5 s).

If the time is found to be 3 seconds, the 0.5 second error is of significance but if the time is 250 seconds the 0.5 s has much less importance.

The percentage error gives some indication of this.

First case: percentage error $= \dfrac{\text{absolute error}}{\text{actual measurement}} \times 100$

$$= \pm \frac{0.5}{3.0} \times 100 = \pm 17\%$$

Second case: percentage error $= \pm \dfrac{0.5}{250} \times 100 = \pm 0.2\%$

Example 2

Calculate the percentage errors in the following.

a) (5.00 ± 0.01) cm

b) (12.5 ± 0.1) volts

c) (85 ± 2) mA

a) percentage error $= \dfrac{0.01}{5.00} \times 100 = \pm 0.2\%$

b) percentage error $= \dfrac{0.1}{12.5} \times 100 = \pm 0.8\%$

c) percentage error $= \dfrac{2}{85} \times 100 = \pm 2.4\%$

Systematic errors

When measurements are taken in an experiment, there is often a constant factor present which affects all the results in the same direction. This error is called a **systematic error** and can arise due to several causes. There may be a zero setting error in the equipment, the procedure adopted may not be correct, or the operator may be taking the measurements wrongly.

The needle on the meter is not set at zero so that all readings will be too low, Figure 5.

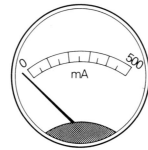

Figure 5

The end of the metre stick is worn so that all readings are too high, Figure 6.

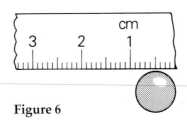

Figure 6

The intensity of light from a light source is measured in a room which is not darkened. Each reading will be too high because the light level of the background is added to it.

The graph in Figure 7 shows intensity plotted against distance from the source. The readings level off at the background level instead of tending towards zero.

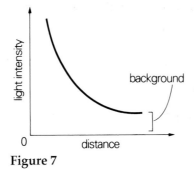

Figure 7

Reading errors

When only one reading is taken from an instrument, the procedure for calculating the mean and then the random error cannot be carried out.

In such cases, the error must be estimated from the scale divisions on the instrument. There is no hard and fast rule for this, but a reasonable working 'rule of thumb' is to take plus or minus half a division of the scale.

In the manometer shown, Figure 8,

difference in levels = 48.5 − 11.0 = 37.5 mm

Taking a random error of half a division gives a value of ± 0.5 mm.

The reading lies between 37 mm and 38 mm.

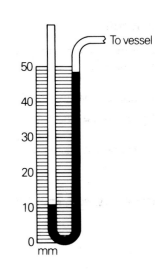

Figure 8

Example 3

Estimate the percentage error in the ammeter reading shown.

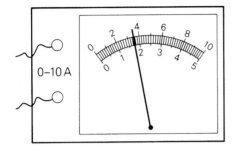

The reading is 3.5 A

absolute error = half a division

$$= 0.1 \text{ A}$$

percentage error $= \dfrac{0.1}{3.5} \times 100$

$$= \pm 2.9\%$$

Percentage error is $\pm 2.9\%$

In some circumstances, plus or minus half a division on the scale gives an error which is much too pessimistic.

In a Bourdon gauge, for example, the divisions are widely spaced and a more realistic estimation of the error would be plus or minus one-fifth of a division.

The reading on the gauge shown is about 1.34×10^5 Pa.

The error is one-fifth of a division which is $\dfrac{0.1}{5} = 0.02$.

The reading would be stated as $(1.34 \pm 0.02) \times 10^5$ Pa.

The percentage error is therefore $\pm \dfrac{0.02}{1.34} \times 100 = \pm 1.5\%$.

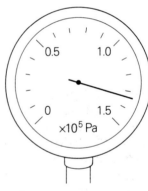

Figure 9

Example 4

A volume of air is trapped in a capillary tube as shown. Estimate the percentage error in the reading.

Estimated reading is 2.15 cm³.

Error is about quarter of a division which is ± 0.05 cm³.

percentage error $= \pm \dfrac{0.05}{2.15} \times 100$

$$= \pm 2.3\%$$

Percentage error is $\pm 2.3\%$

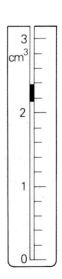

Appendix

Digital instruments

Many instruments at present in use have a digital readout: the numbers are simply read off the output.

Digital instruments sample the quantity being measured and compare it with a standard reference. Depending on the instrument, this sampling will take a certain amount of time so that the final reading is not obtained immediately.

Once the readout is established, there is always some uncertainty in the last digit and manufacturers usually specify this as plus or minus one on the last digit.

This means that for a reading of 3.26 V the voltage will lie between 3.25 V and 3.27 V.

Error bars on a graph

When a measurement is taken and then plotted on a graph the presence of errors is indicated by error bars on the graph, Figure 11.

Figure 11

Figure 10

The length of the bar indicates the magnitude of the error.

A typical example is the calculation of a resistance from a graph where current is plotted against voltage. A variable voltage supply is connected to the resistor and the voltage increased in stages. The corresponding value of current is noted. If the meters shown in Figure 12 are used, the errors are:

ammeter ± 0.05 A   voltmeter ± 0.1 V

When the results are plotted on the graph, the error bars indicate the possible error in each reading of voltage and current, Figure 13.

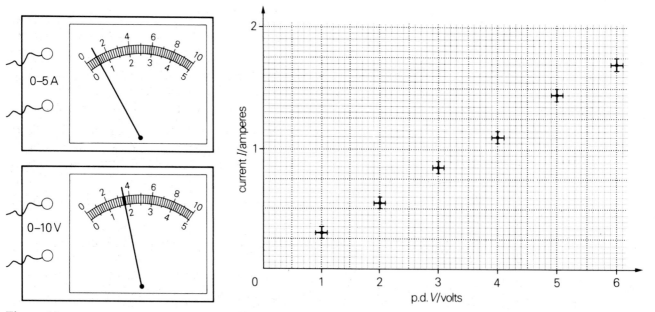

Figure 12   **Figure 13**

Combining errors

Often two measurements are taken and then used in a calculation to give a physical quantity, for example:

$$\text{speed} = \frac{\text{distance}}{\text{time}}$$

$$\text{power} = \text{voltage} \times \text{current}$$

The errors in each measurement contribute to the error in the final value.

There are a number of ways of combining errors, some using fairly advanced mathematics. However a reasonably good estimate of the final error can be arrived at by working out the individual percentages and taking the larger or largest one, the others being neglected.

To illustrate this, imagine the typical experiment where a card fitted to a trolley cuts a light beam which operates a timer. The speed is found by dividing the length of the card by the recorded time.

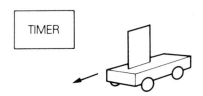

Figure 14

mean time = 0.028 ± 0.001 second

length of card = 120 ± 1 mm

$$\text{percentage error in time} = \frac{0.001}{0.028} \times 100 = \pm 3.6\%$$

$$\text{percentage error in length} = \frac{1}{120} \times 100 = \pm 0.8\%$$

The larger value is taken because it contributes most to the total error.

percentage error in speed = ± 3.6%

The mean speed is $\dfrac{120 \times 10^{-3}}{0.028} = 4.3$ m s^{-1} plus or minus 3.6%.

Summary

A random error is one which has an equal chance of being positive or negative compared with the true value.

Random errors are revealed by repeated observation of the quantity being measured.

The best estimate of a set of readings is given by the mean value.

$$\text{mean value} = \frac{\text{sum of all the measured values}}{\text{number of measurements taken}}$$

The approximate random error in the mean value of a set of measurements is given by

$$\frac{\text{highest value} - \text{lowest value}}{\text{number of observations made}}$$

$$\text{percentage error} = \frac{\text{absolute error}}{\text{actual value of measurement}} \times 100\%$$

Systematic errors are due to faulty equipment or incorrect experimental technique. All readings are higher or lower than the true value due to a systematic error.

Reading errors arise as a result of inadequate divisions on a scale, of incorrect reading by the operator, or of variations due to unknown fluctuations in the instrument.

In analogue instruments, the reading error is often taken as plus or minus half a division on the scale but a common sense judgement should be made to assess the error.

In digital instruments, the reading error is plus or minus one digit.

When combining errors from two or more quantities, the largest percentage error contributes most to the final value. This largest percentage error is a reasonably good estimate in the final numerical result.

Questions

1 Estimate the reading on the thermometer.
Suggest a possible error in the reading.

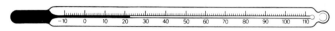

2 An experiment is carried out to find the specific heat capacity of water. Which of the following will contribute most to the final error in the specific heat capacity?

voltage	5.3	± 0.1 V
current	1.2	± 0.1 A
time	200	± 1 s
temperature	5	± 0.5 °C
mass	1	± 0.01 kg

3 Describe clearly the difference between a systematic error and a random error.
Give one example of each.

4 An experiment is conducted to measure the mass of water flowing through a water heater per minute.
The table shows the results obtained.

Mass flowing in kg per minute

5.24	5.31	5.26	5.29	5.28	5.30
5.26	5.31	5.27	5.32	5.25	5.26

Calculate the mean value for the mass flow and also determine the approximate random error in the mean.

5 An ammeter gives the reading indicated.
State the reading and estimate the uncertainty in the reading.

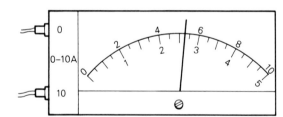

6 The ammeter and voltmeter shown are used to calculate a value for resistance.
Calculate a value for the resistance and estimate the percentage error in the value.

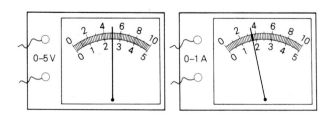

7 A section from a graph is shown.
Find the absolute errors in voltage V and in resistance R.

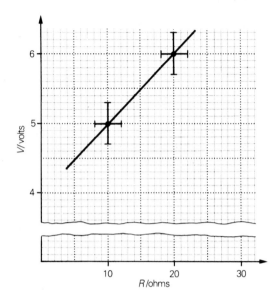

8 Estimate the percentage error in the ammeter reading shown.

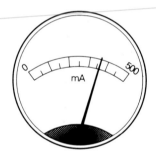

9 The density of a liquid is calculated using the formula

$$\text{density} = \frac{\text{mass}}{\text{volume}}$$

If the mass is 62.7 ± 0.1 g and the volume is 50 ± 1 cm^3, estimate the percentage error in the value of the density.

10 Part of a graph drawn to show the relationship between the force of attraction exerted by an electromagnet and the current in the coil, is shown below.

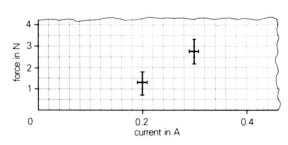

Explain why the readings have been plotted in this way. *SQA*

11 A beam of yellow light from a single slit falls on a double slit ruled on a blackened microscope slide, which is mounted on the end of a cardboard tube as shown in Figure 1.

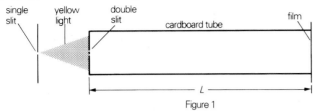

Figure 1

The interference pattern formed is recorded on a piece of photographic film placed over the end of the tube. When the film is developed a series of black lines can be seen. One such film is shown in Figure 2.

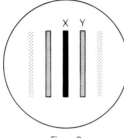

Figure 2

The separation Δx of the black lines is given by the relationship

$\Delta x = \lambda \cdot \dfrac{L}{d}$ where λ is the wavelength of light, d is the double slit separation and L the length of the tube.

a) In one experiment a pupil obtains an estimate Δx by measuring the separation of lines X and Y (Figure 2) and obtains (7 ± 1) mm. His measurement for d was (0.20 ± 0.01) mm and for L was (2.40 ± 0.01) m.

From these measurements, calculate:
  i) the best value for the wavelength of yellow light;
  ii) the uncertainty in this value.

b) **i)** Describe one method of measuring the double slit separation to the stated degree of accuracy.
  ii) Give one way in which the uncertainty in the measurement of the separation of the black lines on the film could be reduced. *SQA*

12 In an experiment to investigate the relationship between the pressure and the volume of a gas, it is necessary to read the pressure of the gas on a Bourdon gauge and the length of a column of trapped air by a metre stick.

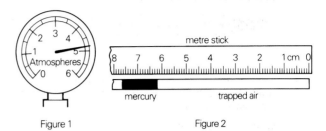

Figure 1   Figure 2

From the sketches of the Bourdon gauge in Figure 1 and the column of trapped gas and metre stick in Figure 2, estimate the values of pressure and length of gas column and the degree of uncertainty in each value.

Estimate also the upper and lower limits of the product of pressure multiplied by length of gas column. *SQA*

Appendix

Quantities, symbols and units

physical quantity	symbol	unit	abbreviation
time	t	second	s
distance, displacement	s	metre	m
speed, velocity	v	metre per second	$m\,s^{-1}$
initial velocity, final velocity	u, v	metre per second	$m\,s^{-1}$
average velocity	$\bar{v}$	metre per second	$m\,s^{-1}$
acceleration	a	metre per second square	$m\,s^{-2}$
acceleration due to gravity	g	metre per second square	$m\,s^{-2}$
mass	m	kilogram	kg
weight	W	newton	N
force	F	newton	N
momentum	p	kilogram metre per second	$kg\,m\,s^{-1}$
energy	E	joule	J
power	P	watt	W
density	ρ	kilogram per metre cube	$kg\,m^{-3}$
pressure	p	pascal	Pa
specific heat capacity	c	joule per kilogram kelvin	$J\,kg^{-1}\,K^{-1}$
specific latent heat	l	joule per kilogram	$J\,kg^{1}$
temperature	T	kelvin (degree Celsius)	K (°C)
electric charge	Q	coulomb	C
current	I	ampere	A
potential difference	V	volt	V
e.m.f.	E	volt	V
resistance	R	ohm	Ω
capacitance	C	farad	F
voltage gain	A_o	*no unit*	
period	T	second	s
frequency	f	hertz	Hz
wavelength	λ	metre	m
refractive index	n	*no unit*	
intensity of radiation	I	watt per metre square	$W\,m^{-2}$
activity	A	becquerel	Bq
absorbed dose	D	gray	Gy
dose equivalent	H	sievert	Sv
half life	T	second	s

Numerical Answers to Questions

Topic 1.1 *pages 9–10*
1. 6 m at 30° above the horizontal
2. 36 cm 56.3° to the vertical
3. a) 22.98 N   b) 22.98 N   c) 19.28 N
4. a) 240 m   b) 176 m, 29° to vertical   c) 176 m at 28.3° to line WX   d) 3.7 ms^{-1}, 29° to vertical
5. 334 N at 29.4° below centre line
6. b) i) 536 m at 67.5°   ii) 1.2 m s^{-1} 67.5° East of North   iii) 2.5 m s^{-1} 67.5° East of North
7. 5.2 m s^{-1} at 67.4° to the river
8. a) i) 1.81×10^6 N   ii) 0.09 m s^{-2}
9. 390 N
10. 1728 N

Topic 1.2 *pages 27–28*
1. a) 0.5 s   b) $a_1 = 0$ $a_2 = -6$ ms^{-2} c) 47.25 m
2. a) 8 m s^{-1} b) 17 m   c) 5.7 m s^{-1}
3. a) 5 m   b) constant at -10 m s^{-2} c) 0.8 m
4. a) 237.5 m
5. a) 21.4 m s^{-1} b) 20.1 m
6. a) 131.25 m   b) i) 12.5 m s^{-1} ii) 15.4 s   d) hare 14.3 s dog 15.4 s
7. a) 5 s   b) $P = 8.0$ m s^{-1} $Q = 6.0$ m s^{-1} c) 5 m
8. a) 1.5 s   b) $a_1 = +3$ m s^{-2} $a_2 = -1.5$ m s^{-2} $a_3 = -0.5$ m s^{-2}
10. a) i) 7.86 m s^{-1} ii) 5.86 m s^{-1} b) i) 1.74 m   ii) ±0.012 m

Topic 1.3 *pages 43–44*
1. a) 6 N   b) 9 N   c) 360 J   d) 72 J   e) 288 J   f) 48 m
2. a) 3.92 J   b) 1.60 J   c) 2.32 J   d) 1.16 N
3. a) 8 kW   b) 3.6×10^5 J   c) 900 m
4. 3.3 m s^{-2}
5. 588 J
6. a) i) 137 N   ii) 2.87 m s^{-2}
7. b) i) 0.1 m s^{-2} ii) 0.2 m s^{-1} iii) 19.8 m
8. a) -1.3 m s^{-2} b) 2.6 s
9. a) 13.7 m s^{-2}
10. a) E_p 5.9 9.8 13.7 17.6 E_k 3.1 7.4 12.0 16.8
    b) 1.20 n   c) ii) 0.34 m approximately

Topic 1.4 *pages 61–63*
1. a) 12.9 m s^{-1} b) 1.3×10^5 J   c) 5200 N
2. a) 2.4 m s^{-1} b) 18 J before and after   c) 14.4 N s   d) 720 N
3. a) 0.032 kg m s^{-1} b) 0.71 N   c) 6.4×10^{-3} J
4. 0.24 n s, 0.96 N
5. a) 1.5 m s^{-1} b) 0.195 J
6. a) 4.9 m s^{-1} to the right   b) i) 5000 N   ii) 1.0×10^7 Pa
7. a) 0.027 J 0.046 J   d) 1.1 N
8. a) -9 m s^{-2} c) 6.8 kg m s^{-1} d) 136 N
9. a) 1.67 N
10. b) i) 20 m s^{-1} ii) 13500 N

Topic 1.5 *pages 82–84*
1. a) 18.6 N   b) 1.1×10^{-4} m^3
2. a) 0.3 kg   b) 2.94 N   c) 2.94 N   d) 4 cm
3. 60 kPa
4. 490 Pa
5. 2.5×10^5 Pa
6. a) 49000 N   b) i) 20 000 N
7. a) ii) 5650 N   iii) 750 N   b) 414 N
8. 1.1 kg m^{-3}
9. a) ii) 1250 N   b) 1200 N
10. c) 30912 N   d) 98% of original

Numerical Answers to Questions

Topic 1.6 *pages 94–96*

 1   80 kPa density ⅔ of the original
 2   136.5 kPa
 3   p × V approximately constant
 4   87 °C
 5   I a) 0K   b) 123 K   c) 773 K
     II a) –273 °C   b) –1 °C   c) 227 °C
 6   a) i) 1.47×10^5 Pa   ii) 733 N
 7   b) 120 kPa   c) 120 N
 8   a) 1600 cm^3 c) 750 K
 9   a) i) 253 K, 273 K, 293 K, 313 K, 333 K   b) 68 K
10   a) i) 125 N   b) 527 K

Topic 2.1 *pages 118–119*

 1   b) ii) 5 V 2.5 Ω
 2   a) i) 9 W   ii) 3 V   b) ii) 3 Ω   iii) 6 Ω
 3   a) i) 0.5 A   ii) 5.0 V   b) iii) (a) 4.0 A   (b) 0.25 Ω   (c) 1.0 V
 4   a) 50 Ω
 7   a) 108 Ω
 8   200 Ω
 9   a) 10k Ω
10   1 A

Topic 2.2 *pages 127–128*

 2   17 V
 3   24 W
 4   45 V
 5   7 V
 6   a) 625 Hz b) 8.4 V
 9   C
10   2.8 A

Topic 2.3 *pages 139–140*

 3   a) 0.1 A   b) 10 V   c) 1×10^{-3} C
 4   5000 μF
 5   c) 0–1 μA
 6   a) i) 6×10^{-3} C
 8   i) 32 μF   ii) 1.44 J
 9   a) 7.5 mA   b) 4.23 mC
10   i) 9 mC   ii) 0.054 J

Topic 2.4 *pages 161–163*

 2   $R_f/R_1 \geq 5$, 15 V approx
 3   c) zero volts
 4   c) 3 V
 6   input 60 kΩ, feedback 60×10^6 Ω
 8   a) ii) 10.0 V
 9   b) ii) –1.8 V   c) i) –5.0 V   ii) maximum zero, mimimum –7 V
10   a) ii) 2.55 V   b) ii) +4.1 V   c) 0.2 V, 1 kHz   d) i) 0 °C   ii)$R_f = R_3 = 164$ kΩ

Topic 3.1 *pages 188–189*

 1   1.2 a) 0.005 m   b) 0.025 m s^{-1} c) 5 Hz
 7   a) 7×10^{-7} m   b) 2.5×10^{-5} m   c) 7×10^{-7} m   d) 4×10^{-7} m
 8   a) 0.66 μ   b) 660 nm   c) 6.6×10^3 Å

Topic 3.2 *pages 198–200*

   1 a) 0.7 b) 4.85×10^{14} Hz

   2 1.35

   3 3.3×10^{-7} m

   5 b) $0.5°$

   6 a) 1.47

   7 a) 1.51 c) 1.99×10^8 m s^{-1}

   9 a) 1.49 b) i) $44°$

  10 a) i) $41°$

Topic 3.3 *pages 236–238*

   3 a) 5.0×10^{14} Hz b) i) no ii) yes

   4 a) 4.4 A

   5 a) 6 b) 1×10^{-7} m; 5×10^{-7} m

   7 ii) 2.9×10^{-19} J

Topic 3.4 *pages 262–263*

   2 b) $A = 14$, $Z = 7$

   3 b) 1.90×10^{-11} J

   5 b) 3.825×10^{-12} J

   6 c) 17 days

   8 b) 2.79×10^{-12} J

   9 a) i) 1.2 mm ii) 1000 cpm

Topic 3.5 *pages 275–276*

   1 12.0 μSv per hour

   2 7.5 mm

   3 108 mSv per hour, 200 μSv per hour, 541 mSv

   4 20.9 mSv

   5 11.4 μSv per hour

   6 2.83 m

   7 3 mSv

   8 b) i) 1.25 hours ii) 2×10^{-5} J c) i) $\frac{1}{32}$

   9 a) 1.8×10^{10} b) 3.125 hours c) ii) 9 mm

  10 a) i) 11 mm approximately b) 32.5 cpm

  11 b) i) 500 μSv ii) 24 mm

Appendix *pages 288–289*

   1 $22.5°C \pm 0.5°C$

   2 temperature $\pm 10°$

   4 5.28 kg min^{-1} $\pm 7 \times 10^{-3}$ kg min^{-1}

   5 5.3 A $\pm$ 0.1 A

   6 7.1 $\Omega \pm 3\%$

   7 $\pm$ 0.3 V, $\pm$ 2 Ω

   8 percentage error $\pm 3\%$

   9 1250 kg m^{-3} $\pm 2\%$

  11 a) i) 583 nm ii) $\pm$ 115 nm

  12 $p = 4.8 \pm 0.1$ atm, $L = 6.2 \pm 0.05$cm; upper limit: 30.6, lower limit: 28.9

Index

Acknowledgements

The publishers and authors are grateful to the following for permission to reproduce their photographs:

Cover photo supplied by The Stock Market Photo Agency Inc.

Amstrad/Michael Joyce p.145 (centre); Associated Press p.145 (top); Paul Brierley p.177, p.178; Camera Press p.81 (centre); J Allan Cash Photo Library p.15, p.81 (bottom); Casio p.233 (left); Coherent p.223 (centre); Peter Gould p.169 (bottom left, bottom right), p.173 (centre right), p.174 (top right, centre right); Griffin & George p.126; Hulton Getty Picture Library p.169 (top); Imperial War Museum p.68; The Johns Hopkins University p.106 (bottom); Keymed p.223 (bottom); The Los Alamos National Laboratory p.254; NASA p.225; The National Meteorological Library/Bodford-Cousins p.103, p.227; D M Nicholas p.187; Oxford Lasers p.223 (top); Photographs and All That p.106 (top), p.131, p.133, p.134, p.184; Popperfoto p.169 (centre); Science and Society Picture Library p.171, p.175; Science Photo Library/Martin Bond p.169 (bottom right), /Adam Hart p.173 (bottom right), p.224 (centre left and right), p.233 (right); Smiths Industries p.69; UKAEA p.224 (bottom), p.258 (left and right), p.261, p.282.

Additional photography by Peter Gould and Robb & Campbell Harper Studios. Special thanks to Beevers Models, Department of Chemistry, Edinburgh University.

Every reasonable effort has been made to contact copyright owners, but we apologise for any unknown errors or omissions. The list will be corrected, if necessary, in the next reprint.